D1626456

BS – WL

Aviation
THE
PIONEER YEARS

THE MONTGOLFIER HOT-AIR BALLOON OF PILATRE DE ROZIER AND THE MARQUIS D'ARLANDES, THE FIRST MEN TO
LEAVE THE EARTH (21 NOVEMBER 1783)

Aviation

THE PIONEER YEARS

Researched and edited by
BEN MACKWORTH-PRAED

STUDIO EDITIONS
LONDON

Aviation: The Pioneer Years
first published 1990 by Studio Editions Ltd.
Princess House, 50 Eastcastle Street
London W1N 7AP, England.

ISBN 1 85170 349 7

Printed and bound in Italy

CONTENTS

Listed below are the main subjects treated in the periods covered by the various chapters. Specific subjects may be more precisely located by referring to the General Index.

PREFACE

Aviation: The Pioneer Years divides the story of flight into five main periods and dedicates a chapter to each:
— the pre-mechanical period, the age of balloons without steering, and of attempts to fly using human power alone;
— the experimental stage, when the new steam and electrical motors were applied successfully to balloons, and when heavier-than-air machines were brought to the point where only the means of propulsion was missing;
— the age of the petrol engine when at last flight could be sustained and the pent-up energies of the aviation experimenters unleashed;
— the interruption of the First World War;
— the period between the wars in which the aeroplane and the aircraft industry developed into recognisably their present forms.

In the first of these periods the book briefly reviews the known, or legendary, attempts at flight before the eighteenth century, passing from Icarus, through the notebooks of Leonardo da Vinci, the seventeenth century speculations of Lana and Schott, the first practical experiments of Besnier, Gusmão and Desforges, to the ultimate success of Montgolfier and Charles, who within twelve weeks of each other had invented both the hot-air and the hydrogen balloon. It then follows the story on through the immediate enormous explosion of interest that these twin inventions inspired, to the inevitable reaction, as for the next sixty years men grappled with the frustration of having this marvellous new method of travel almost within their grasp, but without being able to control its direction of movement with the powers available to them.

By the beginning of the second period it was clear that human power alone would never be sufficient either to lift a man in a heavier-than-air machine, or to steer him against the wind in a lighter; indeed clear thinkers such as Cayley in England had reached these conclusions far earlier. But by the mid-nineteenth century it was also clear from events in other fields that sources of sufficient power already existed, and that it was only a question of time before both the steam engine and the electric motor were sufficiently developed to make controlled flight a possibility. In 1843 Henson, in England, published the plans of a complete steam aeroplane, and within five years his collaborator Stringfellow had successfully flown a steam-powered model of one. Curiously it was not until 1852 that a steam engine was successfully applied to a balloon, by Giffard in France, and even then this momentous advance was ignored and forgotten for over thirty years until first the Tissandier brothers and then Renard and Krebs repeated and informed on his experiments, using an electric motor. Even more curiously, nearly twelve years before Renard and Kreb's first controlled journeys an *internal combustion* engine had been fitted to an airship, and the project allowed to die for lack of funds. The second period ends with the emergence of two separate lines of investigation, on one side the motor-men like Ader who almost succeeded in raising steam-powered aircraft from the ground but who lacked the means to control them in flight, and the glider-men like Lilienthal who correctly insisted that "man must first learn his role as a bird."

By 1901, and the third chapter, the strands were beginning to come together again.

Wilhelm Kress in Austria was the first to put a petrol engine in an aeroplane, though it was still too heavy for the airframe provided; Chanute and the Wrights in America had continued Lilenthal's work on control, and the Wrights had solved on gliders the vital problem of directional stability by their system of warping the wings to increase and reduce lift as required; ever lighter and more powerful petrol engines were being produced for the automobile industry, a fact which Santos Dumont in France put to good use in the service of the airship. In 1903 the Wrights married a petrol engine of a suitable power and weight to their controllable glider and the thing was done. The logic and ease of their success seem almost an anticlimax after the struggles of others to reach this point. Nor were the struggles over; it was another three years before anyone in Europe could duplicate their success.

Once done however both the aeroplane and the airship went from strength to strength. In ten short years the aeroplane developed from the Wrights' construction of wood and canvas to the 124 mph. Deperdussin monocoque monoplane of 1913, the airship from Santos Dumont's 3 horse power *No 9.* of 1903 to the Zeppelins, *Victoria Luise, Hansa* and *Sachsen* that between them carried a total of 19,109 people in the twenty months to November 1913 and this without a single accident. All this progress is recounted in detail, as are the first long-distance journeys to Africa and Russia.

The fourth stage is concerned with that aberration in the logical progress of the aeroplane (and of much else) the First World War. For four years, money was literally thrown at the aircraft industry, but little went on fundamental advance. At the end of the four years the most advanced fighters could fly as fast, but no faster, than the racing Deperdussin of 1913. The aircraft of 1918 were essentially the same as those of 1914. The only difference was in the scale of production; where France had produced 1574 aircraft in 1913, during the next four years she produced 67,982, an average of more than 10 times as many per year. Great Britain from a lower starting point made an even greater increase in production. The aeroplane may not have gained technically from the war but in spite of losses of almost 50% the three major powers ended the war with nearly fifty thousand flying personnel between them and perhaps ten times that number of people who had been engaged in aircraft production.

The effect of this vast increase in the world's stock of both fliers and machines is charted in the fifth and final chapter as the main thrust of aviation changed from the individual efforts of fliers, solo or in small groups to those of powerful commercial companies to open up not only the geographical world but also to extend the frontiers of performance in speed, in altitude, in duration and above all in safety.

CHAPTER I

ORIGINS

PRE-1843

The first few pages of this book are devoted to the ancient legends of flight and to early attempts and projects in which the figures of Leonardo da Vinci and Father Lana dominate. It is the discovery of the balloon, however, which is the most important step in man's journey to the skies; further discoveries served only to perfect the method of airborne travel.

The first years of the history of ballooning are dazzling, and are matched by the beauty of the many works of art which were produced during this incomparable era, as artists and craftsmen alike enthusiastically reproduced the attractive form and bright colours of the balloons.

One is struck by the rapidity with which the new invention developed at this period, by the boldness of the achievements – the size of the balloons, the production of gas in unprecedented quantities – by the frequent success of the operations and by the unmatched courage of those who were the first to leave the earth. The boldness was widely shared; it is worth noting the fact that, even at the very first ascents, places in the basket were vigorously disputed. Such confidence was justified; the first airborne travellers generally manoeuvred their primitive craft with remarkable

skill, and rough landings were the exception.

It would hardly be claiming too much to say that no event in history has ever given rise to such enthusiasm. Neither the greatest political or national events nor any other invention ever aroused the profound popular emotion which greeted the 1783 ascents.

A brief resumé explains this feeling: first demonstrated on 4 June 1783, the invention became known in Paris at the end of July; on 27 August, the Parisians saw the first hydrogen balloon; on 15 October, Pilâtre de Rozier himself went up in a balloon, though ten weeks passed before the discovery was published. On 21 November Pilâtre and d'Arlandes made the first aerial journey and ten days later Charles and Robert set off from the Tuileries before the whole of Paris.

The glory of France in this invention is total; the balloon, born of the genius of the Montgolfier brothers, and perfected by Charles, counts only French names amongst its earliest exponents.

Enthusiasm was succeeded by familiarity, then by a measure of doubt in the face of the failure of all attempts at steering. The Revolution suspended experiments, but gave rise to the invention of the military observation balloon, a project

organised with the perfection which the Committee for Public Safety was sometimes capable of imposing. In the years which followed, the first parachute jump, by Garnerin, remains an event important as much for the element of security which it brought as for the courage of the man who performed it.

During that period heavier-than-air machines were not much in the public eye, and the work of George Cayley passed unnoticed; it is only in recent years that it has been accorded its true value, and it shows that the "idée claire" of the aeroplane, identical in all essentials to modern aircraft, was developed in 1809 in England, a country already rich in the possession of almost all the mechanical inventions which have contributed to the creation of modern civilisation.

The period covered by this chapter ends between 1840 and 1850, years of transition in the history of aerial travel, with the substitution of mechanical power for human effort. The steam engine, Newcomen's "steam pump" or Watt's beam engine, the invention of which was contemporary with the first balloons, had now reached a stage of development which rendered its use on flying machines a real possibility.

Egyptian bronze of Isis, with wings outspread.

FLIGHT IN LEGEND

The idea of human flight is as old as humanity itself. Nevertheless, and contrary to what has often been maintained, there are a very limited number of traditions in ancient civilisations which relate to actual attempts at building and testing artificial wings or flying machines, and even fewer of lighter-than-air vehicles. This fact is all the more surprising since the ancients possessed all the means to construct devices similar to our present-day gliders and hot-air balloons, and one might think that the Egyptians or the Chinese would have exercised their knowledge in this area. On the other hand, both winged deities and journeys through the air by magical or fantastical means abound in the majority of ancient legends.

There are innumerable examples of such tales: Pegasus; Phaeton; the bird Roc or Ganza; the golden arrows of Abaris, or the prophet Elijah's chariot of fire; clouds which carried men, like the one which deposited inhabitants of an unknown land near Lyons at the time of Bishop Agobard; or the Capnobates, a people from Asia Minor, who lifted themselves into the air with smoke, a method also found in a legend of Oceania.

At the head of this chapter is a reproduction of a late Egyptian bronze, which is often presented as an illustration of a flying man; it is however purely as an ornament that it opens this story, because in fact it depicts a winged divinity, Isis or Nephtys, and her wings are the symbol, not of flight, but of maternal protection.

In Europe, all the classical legends appear to be mythical, with the possible exception of that of Daedalus and Icarus which, of all the stories told in antiquity, bears the closest relation to a genuine human attempt at flight.

The father and son escaping from the Labyrinth where Minos had imprisoned them, by means of feathered wings held together with wax, the success of Daedalus in crossing the Aegean sea, Icarus' fatal fall, his wings melted by the sun – these are all images well known to us. The iconography on the subject is copious in Greek and, more particularly, Roman art; in a later period many seventeenth century Flemish artists were inspired by the beauty of the story and used it as a subject for both paintings and engravings.

In China, amongst the most remarkable tradi-

Seventeenth century Chinese engraving of an inhabitant of Ki Kuang in his flying chariot.

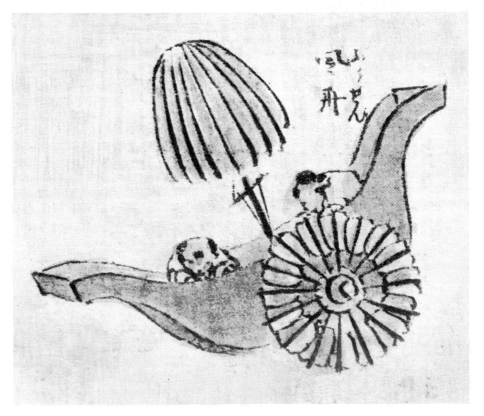

The flying chariot of the inhabitants of Ki Kuang. Japanese engraving by Hokusai (eighteenth century).

tions is one which is found in the *Chan Mai King*, "The Book of the Mountains and Seas", which dates back approximately two thousand years to the Han dynasty; this is the description of the inhabitants of the fabulous kingdom of Ki Kouang, who have one arm and three eyes and who make long journeys in flying chariots. Here we show examples of how they were perceived according to a seventeenth century Chinese print and an eighteenth century Japanese drawing from the *Mangwa* of Hokusai. The same features always appear: a box or a gondola, fitted with two wheels with blades and little wings. Hokusai adds a parasol, probably meant as a kind of parachute.

In Persia it is the story of King Ke Kaous, which is told in the ancient book of the *Shah Nameh*, which dominates. It is said that this legendary king made an ascent in a litter, drawn by four tame cranes. This means of airborne travel is found in many legends; Aesop is sup-

Sixteenth century Persian miniature showing the ascent of King Ke Kaous on a litter harnessed with cranes.

posed to have tamed eagles which could carry young children into the air; Alexander the Great is held to have made a flight supported by birds in front of which he dangled bait at the end of a stick; similarly, Nimrod had himself lifted up in a chariot harnessed to four eagles.

It is possible that these tales were inspired by the ancient legends of India, because the same idea appears again and again. Flying mechanical horses also exist in these legends, such as in the *Sidi Kur*. In *Orlando Furioso* occurs the tale of an aerial journey made by the knight Astolphe on a hippogriff.

Legends apart, Archytas of Tarentum, a friend and contemporary of Plato, certainly made attempts with flying machines in the course of his life as a physicist and engineer. He is supposed to have invented the kite, though this is extremely doubtful, but most importantly he constructed an artificial dove out of wood "which flew by means of a mechanical device. It was held up by vibrations and was moved or excited by the secret blowing of air enclosed inside," according to Aulus-Gellus in his *Attic Nights*. Favorinus too states that Archytas "made a wooden dove which flew; but if ever it fell, it could not rise again".

Suetonius reports the fatal fall of a man who was attempting to fly during the games given by Nero in the Roman year 814 (60 AD) to celebrate the eternity of the Empire.

In Christian times, the fatal flight of Simon the Magician at Rome appears closer to a real attempt, while in England the fabulous life of King Bladud, father of King Lear, is supposed likewise to have ended in a mortal fall in the course of an attempt at artificial flight.

The earliest references to kites in Europe stem from the early XIVth Century. It seems probable that the idea was imported, either directly or indirectly, from China as they generally took the form of a dragon with a type of box kite for the head and a long pennon-like tail to simulate the body. In China, the "dragon", as it is still called in Germany, seems to have been known since the earliest times. The most ancient document on this subject dates back to the Han dynasty; around 206 BC General Han Sin, wanting to calculate the distance which separated him from the centre of a city which he was besieging, had a kite constructed which he flew above the city, and then measured the length of its string. As a result Han Sin is often credited with the invention of the kite; it seems more likely that he used an idea already familiar to him. However, the oldest Chinese encyclopaedias relate that "it was only several centuries later that it occurred to people to use them for the amusement of children".

Certain Cambodian and Siamese traditions are probably based on real experiments. It is well known that for centuries in Siam there have been acrobats who vault upwards, using a pole, and who remain in the air with the help of two large parasols which serve as parachutes.

Apart from this, the Cambodians are particularly adept at launching paper hot-air balloons and this custom – which was first noticed over a century ago – could stem from the fact that these types of balloons were known in the country before the Montgolfier brothers made their discovery; indeed, very ancient accounts refer to *koh mos*, which means "flying lanterns". Nevertheless, not one of the innumerable drawings of the Ancient Orient shows anything which can really be considered a balloon.

The tradition was recorded in the eighteenth century by missionaries in the Carolina Islands, in the Pacific, of a young Oulefat, the son of a benevolent spirit and a mortal woman, who having discovered his divine origins, wanted to see his father and "lit a great fire and, with the aid of the smoke, was carried . . . into the air". It is

quite possible to see this as a primitive experiment with a hot-air balloon.

An Arab legend, dating back to the eleventh century, claims that the Israelite architect of the tower of Mansourah, which still exists just outside Tlemcen in Algeria, made a flight from the top of the monument with the aid of a kind of vast kite – in all probability a glider – and landed on a hill quite some distance away. It is possible that in this tradition lies the much distorted memory of a real event. A similar story is told by Bishop Wilkins of Chester in 1640 of a "certain English monk called Elmerus" who about the time of Edward the Confessor (1042–1066 AD) flew more than a furlong (220 yds.) "from a town in Spain".

At Constantinople, in the presence of the Emperor Emmanuel Komneni, a Saracen wearing artificial wings is reported to have thrown himself from the top of a tower and crashed to the ground; this would appear to be a historical fact.

Even better attested to is the account of an

15th Century European Pennon Kite

Italian alchemist in the time of James IV of Scotland (1488–1513 AD), who, having broken his thigh-bone in an attempt to fly to France from the walls of Stirling Castle, attributed his downfall to having included in his wings some fowls' feathers, which "had an affinity for the dunghill", whereas had he been able to use only eagles' feathers, "they would have been attracted to the air".

We will cite in addition only the old legend of the flying cat of Verviers, in Belgium, and a fairly common practice found in several towns in France and Italy in the Middle Ages and even as late as the nineteenth century; on the occasion of a public celebration, the villagers would throw a live animal, notably a donkey, from the top of a tower, with the animal harnessed to lightweight fabric which floated up to form a parachute and saved it in its descent.

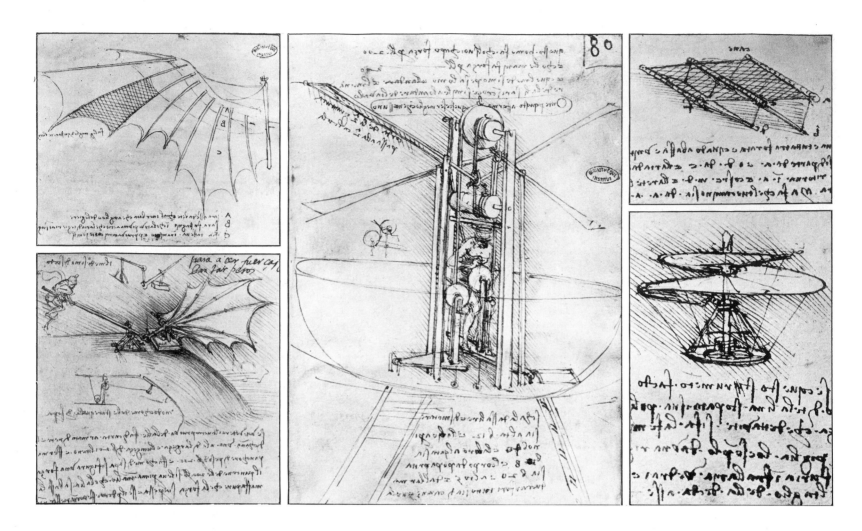

Drawings of flying machines by Leonardo da Vinci. Top left: structure of an artificial wing; bottom left: an experiment with a beating wing; centre: flying machine with four wings, worked by a man; top right: wing with valves; bottom right: helicopter.

LEONARDO DA VINCI

The first known scientific studies of the flight of birds and its mechanical imitation are by the greatest engineer and artist of the Renaissance, Leonardo da Vinci.

The manuscripts which he left on the subject are numerous and important: the Ambrosian Library in Milan, the French Institute, the Castles of Windsor and Chantilly, and the British Museum possess the precious notebooks in which Leonardo wrote his observations, his ideas and his inventions, sketching them out in vigorous ink illustrations. Leonardo's left-handed, mirror-image notes are written in old Italian and are often very difficult to interpret. However, thanks to the work of Govi, Richter, Ravaisson Mollien and Sabachnikoff, his notebooks have been translated and published.

The notebooks contain direct observations on the flight of birds, on gliding, on the anatomy of flying vertebrates, attempts at elementary aerodynamics and a variety of drawings of machines designed to enable human flight: wings which imitate either cheiropters or birds, whose structure he attempted to recreate mechanically, but without limiting himself to slavish mirroring of nature.

It is, in fact, a prominent feature of these drawings that Leonardo, this great genius, takes advantage of the means of mechanical command –

Leonardo da Vinci (Self-portrait). (Biblioteca Ambrosiana, Milan)

double sided screws, return pulleys, pendulums – and depicts only equipment which can be made from materials that existed in his day: wood, reeds, metals, fabric and ropes.

Apart from some experiments with models or with portions of larger machines, it is not possible to ascertain from these notes, how far in fact Leonardo went towards the construction of these machines: some involve wings which are tied to the feet and hands of the experimenter, who lies flat on his stomach; others consist of carriages with wings directly attached, moved by means of levers and pulleys, or with a pylon fixed overhead with wings that move in synchronisation, whilst the pilot, comfortably seated, operates the machine with his feet by means of stirrups.

Two sketches are of particular importance: the first is the earliest illustration of a helicopter, constructed with a large propeller with a continuous spiral, which is set in motion by a man turning a revolving stand. The description which accompanies it is perfectly clear and it can be seen as the earliest example of an active propeller. Leonardo specifies that he succeeded in flying some small, spring-operated helicopters.

The second sketch features a parachute in the form of a pyramid and it too is accompanied by a very clear description explaining the principle of the machine and the method of construction.

Frontispiece from a French edition of *The Man in the Moon*, by Godwin (1666).

FLIGHT IN LITERATURE

François de Belle-Forest's *Ten Remarkable Tales*, published in 1581, gives an account of the appearance above Paris of an enormous dragon during the entire afternoon of 18 February 1579. Belle-Forest writes: "It was prodigiously large, being . . . about fifty feet in length . . . with several feet, and a large head – or two, for when it turned around, as it often did, it seemed to have two heads, with a very long tail, which waved in the wind . . . the wings of which were of great size and membranous". The dragon remained in the

From *Ten Remarkable Tales*, by de Belle-Forest (1581).

sky between La Tournelle and the church of Saint Paul, and "catching the wind, flew almost over the bridge of Notre Dame". After discussing the opinions of the public and the philosophers, who had decided that it was a diabolic apparition announcing pestilence and public ills, Belle-Forest concludes: "My opinion is . . . that the skin of this monster came from . . . a merchant in silk . . . fashioned by some prankster into the form of a dragon (a kind of thing which nevertheless should not be tolerated), carried to . . . a tower somewhere, then thrown into the wind, the creator or master of this foolishness . . . holding it by a little cord."

A substantial number of novels in European literature of the sixteenth to eighteenth centuries envisage aerial travel as a means of transport to the stars or fantastic, inaccessible countries.

Des Maretz's *Ariane*, a novel published in 1639, tells of a prisoner escaping by means of a parachute made from sheets. This method was actually used by several prisoners in the seventeenth and eighteenth centuries, notably by Lavin, a forger, who escaped from Fort Molians, and Drouet, who held up Louis XVI and tried to escape from the fortress of Spielberg.

From 1641 onwards, many editions were published in several languages of *The Man in the Moon*, by Francis Godwin, whose hero, a Spanish adventurer, becomes an aeronaut, using a machine kept aloft by ten wild swans; similar means are employed in *Voyage to Cacklogallinia*, by Samuel Blunt, published 1727, but his hero uses cockerels attached to a litter, flying from Jamaica to imaginary countries.

Cyrano de Bergerac's *The Comic History of the States and Empire of the Moon* and *The Comic History of the States and Empire of the Sun*, give a variety of ways of rising in the air: phials of dew which the morning sun draws to itself and which aid the ascent of the person who has attached them to his belt; beef marrow, whose attraction to the moon has a long and strange tradition; a magnet thrown into the air, attracting a metal chair; the rarefaction of air in a facetted crystal ball reacting to the sunlight; vases filled with smoke, and, finally, a cage equipped with rockets, the action of which aid the ascent. The idea of making an ascent by means of rockets is worth noting; in the eighteenth century, and probably earlier, animals such as dogs were often sent up by rocket, coming down again by parachute, which was known as a "fire parachute".

Robert Paltock, in *Flying Men or the Adventures of Peter Wilkins* (1763), introduces us to the Glums

From *The Discovery of the South*, by Restif (1781).

and Gawris, winged men and women, whose equipment can also serve as a boat. The name Wilkins, adopted by the author, recalls the Bishop of Chester who, a century earlier, made a scholarly study of voyages between stars and of flying machines in general in his *Mathematical Magick*.

Electric machines – two turning globes of glass – are the key to ascent in *The Philosopher without Pretention or the Rare Man*, by La Follie, of 1775.

The last aeronautical novel to appear before the invention of balloons was *The Discovery of the South by a Flying Man*, by Restif de La Bretonne, in which the means of flight were a pair of wings and a parasol, which is not, as has been suggested, a parachute, but a wing worked by springs.

Frontispiece from *A Voyage to Cacklogallinia*, by Samuel Brunt (1727).

Mélinte escaping by parachute. Plate from *Ariane*, by Des Maretz (1639).

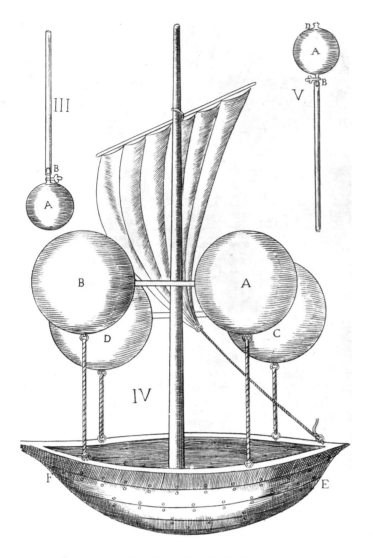

Francesco Lana's plan for a flying ship (1670). Plate from *Prodromo overo saggio di alcune inventioni nuove promesso all'Arte Maestra*.

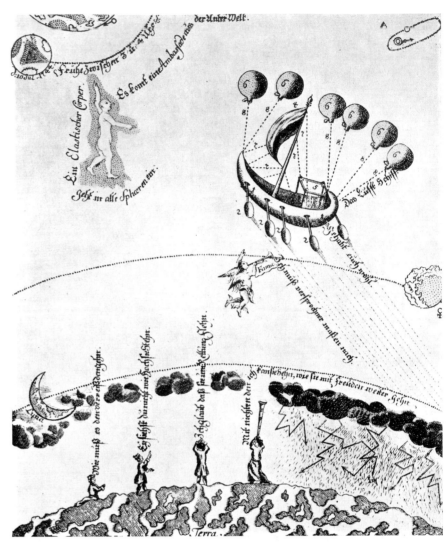

Lana's flying ship, used for an interplanetary voyage. Plate from *Geschwinde Reise auf dem Lufft Schiff nach der obern Welt*, by Eberhard Christian Kinderman (1744).

EXPERIMENTS WITH FLIGHT IN THE SEVENTEENTH AND EIGHTEENTH CENTURIES

It would be impossible here to examine in detail all the numerous attempts at flight which have been reported from the Middle Ages to the eighteenth century: Oliver of Malmesbury, in England in 1060; Dante of Perugia and Paolo Guidotti, in Italy in the fifteenth century; Bolori, at Troyes in 1536; in France, in the seventeenth century, Du Perrier, a member of the Comédie Française, an engineer and the founder of the Paris Fire Brigade; the tightrope walker Allard, at Saint-Germain in 1660, in the presence of Louis XIV; Bernoin, in Frankfurt in 1673; an un-named Russian peasant in 1680; almost all of which were unsuccessful, although in some cases a short flight or glide was achieved.

In the Middle Ages vague ideas also appeared of some ethereal substance so light that vessels containing it would remain suspended in the air. Roger Bacon (1214–1294) imagined a large hollow globe made of very thin metal and filled with ethereal air or liquid fire, which would float on the atmosphere like a ship on water. Albert of Saxony, who was Bishop of Halberstadt from

1366 to 1390 had a similar notion, and considered that a small portion of the principle of fire enclosed in a light sphere would raise it and keep it suspended.

The same speculation was advanced by Francis Mendoza (1580–1626), a Portuguese Jesuit, and by Gaspar Schott (1608–1666), also a Jesuit and Professor of mathematics at Wurzburg, though for fire he substituted the thin ethereal fluid which he believed to float above the atmosphere. But the most complete study is due to Francesco Lana, another Jesuit, who in 1670 published in Brescia a work of major importance, the *Prodromo overo saggio di alcune inventioni nuove promesso all'Arte Maestra*.

Having established that a spherical body in which a vacuum has been created will be subject to an upwards force when released in air, he proposes to construct four globes made from copper or tin, the diameters of which he calculates should be about 25 ft. in order to produce an upwards force or lift of some 1200 lb., taking into account the weight of the copper, which he estimates at three ounces per square foot. This should be sufficient to raise the wooden boat to which the globes are to be attached, together with a mast and sail, oars and passengers. The vacuum is to be obtained in the following manner: each air-filled globe, which has a tap at its base, is placed at a certain height and the tap attached to a

tube which descends to a depth of one hundred and forty seven Roman palms (35 ft. 6 in. approximately) and has its end immersed in a tank of water. The globe is filled with water via an opening at its top, which is then sealed; the tap is next opened at the base and the water flows out, leaving the globe empty, using the barometric effect. The idea is ingenious, though impracticable as a globe of the dimensions indicated would be quite unable to resist a pressure of one atmosphere. Lana was not unaware of the problem but thought that the symmetry of the sphere would permit the skin to be everywhere in compression and thus resist the forces after the manner of an arch.

He expresses perfectly sound views on the control of the vertical movements of his aerial ship by using ballast and letting measured quantities of air into the globes by means of taps. On the subject of the use of oars for navigation, he shows that he had some understanding of the notion of air resistance. Comparing aerial to maritime navigation, he finds that the former has the advantage of avoiding the necessity for ports, "since the pilot can descend to earth at the slightest sign of danger if he sees fit to do so". He is concerned only by the violence of the wind and advises using anchors for landing.

Lana, who had a clear idea of the constitution of the atmosphere, was also worried about its effect on the aeronauts, but concluded that, since a perfect vacuum could not be obtained, the globes would reach their point of equilibrium below the height at which the atmosphere becomes too thin to breathe.

No other project undertaken before that of the Montgolfiers can be compared to this study for its scientific and technical value. It does not in any way follow that the Montgolfiers imitated Lana, whose machine was, in fact, unworkable, but the greatest respect is due to this Italian scholar.

Moreover, his airborne ship did not pass unnoticed, and it is reproduced in several contemporary works; Leibnitz himself dedicated a study to it, which is full of praise for the principle, but doubtful of its feasibility.

Shortly after the publication of Lana's *Arte Maestra*, the *Journal des Sçavans* published a very interesting account of the experiments carried out by a locksmith, named Besnier, with a flying machine at Sablé, in the Province of Maine. These are the first attempts of which there exists a reliable account, in addition to a schematic description.

"This machine consists of two sticks which have at each end an oblong frame covered with fabric, the frame folding from top to bottom in the manner of shutters. In order to fly, the sticks are placed on the shoulders, so that there are two frames in front and two behind. The front frames are moved by the hands and those at the back by the feet, pulling on a cord which is attached to them. The way of moving these 'wings' is such that when the right hand makes the right wing move down, the left foot, by means of the cord marked E, makes the back left wing marked B move down. Then, as the left hand makes the left wing move down . . . , the right foot makes the . . . right wing move down . . . and so on alternately in diagonal. The idea of the diagonal movement seemed very well conceived, since it is the movement which is most natural to quad-

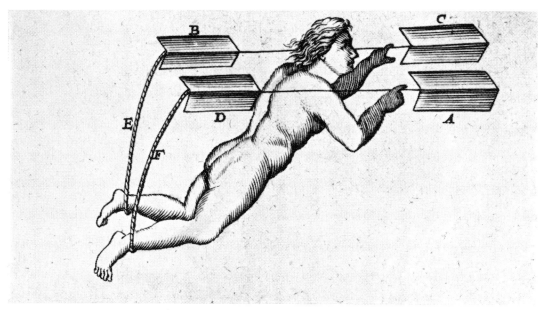

Besnier's flying machine. *Journal des Sçavans*, 12 December 1678.

rupeds . . . when they walk or swim."

Besnier's experiments, the authenticity of which is undoubted and which created a long tradition at Sablé, were conducted in gradual and logical steps:

"He does not claim to be able . . . to lift himself in the air with his machine, nor to be able to stay in the air for long . . . but he maintains that, if he set off from a fairly high point, he would easily be able to cross over a river of considerable width, having already achieved this feat over several distances and from different heights. He started first of all by throwing himself from the top of a stool, then . . . from the top of a table, following this from a first floor window, then from a second floor window and finally from an attic, from which he passed over neighbouring houses and thus, by exerting himself little by little in this way, he created the machine which he now uses."

The journal adds that his first pair of wings

were taken to the fair at Guibray, "where a wandering player bought them and now uses them with great success".

After Italy, it is Brazil which has claimed the honour of the invention of the balloon, by a monk from Santos, Bartholomeu Lourenço de Gusmão (1685–1724), who is supposed to have experimented with a flying machine in Lisbon, in 1709, which some see as a hot-air balloon.

It is certain that Gusmão carried out several experiments at that period, notably in the presence of the king of Portugal, John V, who granted him a royal privilege for his invention, but the accounts are numerous and confused, even contradictory. It is difficult to separate the experiments with models on a reduced scale, which were carried out in the Ambassadors' Room at the Casa de India, from the full-scale experiments which took place outside in August, and in October, 1709.

According to contemporary drawings and prints, the most important machine was made up of a winged basket, with a rudder attached and with an immense piece of material stretched horizontally over it, although some sources describe it as pyramidal in shape. Another fact which has been established is that fire was used in lifting this machine into the air. We do not think that Gusmão's machine can properly be considered as a hot-air balloon; it most probably relied on rockets to raise it, following the system described by Cyrano de Bergerac and which was practised in the eighteenth century by pyrotechnists. The piece of material was most likely not the casing of a balloon, but a parachute added to ensure a safe descent.

It is nevertheless possible that Gusmão experimented with many types of air machine and that one of the small-scale experiments carried out at the Casa de India was the indoor ascent of a paper globe inflated with hot air; however, if that is the case, these experiments have remained without any technical posterity.

In about 1742, the Marquis de Bacqueville, "a slightly eccentric, but most intelligent man", who was over sixty years old, resolutely threw himself from the roof of his mansion in the Quai des

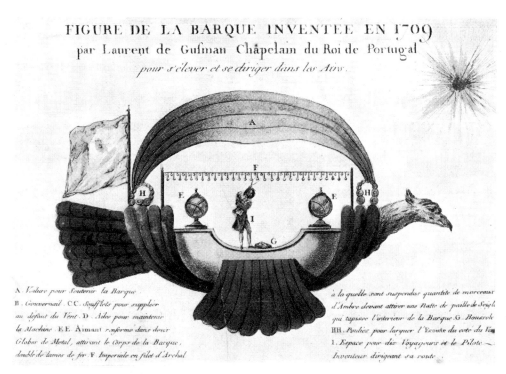

Gusmão's flying machine (1709). Engraving published in France in 1784.

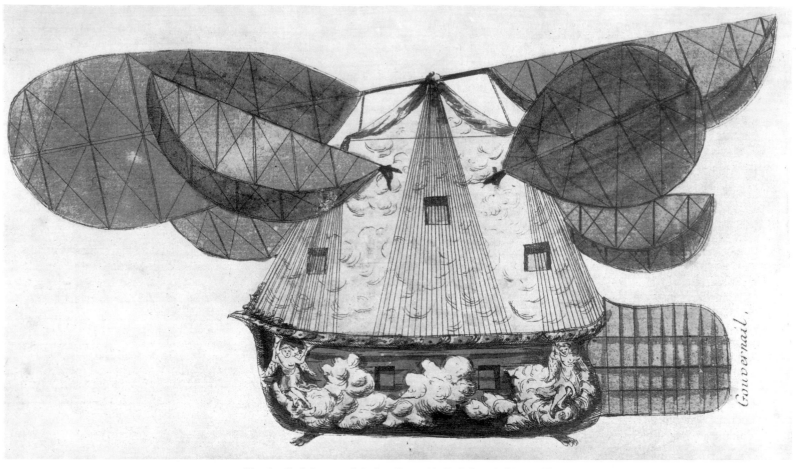

Blanchard's flying vessel, built and tested in Paris from 1781 to 1783.

Théatins, and would have succeeded in crossing the Seine with his artificial wings, had he not fallen on to a laundry boat at the edge of the Right Bank and broken his thigh. No details of his machine have been preserved.

Later, a French monk, named Galien, published in Avignon in 1755 and 1757 a small book, *L'Art de naviguer dans les airs*, in which, echoing Schott, he presents the idea of a ship made out of leather with dimensions of more than a mile in all directions which could float in space by virtue of the particularly rarefied air which it contained, and which would be capable of carrying fifty-four times the cargo of Noah's ark. Father Galien believed that this air could be found in the atmosphere itself, and was going to construct the machine on the top of a high mountain.

On 13 and 14 September 1757, John Childs made several "flights" – more probably a kind of parachute jump – by throwing himself from the top of the bell tower of a church in Boston; this is the first recorded aerial experiment in America. Childs had already carried out this exercise in England.

In 1772, a Canon from Etampes, Abbot Desforges, constructed a flying machine made from willow, which had wings that he could move very quickly in order to keep the machine aloft and, above all, to propel it through the air. It was surmounted by a vast parachute designed to facilitate gliding. This machine already showed some similarity in idea to that of the aeroplane, as well as that of the ornithopter. Desforges carried out some trial runs on the hills near Etampes, then one day threw himself from the top of the tower of Guinette. He crashed at the foot of the monu-

ment, but with no worse injury than a few bruises.

The Canon calculated that the machine was capable of flying 300 leagues per day, at a speed of 30 leagues per hour – figures not dissimilar to those for actual aeroplanes. The pilot was to be provided with a crash helmet and goggles.

In 1781, Blanchard, whom we will mention again many times in his capacity as an aeronaut, built, at La Villette and in Paris, at the home of

Blocking stamp from the binding of the *Royal Almanach* for 1773, showing Canon Desforges' flying machine.

the Abbot of Viennay, a "flying vessel", consisting of a kind of light gondola with a pointed roof, the top of which supported the axle of two large, beating wings; four more wings extended transversally. The larger wings were operated by means of pedals, the others by movement of the arms. The wings, which were shaped like walnut leaves, were, like those of Besnier, designed with a central hinge. An enormous parachute completed the machine.

Blanchard, who had built his apparatus with extreme care, tested it methodically by suspending it from a cord which had a counter-weight attached; as he perfected his machine, he endeavoured to reduce the counter-weight.

Blanchard at the same period carried out an experiment with a full-size helicopter, made from a broad wheel with blades set at an oblique angle, with a vertical axle. He most certainly gained useful knowledge from this attempt, which was carried out in August 1781 at the home of M. de Monville, near Saint-Germain.

A helicopter was also described by Paucton as early as 1768, in his *Théorie de la vis d'Archimède*; it was a chair fitted with two "pterophores", or propellers, one on a vertical axle for upward movement, the other on a horizontal axle for directional movement.

In 1781 and 1782, Black and Cavallo in England, and Barbier of Tinan and Volta in Geneva, had simultaneously the idea of filling bladders and soap bubbles with hydrogen; the power of the new gas to move upwards was demonstrated by the bubbles, but the bladders were too heavy to do so, and the honour of inventing the balloon finally fell to France.

Joseph Montgolfier (1740–1810). Drawn from life by J.–J. de Boisseau.

Etienne Montgolfier (1745–1799). Drawn from life by A. Pujos.

THE FIRST BALLOON

More precisely it is to Joseph and Etienne Montgolfier that the invention of the balloon must be credited. More precisely still, it was Joseph Montgolfier who made the discovery, and the two brothers together brought it to perfection.

The sons of a paper maker in Annonay, both of them scientifically and practically minded, the brothers had long dreamed of the possibility of flight. In November 1782, probably on the 5th, Joseph had the inspired idea of making use of the fact that smoke rises.

His first experiment with a hot-air balloon is recounted in the following manner by one of his biographers, the Baron of Gerando, and has been confirmed by Joseph himself.

"He was staying in Avignon at this period, during the time when the combined forces of France and Spain were attempting the seige of Gibraltar. Sitting alone by the hearth, dreaming, as was his wont, he was looking at an engraving which depicted the preparations for the seige; it frustrated him to see that there was no way of reaching the heart of the place either by land or by water. But could one not at least reach it by air? Smoke travels up the chimney; why should it not be possible to store the smoke so that it could be used? . . . He begged the young lady with whom he was staying to procure several ells of old fabric for him, . . . constructed a little balloon, lit a flame under it, then watched it rise up to the ceiling, to the great surprise of his hostess and to

his immense joy. He wrote immediately to his brother Etienne, who was in Annonay at that time (the letter is still in existence): 'With all haste gather together provisions of fabric and ropes, and you will surely see the most astonishing

The first public experiment with a hot air balloon, at Annonay, 5 June 1783.

things in the world.'"

After several private trials, on 4 June 1783, the Montgolfier brothers invited the Representative Assembly of Vivarais, which was gathered in Annonay, to witness on the following day, in one of the town squares, the ascent of their new balloon; this, which measured 35 ft. in diameter and was made of sections of fabric reinforced with paper, simply buttoned together, was swiftly inflated by burning straw and wool beneath it. It rose quickly, despite the rain, reached a great height, then came down again very gently, ten minutes later, on to a vine on a wall where the sparks from its burner set it alight.

The event was minuted in the records of the Representative Assembly of the Region of Vivarais (reproduced overleaf) and a report was sent to the Academy of Science in Paris, where the news had an immediate effect. It is a remarkable fact that nobody at the time doubted its veracity, nor the importance of the discovery. Coming at the right moment, when the idea of aerial navigation was very much in people's minds, this great discovery was greeted with an enthusiasm unprecedented in the history of inventions; in the middle of a century of scientific discoveries, it opened up a new world. The concept of a scientific and human revolution was widely held and there was immediate talk of using the new machine for aerial voyages. The academy asked for the experiments to be repeated, and Etienne Montgolfier, who was more sociable in character than the learned but eccentric Joseph, was sent in haste to Paris.

THE FIRST HYDROGEN BALLOON

Even before the arrival of Etienne Montgolfier in Paris, a physicist, Dr. J.A.C. Charles, had undertaken to repeat the balloon ascent for a Parisian audience. He worked in collaboration with two excellent builders of scientific instruments, the Robert brothers, and was aided by a subscription opened by Barthélemi Faujas de Saint-Fond.

Charles, although perfectly aware of the simple methods used by the Montgolfier brothers, preferred to make use of the lightness of "inflammable air", or hydrogen, which had been discovered only nine years earlier by Priestley, and which was being studied by all the scholars of that period.

Charles and his collaborators ingeniously made the silk covering of their balloon impermeable by varnishing it with a solution of elastic gum, and produced the necessary large quantities of the gas by the action of sulphuric acid on iron filings. The gas was fed into the balloon through lead pipes, but great difficulty was experienced in filling the balloon entirely, and about 500 lb. of sulphuric acid and 1000 lb. of iron filings were needed.

The balloon, which was about 13 ft. in diameter, and had a capacity of over 2000 cu. ft. of gas, was inflated over four days at a house in the Place des Victoires, and daily bulletins were issued of the progress of the inflation. So great were the crowds outside the house that the balloon had to be taken secretly by night to the Champ-de-Mars, where it was released, on 27 August 1783, at 5 o'clock, before a crowd breathless with emotion. The release was signalled by a cannon, and the balloon rose rapidly to about 3000 ft.

Faujas de Saint-Ford gives the following account of the event:

"The violent rain which started to fall just at the moment when the balloon was leaving the ground did not prevent it from rising with extreme rapidity; the experiment had the greatest success, and astonished everyone. The idea that a body leaving the earth could travel in space was so very remarkable and so sublime; it seemed so very far removed from the ordinary laws of nature that the spectators could not restrain themselves from feelings of enthusiasm. Their satisfaction was so great that the ladies, elegantly dressed, their eyes fixed on the balloon, stood in the heavy, driving rain without heeding it, more occupied with watching such an extraodinary feat than with trying to avoid the storm."

The balloon, after remaining in the air for three quarters of an hour and travelling north-east for about fifteen miles, split under the pressure of the expanding gas and crashed at Gonesse, where two peasants, terrified by the fall of this monster, dragged it all the way back to the village, where the inhabitants beat it.

The government considered that it was its duty to publish throughout France a "Warning to the People", in which they were told not to be frightened at the appearance of these "globes which resemble the moon turned dark", adding that "far from being an object to fear, it is simply a machine made from fabric and light cloth which can cause no harm and which we expect will one day be put to a use for the needs of society".

The names most commonly given to the balloon at the time were flying globe or aerostatic sphere. Later, it was called an aerostatic machine or aerostat, but very quickly the names balloon and aerostat prevailed, and even this last disappeared with time. More misleading were the popular words of the time: air balloon and fire balloon. Charles' balloon described above was an air balloon because it was filled with "inflammable air", while that of the Montgolfiers (which we nowadays would call a hot-air balloon) was termed a fire balloon in reference to its method of initiation. The French alternative of calling them charlères and montgolfières was much simpler, though even that does not seem to have prevented confusion in the mind of the engraver of the plate overleaf of Montgolfier's demonstration at Versailles.

Extract from the minutes of the Representative Assembly of the Region of Vivarais, dated 5 June 1783.

TRANSLATION

Extract from the minutes of the Representative Assembly of the Region of Viverais.

On the morning of Thursday 5 June 1783.

M. Le Syndic has affirmed that, the Assembly having been invited yesterday to witness a trial of the aerostatic machine invented by the Montgolfier Brothers of this town, the majority of its members were present in the Place des Cordelliers, where they saw a vessel with a capacity of about twenty-eight thousand cubic feet in the form of a sphere, thirty-five feet in diameter, constructed of cloth and reinforced internally by several layers of paper applied one on top of the other, strengthened by a number of ropes, and pieces of wood, and wire; the sphere after being inflated imperceptibly, to the great astonishment of all the onlookers rose into the air with increasing speed, up to the height of five hundred toises (3250 ft.), and after having remained in the air for about ten minutes descended slowly to the ground, at a distance of about seven hundred toises (1500 yds.) from its starting point. And because this discovery may prove useful M. Le Syndic has thought it his duty to propose to the assembly that the account of this experiment be written into its minutes, . . . to do honour to those who have invented the aerostatic machine.

And the Asembly has thus agreed.

Confirmed. Illegible signature(s).

Ascent of the first hydrogen balloon in the Champ-de-Mars, 27 August 1783.

(Right) The alarm caused by the fall of the balloon at Gonesse.

Jacques Alexandre César Charles, 1746–1823, drawn from life in pastel by J. Boze. (Musée Jean Houdon, Versailles)

Alarme causée par la Chûte du Ballon à Gonesse.

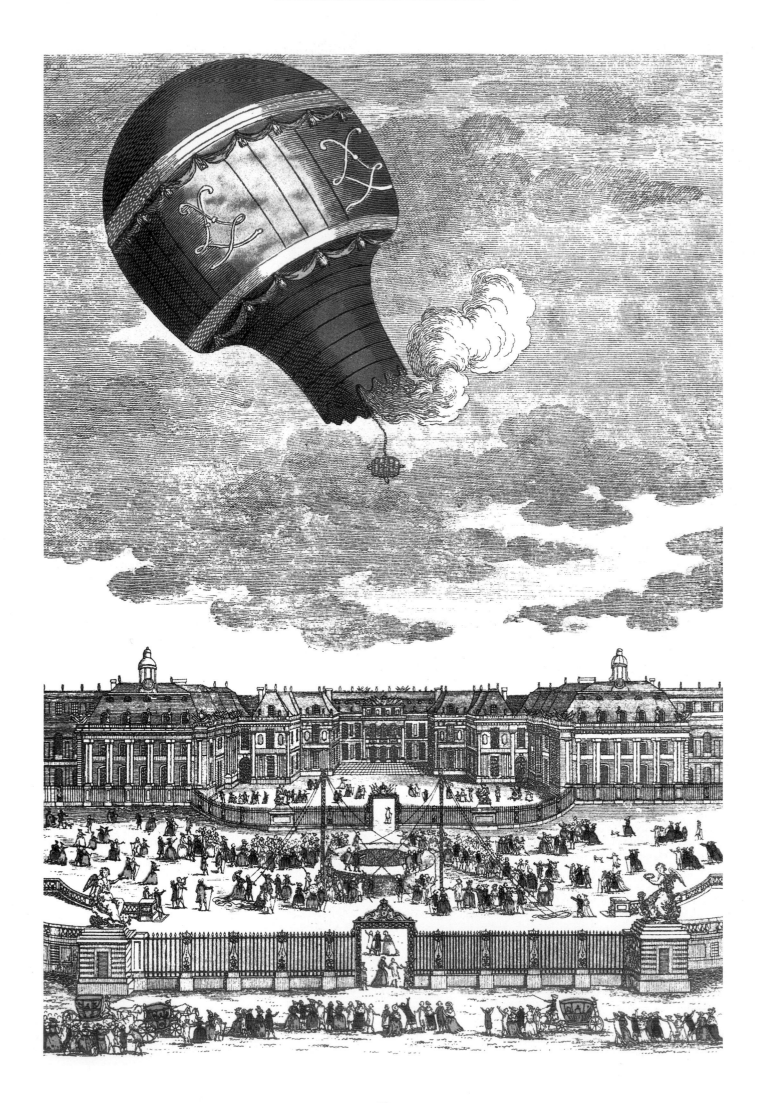

THE VERSAILLES ASCENT

Once arrived in Paris Etienne Montgolfier constructed a large hot-air balloon, to be demonstrated before Louis XVI at Versailles, but, in the course of a preliminary trial, the machine was destroyed by the wind and rain. In five days Montgolfier made another balloon in blue cotton, decorated with the royal monogram in gold.

On 19 September 1783, this vast machine, 41 ft. in diameter, was inflated in a few minutes on a platform which had been set up in the courtyard at the Palace of Versailles. Under the montgolfière a basket was hung in which had been placed a sheep, a cockerel and a duck, in order to ascertain whether the atmosphere could be breathed at some distance from the ground – a fact about which no one could yet have any information.

The balloon rose unsteadily, but it had been torn on its departure and came down after only 8 minutes at Vaucresson, where the first rider to arrive was Pilâtre de Rozier, who was later to become the first aeronaut. The animals were unharmed, except the cock, which had a damaged right wing as a result of a kick that it had received from the sheep before the ascent; the sheep was afterwards kept in the Royal Menagerie.

Etienne Montgolfier wrote that night to his brother in Annonay:

". . . we assembled, washed, and left at five, reaching Versailles at eight where people were beginning to get impatient at not seeing us arrive. The clerk of entertainments presented me to M. le Maréchal de Duras: I explained to him the probable outcome of the experiment, he asked for a report to show to the King fearing that he might give a false impression of the height and distance which ought to be achieved; I was about to obey his orders, a moment later he told me that he thought it would be better if I myself gave the report to His Majesty; at half past eleven I was conducted to the levée, I handed in my report; I returned to the machine, spread it out, got it ready, etc.

A few moments later the King and Queen arrived, together with the Prince and Princess, the Count of Artois, Mme Elizabeth, etc. who came one after the other, passed under our scaffold, entered the space under the machine, asked how it worked, and saw among all the other apparatus a stove filled with straw. M. de Cubières who had accompanied the King shouted to M. Reveillon to call me because I had not seen them, being on the other side of the scaffold; the King who had my report in his hand said to him: 'It's all right. Don't worry. Here is little Montgolfier who will explain it to me in any case.'

At one o'clock a flare (?) went off, and the fire was lit; two or three gusts of wind made us doubt the success of the experiment, nevertheless by the strength of our arms and of the smoke we overcame its resistance and in 4 (?) minutes the machine was full, it was only restrained by the ropes and the combined efforts of 15 or 16 men; a second flare went off, the smoke was increased, and at the third flare, which perhaps I made go off too soon for fear that the wind was going to give us problems, every one let go at once, the machine rose majestically, pulling after it a cage

Medal by Houdon of the Montgolfier brothers,
inscribed
"For having rendered the air navigable".

containing a sheep, a cock and a duck. A short moment after take-off a sudden gust of wind came which laid it over on its side, the ballast being insufficient to keep it upright because the upper part presented a much greater surface to the wind than the part where the animals were. I was afraid for a moment that it was going to crash, it got away with losing about a fifth of its smoke and continued just as majestically on its way up to 1800 toises (11,700 ft. but other accounts say 1500 ft.) where the wind made it heel over again and descend gently to the ground. I immediately went up to the royal apartments, where I found the King still occupied in watching the machine through his telescope, he pointed out to me the place where it had fallen; he assured me of his satisfaction, and at my request, gave orders for someone to go to the place where it was lying, to see in what state the animals were. The Comptroller General was there, who expressed his thanks, and invited me to dine with the Academicians, I went off to excuse myself to M. de Cubières, to whom I had been promised . . .

At the Comptroller General's we talked of nothing but the machine throughout dinner. Someone came to tell me how it had landed, which was at 1800 toises (3900 yds.) from the point of departure; the upper part had been torn, but the animals were well, the sheep peaceful in its cage etc.

I went to tell this to M. le Maréchal de Duras who was with M. d'Ossun; I was taken into a pretty apartment in an attic; in the second room, lit by a pleasing half-light, was an agreeable circle of 20 or 30 ladies, who could have served as models to the painters who have represented the gatherings of Olympus. They were giving a performance of a new opera by Sacchini; Mme d'Ossun said some very flattering things to me, made me sit down to listen to the music etc. After half an hour I left, they tried to restrain me, I put forward the excuse that Marshal de Duras had asked for a report on the state of the machine to give to the King, and that I was going to write it; they made me promise to return and gave orders for the door to be opened for me. I had to see M. de Cubières, I went to his house and found company there, a gentleman told me that he had written about the machine: a book! a poem! composed a song! – of one sheet – of one line, which is: 'Of this globe the inventor is only a man.'

After leaving there to rejoin my companions at a meal I lost my way and walked for three quarters of an hour, I arrived at last worn out with fatigue, and: 'Quick! Go back to the Palace, where the Queen is asking for you.' I took Argand's arm and set off. We arrived at Mme d'Ossun's. 'Where have you been then?' said the Marshal, 'I have sent people to look for you; you have to see the Queen; she has already come out two or three times to talk to you.' I went into the first room, where Mme d'Ossun also reproached me gently because I had not taken up her invitation to return; the Queen came out and I told her about the machine, and read her the report that I had prepared for the King, and told her all about our latest plans . . . "

King Louis XVI granted letters patent of nobility to Pierre Montgolfier, the father of the two brothers, who thus inherited the title, and to whom he also awarded the ribbon of Saint-Michel. The Academy of Science, for its part, gave them the right to attend their proceedings, before receiving the first aerial navigators and accepting Joseph Montgolfier and Charles as members.

Finally, a medal, with a magnificent profile of the Montgolfier brothers by Houdon, was stamped, inscribed "For having rendered the air navigable."

Charles and Montgolfier achieved great popular success with their inventions; people spoke of nothing but the new method of travel. Meanwhile both of the victors – and rivals – set swiftly to work to create a balloon which would be capable of carrying men.

(On opposite page). THE AEROSTATIC GLOBE constructed at Versailles was placed in the first court of the Chateau, called the Ministers' Court, on a scaffold which was 60ft. square and 8 ft. high. About 100 workers helped in the preparations, and the whole apparatus was covered by a cloth so that the public could not see what was happening inside. The globe, which was 60 ft. high and 40 ft. in diameter, coloured bright blue, with the pavilion and ornaments coloured in gold, and containing 4000 cubic feet of gas, could lift a weight of twelve hundred pounds; however, it was carrying only six hundred pounds, not including its own weight, which was from 7 to 8 hundred pounds; a cage was attached to it, with a sheep shut inside, and on 19 September 1783, at one hour past midday, having been filled with inflammable air, (!) it rose in the presence of the King and the Royal Family. Its direction formed an angle of 87 degrees 40 minutes with the western meridian, the angle above the horizon was 1 degree 55 minutes 55 seconds, which gives a height of 3850 feet above the ground floor of the Observatory: the apparent diameter was approximately 6 minutes, which indicated that the machine was approaching the Observatory, and indeed it was carried over Paris, 3900 yards from its point of departure to the Carrefour Maréchal, in the Bois de Vaucresson, near the cattle path, where it fell.

Francois Pilatre de Rozier (1754–†F1785).
(Drawn from life by A. Pujos)

THE FIRST MANNED ASCENT

Four months after the experiment at Annonay, a man left the earth for the first time in the history of the world and rose into the air; five weeks later the first aerial voyage took place. No invention, nor any of man's other great conquests, was as rapid in its development or as complete; it constituted a real extension of human possibilities and the penetration of an element hitherto inviolate.

Etienne Montgolfier had rebuilt the balloon which had collapsed at Versailles, increasing its size and attaching to its base a circular gallery designed to carry men. The balloon was made from cotton coated in alum to reduce its inflammability, and was now 70 feet high and 46 feet in diameter. Its volume was equivalent to 75,000 cu.ft. The gallery was fixed to the circle at the base of the balloon and held up on the outside by cords. The burner weighing 1600 lb. was suspended from chains in the inside of the balloon.

The balloon was beautifully decorated; the inscription on a contemporary engraving describes it in the following terms:

"The upper part was encircled with fleurs-delys; beneath this were the twelve signs of the zodiac. In the middle were the initials of the King, alternating with pictures of the sun. The lower part was decorated with lions' heads and garlands; several eagles with outstretched wings seemed to hold this powerful machine aloft. All the decorations were the colour of gold, on a beautiful blue background, so that this magnificent globe seemed actually to be made from gold and azure. The circular gallery was painted with crimson draperies with golden fringes."

Rigorously methodical experiments were carried out in October 1783 in the garden of the paper manufacturer, Reveillon. The first trials consisted in inflating the balloon and raising it a few feet off the ground; these continued until 15 October, when Francois Pilâtre de Rozier took his place in the gallery and allowed himself to be lifted as high as the cords which were holding the

balloon would permit, which was about 80 ft. from the ground. He remained there for four minutes and twenty-five seconds; then, very gently, came down again. The experiment was repeated the following day before a highly distinguished audience.

On 19 October, Pilâtre went up alone to a height of 250 feet, descending and rising again at will by regulating the fire; then, accompanied by Giroud de Villette, he rose to 324 feet and remained there for nine minutes; finally, the Marquis d'Arlandes accompanied Pilâtre in a third captive ascent.

Pilâtre de Rozier was born in Metz in 1754 into a family of modest means; after a period of rather adventurous living, he succeeded in making a name for himself in Paris through his talents as a physicist and a chemist. He was given the post of Secretary in the cabinet of Madame, then founded a kind of Athenaeum, the Musée de Paris, under the protection of the Count of Paris. Pilâtre's ambition was equalled by his courage, and from the outset he was fired with enthusiasm for the new invention; he was to become its first hero and its first martyr.

The Marquis d'Arlandes was a major in the infantry, born in Anneyron, near Valence in the Daupine. Although his career is somewhat obscure, his name must remain linked with that of Pilâtre, whose companion he was in the first aerial voyage.

On 21 November 1783, after a final captive ascent rendered somewhat perilous by the wind, the balloon rose free in the garden at La Muette, bearing the two first aerial travellers, Francois Pilâtre de Rozier and Francois Laurent, the Marquis d'Arlandes.

The lawyer Thilorier wrote several years after the great event:

"This short journey, made by the world's first aeronauts, will always remain an outstanding event in the history of human courage . . . Openings had been made in opposing sides of the cylinder which encased the flame. As they had to counter-balance each other, Pilâtre and d'Arlandes were denied the satisfaction of being able to see one another; they had taken off their outer garments; their arms were bare and they were continually occupied in keeping alight the fire which was holding them aloft. We could hear their cries as they shouted to one another, and as the distance rendered the cries fainter, the effect became increasingly alarming. As the machine swayed about, emitting clouds of smoke, the two men, each equipped with a poker, stoked the fire with straw to keep it burning; as they raked it, showers of half-burnt straw fell through the air, catching light again as they fell. Never had such a profound silence reigned on earth; admiration, terror and pity were written on the faces of the spectators. The aeronauts moved further away; the river was no longer beneath them. We could see them taking a few moments' rest; the montgolfier descended; it disappeared . . . 'illi robur et aes triplex circa pectus erat . . .'"

The Marquis d'Arlandes also left an account:

"We left at fifty-four minutes past one . . . The people who witnessed the ascent said that the machine rose with great majesty . . . I was sur-

Francois Laurent, Marquis D'Arlandes (1742–1809).

prised by the silence and by how little movement our departure caused amongst the spectators; I thought that, since they must have been amazed, and indeed frightened, by this new spectacle, they needed to be reassured . . . I took out my handkerchief and waved it, and then saw a great deal of movement in the garden at La Muette . . . At that moment, M. Pilâtre said to me:

'We are scarcely rising, and yet you do nothing.'

'Forgive me,' I replied, 'but I had to do something to reassure those unhappy mortals whom we are leaving down there, in a far harder situation than our own.'

I placed a bundle of straw on the fire and turned back again quickly, but I could no longer see La Muette. Astonished, I looked at the river, followed the line of its course, and finally caught sight of the confluent of the Oise . . . I looked down from inside the machine and saw underneath me the Visitation at Chaillot. At that moment, M. Pilâtre said to me:

'There is the river and we are getting lower.'

'Ah well, my dear friend, to work.'

So we set to work; but instead of crossing the river, . . . we went over the Isle des Cygnes, returned along the main river bank and followed it back to the barrier at Conference. I said to my companion:

'This river is very difficult to cross.'

'I agree,' he replied; 'and yet you do nothing.'

'It is only that I am not as strong as you, and it is so pleasant up here.'

I took up my fork and . . . thrust a bundle of straw into the fire. The next moment, I felt as if I were being lifted from under my arms.

'This time, we are rising . . .'

I turned to see where we were, and found that we were between the Ecole Militaire and the Invalides . . . I heard an unfamiliar noise in the machine . . . which prompted me to examine the interior of our dwelling. I saw that the part which faced south was filled with holes, some of which were very large indeed. So I said:

'We must descend.'

'Why?'

'Look . . .'

At the same time, I took my sponge, and without any difficulty extinguished the fire which was threatening some of the holes which I could reach; but, noticing that when I pressed to see if the base of the material was firmly attached to the circle, it came away very easily, I said once more to my companion:

'We must descend.'

He looked down beneath him and said:

'We are above Paris.'

'That is not important.'

'But are you in any danger? Is the gallery secure on your side?'

I examined my side and saw that there was nothing to fear . . . So I said:

'We can cross Paris.'

During this exchange, we had come noticeably closer to the roofs of the houses. We stoked up the fire and rose with the greatest of ease. I looked beneath me and could see the Foreign Missions perfectly . . . On my left I saw a kind of forest which I took to be the Luxembourg Gardens; we crossed the Boulevard, and I cried out:

'For better or worse, let us land!'

We extinguished the fire; M. Pilâtre, who could see in which direction we were going, judging that we were heading towards the windmills which lie between the Petit-Gentilly and the Boulevard, warned me. I threw on a bundle of straw, stirring it to make it catch light . . . we rose up. . . .

M. Pilâtre cried out to me again:

'Take care! The windmills!'

But a look in that direction, confirmed by a glance through the opening at the bottom of the cylinder, allowed me to judge more surely, and I saw that we were not going to collide with them; I said to him:

'We are there.'

We landed on the Butte-aux-Cailles, between the Moulin des Merveilles and the Moulin Vieux, about 100 yds. from either. As we neared the ground, I climbed on to the gallery; I felt the top of the machine pressing lightly on my head; I pushed it back and jumped out of the gallery; turning back towards the machine, I thought to find it fully inflated; imagine my surprise when I saw that it was completely flat. I could not see M. Pilâtre; I ran round to his side to help him to escape from the mass of material which was covering him; but before I had even circled the machine, I saw him emerging from underneath it, in his shirt sleeves, having taken off his coat before we came down . . ."

Amongst the first witnesses to arrive on the scene was the Comte de Laval, closely followed by the Duc de Chartres, who had ridden on horseback cross-country from La Muette.

In the confusion which followed the landing, Pilâtre's jacket was torn up among the crowd for souvenirs, and only the Marquis d'Arlandes was able to return to La Muette, whence he set off to give the account of this first airborne voyage to the Academy "which, at every pause in the account, marked its satisfaction with repeated applause: a thing which it has never done for anyone before."

Amongst the signatures on the report which marked this great experiment were those of Benjamin Franklin, the Dukes of Polignac and Guines, the Comte de Vaudreuil and Faudras de Saint-Fond.

The voyage had lasted twenty-five minutes and had covered about ten kilometres. The aeronauts had risen to a height of over 3000 ft. and had experienced no discomfort in this first exploration of the atmosphere. At the time of landing, two-thirds of the provisions of straw remained on board, but prudence had dictated that the journey should not be continued because of the state of the balloon's casing.

It is a regrettable but true fact that to this day no monument or street name in Paris commemorates this great event and its heroes.

Descent of the Aerostatic Machine on the plain beyond the New Boulevards near the little town of Gentilly, next to the Moulin Croulebarbe; in this place a pyramid should be erected in eternal memory of the glory of M. de Montgolfier, the author of this discovery, and of the Marquis d'Arlandes and Pilâtre de Rozier, the first aerial voyagers.

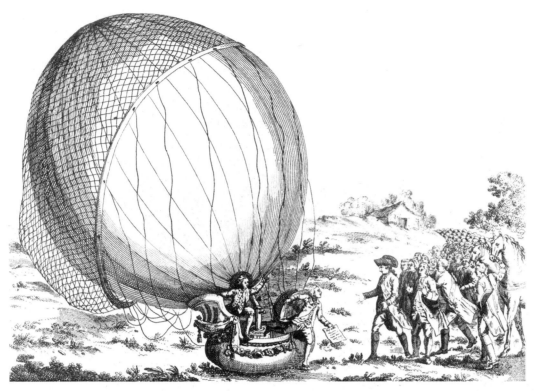

Descent of the Aerostatic Machine of MM. Charles and Robert.

CHARLES AND ROBERT

At a quarter to two on 1 December 1783, Charles and M.N. Robert the younger left from the central ornamental pond in the Tuileries in the basket of the first full size hydrogen balloon. Although Pilâtre's ascent was the first of the two, the fact that it took place in private meant that it had less of an impact; Charles' and Robert's ascent was witnessed by the whole of Paris.

Charles' too was a much more advanced experiment technically. Charles and the Robert brothers had invented the varnished covering of the gas-bag, the net to hold it, the basket, the release-valve, ballast, the use of a barometer – indeed most of the features of all subsequent gas balloons.

After a voyage which lasted two hours and five minutes and was completely trouble free, the aeronauts landed at Nesles, near the Isle-Adam. Here Charles made a second ascent by himself. There was no suitable ballast available at this point to replace the weight of Robert, but the sun having already set Charles gave the order to release the balloon anyway. In consequence it ascended much more rapidly than before to a height of about two miles. After staying in the air for some 35 minutes Charles landed again near Tour-du-Lay, about three miles from where he had left Robert. In this second journey he experienced a second sunset, and violent pain in his jaw and right ear, which was attributed to the rapidity of the ascent.

Lablée, a literary friend of Charles, wrote that same evening to his brother, in Beaugency:

"All the terraces and alleys of the Tuileries were filled with people, as were the crossroads and the roofs of the chateau and the houses which overlook the garden . . . A basket, elegantly shaped and most tastefully decorated, was suspended from the balloon. People had not expected to see M. Charles climb into it. He took his place there with one of the Robert brothers. They drank a toast to the health of the spectators; each took a flag in his hand, one white, the other red, and they waved them to all sides. The ropes were cut and there they were, floating off into the air. Charles never ceased stretching out his arms and waving, but perhaps he was trembling as he did so, as first his hat, then his flag, or perhaps his handkerchief, fell to the earth. However, one must do him justice, and say that as he left he showed great assurance and was full of gaiety. Was there ever anything so beautiful as that departure? . . . It is ten in the evening and the place where the airborne voyagers arrived is still unknown . . . There is not the slightest danger in travelling in this way. It appears that they enjoyed themselves en route; two leagues from here, they threw out an empty bottle . . ."

Charles himself wrote:

". . . We rose up in the midst of a silence intense with emotion and surprise . . . Nothing will ever equal that moment of joy which seized my very being as I felt myself flying away from the earth; it was not simply pleasure, it was happiness . . . This feeling was followed by a sensation which was even more vivid: sheer wonder at the majestic spectacle before us. Everywhere we looked, we could see the tops of people's heads; above us, there was a cloudless sky and in the distance, the most charming view . . . In the course of this delightful voyage, it did not even occur to us to feel the slightest anxiety concerning our fate or that of our machine . . . We spoke constantly with the country people who came running towards us wherever we went; we heard their cries of happiness, their good wishes, their concern, in a word, their wonder and their alarm. We shouted 'Long live the King!' and the wholy countryside answered our cries. We heard distinctly: 'My dear friends, are you not afraid? Do you not feel ill? God, it's beautiful! May God keep you!' I was moved to tears by this tender and genuine concern . . . We waved our flags constantly and noticed that these signals redoubled their happiness and reassured them . . .

. . . We came down towards a large meadow. At its boundary were some bushes and a few trees. I threw out two pounds of ballast and the basket rose above them . . . We travelled more than a hundred yards one or two feet from the ground . . . The peasants ran after us, but could not catch up with us, like children chasing butterflies in a field. Finally, we landed."

"When I left the meadow (on the second flight) the sun had set for the inhabitants of the valleys, but soon it rose for me alone and once more spread its golden light on the balloon and the basket. I was the only object on the horizon still sunlit – I saw the whole of the rest of nature plunged in darkness. Soon the sun itself disappeared and I had the pleasure of seeing it set twice in the same day."

Charles and Robert's balloon brought triumphantly back to the Place des Victoires in Paris.

TO THE HONOUR OF MM. CHARLES AND ROBERT.

THE FAMOUS EXPERIMENT WHICH TOOK PLACE IN PARIS *in the presence of more than eight hundred people, in the royal gardens at the Tuileries, on 1 December 1783, with an aerostatic balloon 26 ft. in diameter. The balloon was made from fabric coated with elastic gum and filled with inflammable air, covered with a net, the bottom of which was a large wooden circle, marking the middle point, to which a cane basket was attached. This was most gracefully shaped, covered in painted cloth and tastefully decorated. At one hour and forty minutes after midday, this superb machine, manned by* M. Charles *and* M. Robert *the younger, was seen, with much private emotion, to rise majestically to a considerable height; following the direction of the wind it was carried to a meadow at Nesle, near L'Isle Adam, 9 leagues from Paris, and, at five minutes past two, they landed peacefully there. Immediately a report was made, signed by the local dignitaries, and by the Duke of Chartres, the Duke of Fitz-James and Mr. Farer, an English gentleman, who had all hastened there, arriving at four-thirty.* M. Charles *went up again alone in the machine, in the presence of a great number of people who arrived from every direction, and having gone up to a height of nearly 10,000 feet, where he felt nothing but a little dry cold, night forced him to bring to an end his famous voyage, and he came down after 35 minutes, landing in the fallow region near* Tour du Lay, *one and a half leagues from his point of departure. This experiment was preceded by one with a small balloon, 4 feet in diameter, which* M. Charles *presented to* M. Montgolfier *to launch; in five minutes it rose to a prodigious height, where it appeared no bigger than a star, and having finally disappeared it came to earth in Vincennes; it had travelled in the opposite direction from the large balloon, which left soon afterwards, although the wind had not changed direction. On sale in Paris at Le Noir, supplier to the Cabinet des Estampes of the King, the Louvre.*

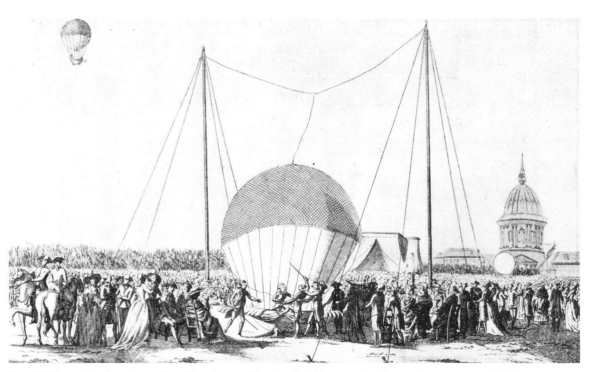

STANCES,

Faites lors de l'Expérience du 2 Mars par M. Blanchard.

Toi qui chantas fi bien
Le Siècle renommé de Mécène & d'Augufte,
Peut-être trop hardi , moins brillant , mais plus jufte;
Je vais chanter le mien.

Le fièce que j'encenfe
L'emporte fur les temps que vantent tes chanfons,
Le fièce de mon Roi , le fièce des ballons
Aura la préférence.

O fage *Montgolfier*;
Et toi qui s'éléva au-deffus des tempêtes;
Approche , viens *Blanchard* , que ma main, fur vos têtes
Pofe un double laurier.

Et favant & modefte;
Montgolfier nous apprend l'art de franchir les airs;
Bientôt nous étonnant par fes refforts divers
Blanchard tente le refte.

Mortel audacieux ,
Malgré la réfiftance & la fureur d'Eole ;
Il voulut à fon gré diriger fa bouffole
Et planer fous les cieux.

Qu'entend-je . . . voici l'heure . . . .
Qu'ai-je vu . . . fur *Blanchard* tout Paris a les yeux . . .
Blanchard dans un inftant va pénétrer des Dieux
La brillante demeure.

Dupont du Chambon, a cadet at the Royal Military School, trying to force his way on to Blanchard's balloon, on the Champ-de-Mars, 2 March 1784.

THE FIRST ATTEMPTS AT STEERING: BLANCHARD

Jean-Pierre Blanchard, mechanic and engineer, who was born on 4 July 1753, the son of a carpenter from the Andelys, had been haunted since childhood by the idea of flight. When he was very young, he made a jump with an umbrella which he used as a parachute. Later, he constructed hydraulic machines, then a mechanical car which carried Benjamin Franklin from Paris to Versailles and Marie-Antoinette to the Trianon.

In Paris, in 1781, he began constructing his flying machine, which he was still testing when the news of the invention of the balloon reached him.

A curious letter, preserved in the library at Andelys, expresses his initial doubts about this non-mechanical means of rising into the air; but he was soon convinced, and he publicly paid homage to Montgolfier, declaring that in the future he would devote his engineering talents to attempting to develop a system of steering for balloons.

Blanchard's difficult personality has often been argued about, wrongly in our opinion; defects in his character should not make us forget his courage, nor his great ability, nor, above all, his achievements in the course of the sixty or so ascents which he made, while preserving throughout his long career a profound enthusiasm for airborne travel.

Towards the end of 1783, still in Paris, he had a magnificent, varnished silk balloon made, to which he attached part of his existing flying machine. The basket of the balloon was, in effect, the lower part of this machine, to which he had given the name of *the flying boat*; this precious object, which predates Montgolfier's discovery,

still exists and has been perfectly preserved. Blanchard equipped the barque with a little rudder and two pairs of hinged paddles which opened and closed as they rotated; the engraving which is reproduced on this page shows clearly how they operated. A parachute, fixed to the hoop between the balloon and the carriage, could be used to slow the descent.

On 2 March 1784, a huge crowd gathered in the Champ-de-Mars around Blanchard's balloon.

At the moment of departure, a pupil of the Military School, Dupont du Chambon, rushed towards the balloon and tried to force his way

Mechanism designed for steering Blanchard's balloon: two double paddles that opened and closed automatically as they rotated, and a rudder; a parachute ensured safety in the event of damage to the balloon.

into it. A struggle ensued between the aeronaut, several members of the crowd and the excited cadet who drew his sword, wounding Blanchard on the wrist, and ripping the parachute and paddles. It has been claimed that the young man was Bonaparte, but this is not true.

Blanchard attempted to leave with his passenger, a monk, Dom Pech, but had to give up the idea. Alone in his balloon, without the use of the apparatus which had been damaged, Blanchard rose up to a great height and noted the existence of cross currents. After an hour and a quarter in the air, he landed safely on the bank of the Seine, at Bilancourt.

A translation of the verses accompanying the engraving at the top of the page.

STANZAS, *composed during M. Blanchard's Experiment on 2 March.*

O you who praise in song the renowned century of Maecenas and Augustus, perhaps too bold, less polished than ours, but more just; I shall praise my own.

The century that I shower praises on outmatches the days that your songs vaunt; the century of my King, the century of balloons shall have preference.

O wise *Montgolfier*; and you who raises himself above the tempests; come, draw night, *Blanchard*, that my hand may place on your heads a double wreath of laurels.

Both learned and modest; *Montgolfier* teaches us the art of breasting the air; now *Blanchard*, amazing us by his versatility, attempts to conquer all that remains.

Audacious mortal, braving the opposition and the fury of Aeolus, he wishes himself to choose his own heading, and to soar through the skies.

What am I hearing . . . now is the time . . . what have I seen . . . all Paris has its eyes on *Blanchard* . . . *Blanchard* is about to enter into the bright abode of the gods.

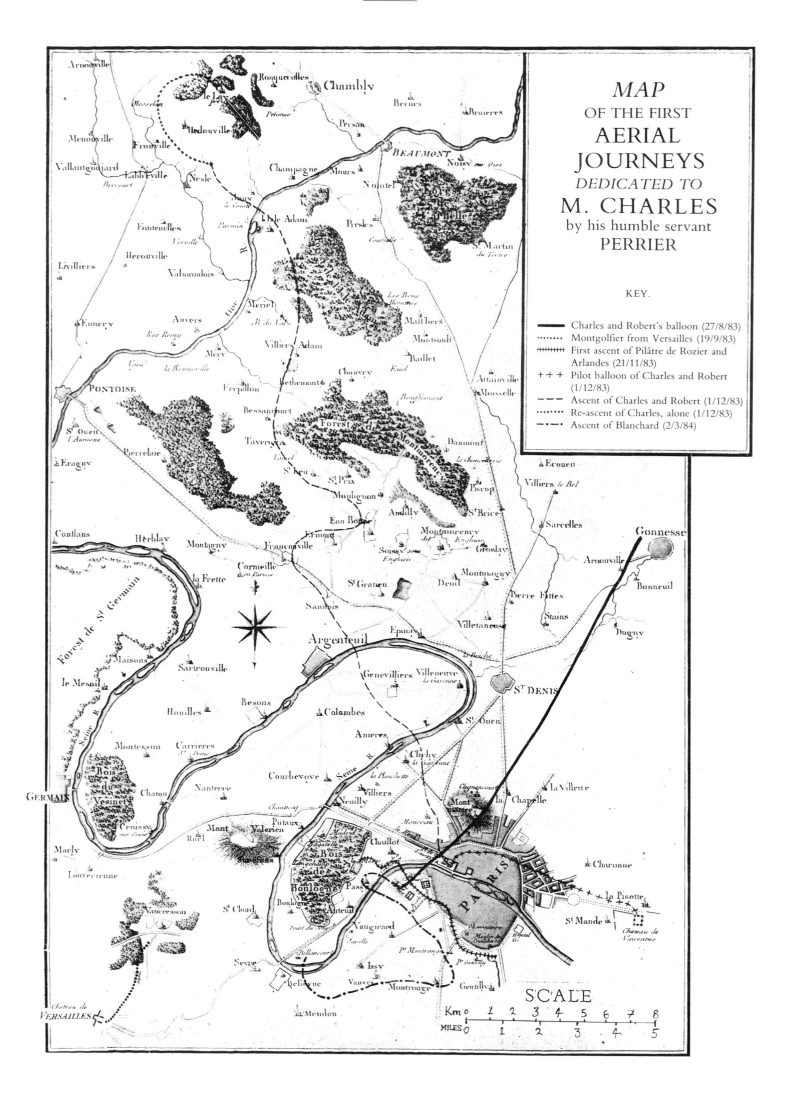

MAP
OF THE FIRST
AERIAL
JOURNEYS
DEDICATED TO
M. CHARLES
by his humble servant
PERRIER

KEY.

—————— Charles and Robert's balloon (27/8/83)
.... Montgolfier from Versailles (19/9/83)
++++++++ First ascent of Pilâtre de Rozier and
Arlandes (21/11/83)
+ + + Pilot balloon of Charles and Robert
(1/12/83)
— — — Ascent of Charles and Robert (1/12/83)
.... Re-ascent of Charles, alone (1/12/83)
—·—·— Ascent of Blanchard (2/3/84)

SCALE

Km 0 1 2 3 4 5 6 7 8
MILES 0   1   2   3   4   5

Snuffbox with engraved glass illustration, showing the ascent of Charles in the Tuileries.

BALLOONS AND ART

In France, the enthusiasm which was aroused by balloons found its expression, from 1783 to 1785, in their use as a decoration in both the fine and the applied arts, on luxury and popular items alike.

After the experiment in the Champ-de-Mars, fashion seized upon the discovery: hairstyles, dresses and waistcoats were adorned with balloons.

China, however, was the medium most used to express their popularity. The factories at Nevers and Strasbourg, and the high quality manufacturers in Moustiers and Marseilles, produced innumerable plates and salad bowls "au ballon". From the Midi and from Lille there are ornamental pieces, basins and pitchers, all decorated in the same way. The great porcelain manufacturers in Sèvres, Saint-Cloud, and Paris painted charming ballooning scenes on cups, bouillons, and even on jardinières.

Another expression of the public enthusiasm

Morocco binding embossed "au ballon".

Chinese style faience plate from Marseilles, with balloon fantasy motif.

Snuffbox with "fixe" showing Charles' second ascent at Nesles.

was the considerable number of fans which appeared, some finely painted on silk, some printed on paper and clumsily coloured, with songs on the same subject written on the back.

Gold watches and clocks – one at least of which belonged to Marie-Antoinette – were decorated with or were made in the form of balloons. The fashion even affected furniture: there are chairs with backs fashioned "au ballon", carved barometers and mirror frames, furniture with inlaid work, chests of drawers with copper handles, bird cages and chimney pieces where the balloon forms the principal motif.

Men used snuffboxes made of ivory, tortoiseshell and gold, the covers of which depicted ascents; as on other items, it is the ascent of Charles and Robert which predominates.

Objects "au ballon" were very rare outside France. It is essentially a French art form, and an ephemeral one; from 1785 onwards, it is only occasionally that the balloon is found as a motif in art, and such an explosion of popular enthusiasm never occurred again with other subjects, not even the storming of the Bastille.

Parisian clock and two cone shaped vases in Delft faience, with decorations "au ballon".

Balloon fashion. 1783 caricature.

Fan, painted on silk, decorated with ballooning subjects (1785). From left to right: Charles and Robert's balloon in the Champ-de-Mars, 27 August 1783; the project of M. D . . . , the Versailles balloon (19 September 1783), Euslen's *Pégase*, launched in 1785, the scene at Gonesse.

Writing box decorated in martin varnish and showing Blanchard's landing at Billancourt, opposite the wooden bridge at Sevres (2 March 1784).

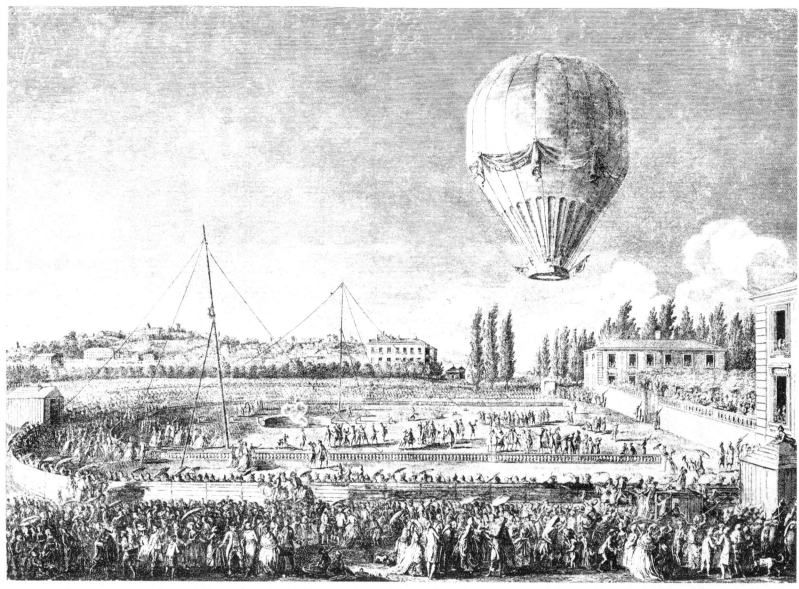

The first ascent by a woman: Mme Thible going up in a hot air balloon, in Lyon, 4 June 1784, accompanied by Fleurant.

OTHER EARLY ASCENTS IN FRANCE

Although enthusiasm never reached the same levels as in Paris, the inhabitants of a number of other French towns formed subscription groups to organise a series of ascents of balloons of various types.

The third aerial voyage took place in Lyons on 19 January 1784. Joseph Montgolfier, Pilâtre de Rozier, the Prince of Ligne, the Counts of Laurencin, Dampierre and Porte d'Anglefort went up in a balloon named *Les Flesselles*, which even in 1932 was still the biggest free balloon to have been constructed. This balloon, made from lightweight cloth lined with paper, was 115 ft. high and 102 ft. in diameter; its volume was over 800,000 cu. ft.

At the last moment, a seventh traveller, a young man named Fontaine, jumped aboard, to become the first airborne stowaway. Despite the appearance during flight of an enormous tear in the cloth, which was too weak for a balloon of this size, it landed safely if a little roughly, after about a quarter of an hour, having reached some 3000 ft.

In Chambéry, not at that time part of France though the event is recorded here for conveni-

A

A

Fig 1 res

Fig. 2

Echelle de soixante et dix pieds de roy:

0 5 10 15 20 25 30 35 40 45 50 55 60 65 70

MACHINE AÉROSTATIQUE

de Monsieur le Chevalier **De CHEVELU**,

montée par deux personnes;

Lancée à Chambéry le 6 May 1784.

Hot air balloon launched at Chambéry, 6 May 1784, by Xavier de Maistre and Brun.

Ascent of Coustard de Massy and Mouchet in the balloon *Le Suffren*, Nantes, 14 June 1784.

Ascent of Rambaud in a hot-air balloon, Aix-en-Provence.

ence, a short but successful flight took place on 6 May 1784 with Brun and Xavier de Maistre acting as pilots.

Blanchard, whom we come across again and again during this period, introduced hydrogen balloons to many of the French provinces. A Norman by birth, he made his second and third ascents at Rouen, with great success, in May and July 1784. He appeared again at Douai, and at Valenciennes with a fleet of five balloons; then at Nancy, Metz and Strasbourg.

An experiment in Lyons, on 14 June 1784, with the balloon *La Gustave*, is worth special mention; for the first time, a woman, Mme Thible, went up in the air, accompanied by the painter Fleurant. She seems to have shown great courage, exchanging couplets from *Zémire and Azor* with her pilot: "What, to travel through the clouds . . ." and "I triumph, I am Queen . . ." In the evening, Mme Thible was crowned at the Comédie Française.

On 14 June and 26 September a fine hydrogen balloon, built in Nantes, made two ascents under the pilotage of Coustard de Massy.

Closer to Paris, Pilâtre de Rozier and a chemist named Proust made an ascent at Versailles on 23 June 1784, in an enormous balloon called *La*

Marie-Antoinette, in the presence of Louis XVI and the King of Sweden. They landed in a clearing in the Forest of Chantilly, which the Prince of Conde named after Pilâtre, and which is still so named today.

Ascent of Abbot Carnus and Louchet, in a hot-air balloon, Rodez, 6 August 1784.

Other ascents were made in 1784 by: Rambaud, in Aix-en-Provence; Bremond and Mazet in Marseilles; in Bordeaux, Darbelet, Chalifour and Desgranges; Abbot Carnus and Louchet, in Rodez; Adorne, Pierre and Degabriel, in Strasbourg.

In general the ascents in the provinces were carried out with balloons which were simpler and more rustic in style than those of Paris, and which were less difficult to construct and to inflate. However none of these primitive balloons, many carrying enormous burners, and totally inexperienced pilots, ever gave rise to a fatal accident.

On the other hand the enthusiasm of the public made failure a formidable prospect; there was painful proof of this in Bordeaux, where a failed ascent degenerated into a riot so serious that two men were killed, two others hanged and nine sent to the galleys.

Predictably the fires which were caused by the landings of, particularly, small scale balloons, which were launched with no precautions, gave rise, on 23 April 1784, to a police order which prohibited the launching of fire-balloons without authorisation: it is the first piece of aviation law, and it was imitated by the Emperor of Austria, the King of Spain and several German princes.

(Above) Engraved fan showing the ascent of Andreani and the Gerli brothers, at Moncuco, on 25 February 1784.

(Below) Portrait of Vincent Lunardi, stipple engraving by Bartolozzi, after Cosway.

EARLY ASCENTS OUTSIDE FRANCE

Italy was the first country, after France, to witness a manned balloon ascent. On 25 February 1784, on his lands at Moncuco, near Milan, a young knight, Paolo Andreani, made a short but entirely successful flight accompanied by two architects, the brothers Carlo and Agostino Gerli, who had built, at his expense, Andreani's magnificent balloon.

This balloon was markedly different from the French hot-air balloons; it did not have a circular gallery, but a basket, over which the burner was placed, a much more dangerous but more comfortable arrangement for the travellers.

The first balloon to ascend from British soil was the unmanned 10 ft. diameter hydrogen balloon of Count Zambeccari, an Italian living in England at the time. This was displayed in London for several days, then launched from the Artillery Ground on 25 November 1783. It landed two and a half hours later at Petworth in Sussex, 48 miles from London. A similar balloon of 5 ft. diameter went up from Sandwich in Kent on 22 February 1784, and reached Warneton in French Flanders 75 miles away, thus becoming the first balloon to cross the channel.

The first manned flight in Britain was that of James Tytler, who had earlier largely edited the Second Edition of the Encyclopaedia Britannica, and who rose from Comely Gardens in Edinburgh on 27 August 1784 in a hot-air balloon of his own construction. This was a short flight of a few minutes' duration, covering a distance of about half a mile, and took place almost without witnesses.

It was only on 15 September, 1784, that England witnessed a manned ascent, carried out in London with a success all the greater because of the scepticism which still dominated the large crowd which had gathered in the Artillery Ground – a scepticism fuelled by the failure of a Frenchman named De Moret to carry out an announced ascent in a hot-air balloon from the grounds of the Chelsea Hospital on 11 August,

and the crowd's consequent destruction of his machine.

The aeronaut was another Italian, Vincento Lunardi, who was Secretary to Prince Caramanico, the Ambassador of the Kingdom of Naples in London. He had intended to take with him an English gentleman named Biggin, but the inflation of the hydrogen balloon having taken longer than anticipated and the crowd becoming restless, Lunardi decided to set off with the balloon partly inflated, accompanied only by a dog, a cat, and a pigeon. The balloon was equipped with oars, one of which fell off shortly after he set off, and was later reported by Lunardi in a letter to his guardian to have caused the death by heart failure some few days later of a lady who had mistaken it for himself. After rising to a great height, Lunardi let his balloon – which had no valve – come

The first ascent in England, by the Italian Lunardi, at the Artillery Ground, London, 15 September 1784.

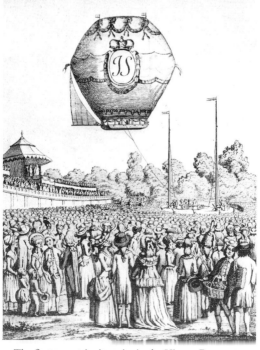

The first ascent in Austria, in the Vienna Prater, on 7 July 1784, by the pyrotechnist Stuver.

Blanchard's ascent at Nuremberg, 12 November 1787.

The first ascent in Germany: Blanchard landing at Weilburg.

down; he made a stop at North Mimms, to set down the cat which was suffering from the cold, set off again and finally landed at Standon, near Ware, in Hertfordshire.

Lunardi was presented to the King and fêted on all sides; he afterwards devoted himself for some years to a career as an aeronaut, most notably in Scotland, Italy, Spain and Portugal.

Shortly after, Blanchard carried out a series of ascents in London, where his passengers were Dr. Sheldon and a Dr. Jeffries, the first American to leave the earth. These two doctors carried out their ascents as scientific experiments, and Dr. Jeffries later accompanied Blanchard on his historic crossing of the Straits of Dover.

The first English aeronaut was James Sadler, at Oxford on 4 October 1784. He continued his career until 1825, being prevented, in October 1812, from being the first man to cross the Irish Sea, by a sudden change of wind that forced him to descend into the sea off Liverpool. His two sons followed in his footsteps, one of whom successfully completed the same crossing on 22 July 1817.

The first ascent in Germany was by Blanchard in Frankfurt on 3 October 1785. He landed at Weilburg, in Nassau. He later frequently made ascents in the larger German cities with great success; the German princes followed his progress with interest, and often gave him "most generous gifts" in reward.

In 1786 Baron von Lutgendorf attempted in vain to set off from Augsburg. It was not until much later that German aeronauts emerged; the first was Bittorf in 1804, then the Reichardts from 1810 onwards.

Blanchard was also the first man to leave the earth in Holland, Belgium, Switzerland, Poland and what is now Czechoslovakia, with ascents in The Hague on 12 July 1785, Gand on 20 Novem-

ber 1785, Basel on 3 May 1788, Warsaw on 30 May 1789 and Prague on 31 October 1789.

In Austria, he was preceded by the pyrotechnist Stuver, who, on 7 July 1784, went up in a vast and strangely shaped balloon, accompanied by three passengers. His intention had been only to effect a captive ascent but the anchor rope broke and the balloon rose freely; the jolt also produced the beginnings of a fire, which was swiftly put out, and the balloon landed without further incident, after having crossed the Danube.

SIC ITUR AD ASTRA

The first ascent in America by Blanchard.

In Spain, a Frenchman, Bouche, began his career in aviation in a rather unfortunate manner: leaving from Aranjuez on 4 June 1784, in a hot air balloon, he forgot to have the rope which anchored the top of the balloon removed; the balloon rose, then turned upside down, the fire falling inside. Badly burned, Bouche jumped from a great height. He was critically injured, but survived.

Ascents in hydrogen balloons did not begin in Spain until 1792, with Lunardi, who also introduced them to the Portuguese in Lisbon on 24 August 1794.

An important ascent was reported from Turkey in March 1785: a balloon, piloted by a Persian physicist, accompanied by two bostangis from the seraglio, is said to have left Constantinople in the presence of the Great Sultan and, after successfully crossing the Bosporus, to have landed at Bursia.

It is difficult to know whether or not this ascent was invented by the journalists of the day, like that of the carpenter, Wilcox, who was supposed to have set off from Philadelphia by means of a bunch of little balloons!

There was, however, definitely an ascent in Constantinople in 1802, made by Barly and Devigne and, in 1825, a Turk, Selim Ogat, went up in a hot-air balloon in Smyrna.

Blanchard's forty-fifth ascent was the first aerial voyage to be made in America. Embarking at Hamburg in September 1792, the great aeronaut took with him provisions of sulphuric acid which he had ordered from London.

The ascent took place on 9 January 1793, in front of President Washington, who presented the pilot with a passport signed in his own hand. The weather was favourable, and Blanchard, leaving from the middle of a large crowd, landed forty-seven minutes later in a forest.

The ascent of Guyton de Morveau and Abbot Bertrand, Dijon, 25 April 1784, in the balloon *L'Académie de Dijon*.

EXPERIMENTS WITH PROPULSION

Though rudimentary, early attempts at controlling balloons are often of interest. The balloon built by the Academy at Dijon, which was tested by Guyton de Morveau with, successively, Abbot Bertrand and M. de Virly, on 25 April and 12 June 1784, carried two oars fixed to the basket, two larger oars on the centre-line of the balloon itself, a rudder behind and a streamlined device in front. The aeronauts could by these means turn and rotate a little.

The Duke of Chartres, later Philippe-Egalité, engaged the Robert brothers to build the first

Descent of the Robert brothers' second long balloon, at Beuvry, in Artois, 19 September 1784.

elongated balloon, which had a small balloon inside the gas-bag, in which air was compressed to control vertical movements. The lengthened basket carried two parasol-like oars. No useful result was obtained; the balloon left Saint-Cloud on 15 July 1784, and rose rapidly to a considerable height; the little balloon blocked the valve of the larger, and in order to avoid a rupture the Duke had to pierce the gas-bag with a flagpole. The highly perilous descent ended safely at Meudon.

Soon afterwards, the Robert brothers built a new balloon of the same shape; cutting their 1783 balloon into two halves and inserting a cylindrical section. The basket had five parasol-oars. The brothers and their brother-in-law Collin-Hulin left from the Tuileries on 19 September 1784 and after six hours and forty minutes landed at Beuvry, near Arras, in front of the castle of the Prince of Ghistelles who had himself just launched a balloon. With their oars the aeronauts had been able to steer some 22 degrees off the wind, and to execute part of an ellipse.

Blanchard experimented with several systems of articulated oars, then with a propeller, but without great success, and it seems without much

The first night flight, Tetu-Brissy, 18 June 1786.

conviction; he declared in a letter that he believed human force to be inadequate, but that steering could probably be achieved by the use of the "fire-pump" or steam-engine. Lunardi too swiftly rejected oars, with which he had obtained only vertical movements. The hot air balloon built by Abbot Miolan, Janinet and Bredin, was designed to be moved by the reaction from escaping air as proposed by Joseph Montgolfier. The launch was a failure and the balloon was destroyed by the furious crowd on 12 July 1784.

Alban and Vallet, directors of a chemical factory at Javel, built a fine balloon by subscription in 1785, which was named after the Comte d'Artois, the future Charles X, who is supposed to have taken part in the captive ascents. The basket was fitted with rotating paddles which could be feathered for any chosen part of each revolution, and thus could control both vertical and horizontal movement, although the principal means of propulsion was a propeller, which gave appreciable cross-wind manoeuvrability.

The first elongated balloon, flown on 15 July 1784 by the Duke of Chartres, the Robert brothers and Collin-Hulin.

On 18 June 1786, Tetu-Brissy made an ascent in Paris, from the Luxembourg, in a balloon with oars. Using these to aid his descent, he touched down near Montmorency, then set off again, in spite of a severe and prolonged storm, on the first nocturnal flight, landing near Breteuil in the early hours of the morning, after eleven hours in the air.

General Meusnier of the Engineering Corps designed in 1785 a gas balloon with a remarkable system of restraining straps and an internal air balloon to give permanence of shape to the gas-bag and control of vertical movements. Propellers worked by hand winches provided the propulsion, and the project included a permanent hangar and a tent for campaigns. Owing to lack of funds and Meusnier's death during the wars of the Revolution, the balloon was never built.

D'Alban and Vallet's dirigible balloon *Le Comte d'Artois*, at Javel, 1785.

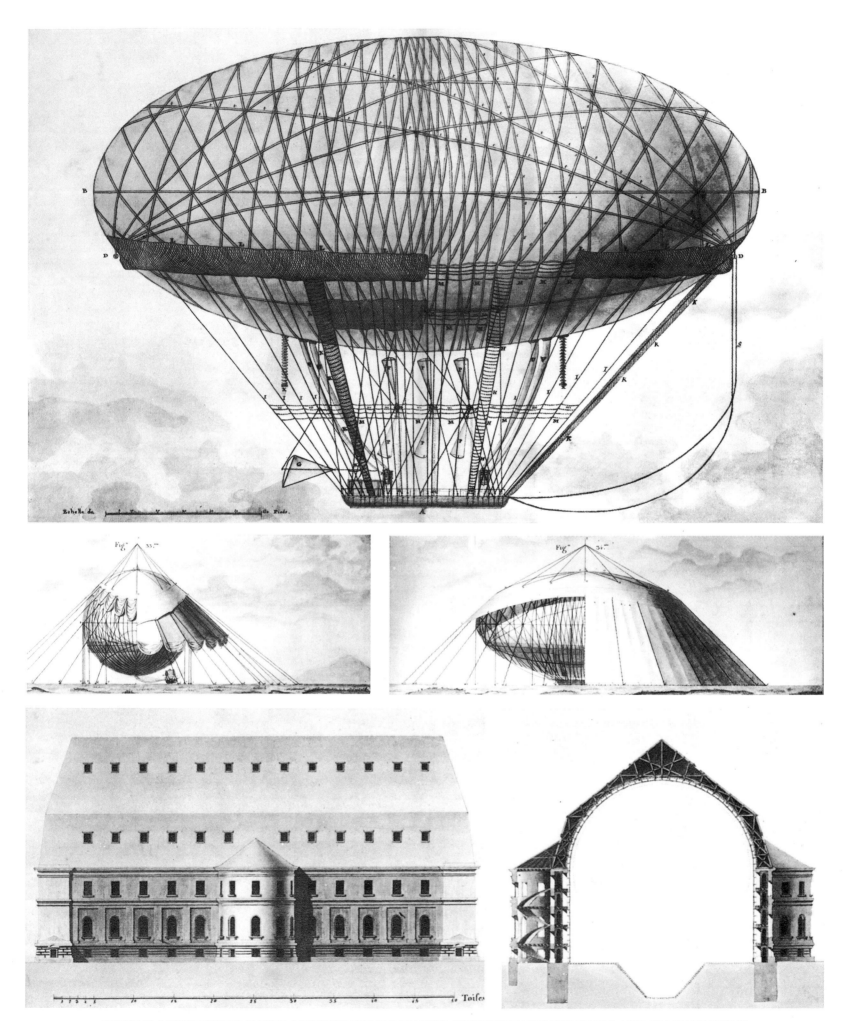

GENERAL MEUSNIER'S PLAN FOR A DIRIGIBLE BALLOON (1785), WITH PERMANENT HANGAR AND CAMPAIGN TENT.
(Original watercolours preserved at the Musée de l'Aéronautique, Chalais-Meudon.)

THE FIRST SEA CROSSING

From the day of his first ascent, Blanchard had dreamed of achieving the "first aerial crossing of the sea" and it was with this in mind that he embarked for England in September 1784.

One of his passengers in London, Doctor John Jeffries, originally from Boston, but then serving in the British army, was attracted by this project and asked to accompany him. It was agreed that the doctor would pay the costs of the ascent.

Once in Dover, the aeronauts did not have long to wait for favourable winds. On 7 January 1785, on a cold, clear morning, Blanchard decided to leave, following his reading of the clouds and of pilot balloons, but contrary to the advice of the sailors. The balloon was quickly inflated, and at five minutes past one it left from the foot of the old castle. The inadequacy of the means which the crew had at their disposal is frightening: the little balloon, which was not even proven to be impermeable, carried only three bags of ballast weighing ten pounds each, a large packet of leaflets, two small anchors, two cork life jackets, several bladders inflated with air, some provisions, a telescope, a barometer, a compass and a large quantity of clothes; in all, about 95 pounds, to which was added the weight of the oars and windlass, the rudder and the ornaments on the basket.

The moment of departure was emotional, Mrs Jeffries and her daughter having begged the doctor in vain to renounce the voyage. The balloon rose into the air, rotating slowly as it moved forward over the calm sea, dotted with boats.

Jeffries, in his account of the journey, describes the pleasure which he felt at the sight of the coast and the English countryside, with the ancient town of Canterbury rising above it, and the strong impression created by the breakers near the Goodwin sands.

At 1350, the balloon began to descend: two bags of ballast were thrown out. The crew profited from the renewed upward movement of the balloon to arrange ropes around the balloon's lower circle to which they could cling if they fell into the sea.

The balloon started to descend again in the middle of the crossing: the rest of the ballast and the leaflets lightened it, but, at 1415, a further movement downwards had to be prevented. The sight of the French coast, from Gris-Nez and Blanc-Nez as far as Calais and Gravelines, delighted the travellers and gave them renewed courage. At 1430, the downward movement increased very rapidly; the provisions, then the two pairs of oars and the rudder went overboard, as did the windlass. This major disposal of ballast did not suffice; the ornaments from the basket had to be sacrificed followed by the only bottle which they had taken with them: it was open when they threw it out, and created a cloud of liquid as it fell.

Still rapidly approaching the sea, they threw out the two anchors, then they undressed, throwing out their coats, jackets and even their trousers; they put on their life jackets. Three quarters of the distance had been covered; Jeffries offered to sacrifice himself; Blanchard refused the offer. At that moment, the balloon started to move upwards again; the countryside,

The first balloon crossing of the Straits of Dover: Blanchard and Jeffries arriving at Calais on 7 January 1785. The engraver plainly did not understand the method either of attaching the gas-bag or of operating the oars (shown clearly in the engraving of Blanchard's first flight). In any case the oars were jettisoned before the French coast was reached.

The column erected in 1786 in the Forest of Guines.

four or five miles in the distance, gradually became clearer to the valiant navigators.

In the course of this last upward surge, the highest of the entire voyage, at three o'clock, they crossed the coast between Gris-Nez and Blanc-Nez. Blanchard threw out a packet of letters, the world's first air mail, which they watched for a long time as it drifted slowly towards the earth.

The wind had become quite strong and the balloon was approaching the Forest of Guines, several leagues from Calais. The life jackets – the final ballast – were thrown out, also the bladders which contained the aeronaut's urine, to lessen the impact with the trees over which the basket was skimming. By grabbing hold of branches and opening the valve, the aeronauts were able to stop between two trees and to deflate the balloon. For a while they remained alone, then they were surrounded by the local inhabitants who came rushing up to them and lent them clothes, since

they were by now suffering from the cold, despite their work and, above all, their joy at having triumphed. Jeffries apparently dipped into his snuff box twenty times in a row and had even embraced Blanchard when they landed.

That evening, the aeronauts were received in Calais, and the following day there was a solemn reception given in their honour by the municipality, which offered Blanchad the title of citizen. Jeffries received the same honour from the town of Dover. The town of Calais bought Blanchard's balloon from him and, like Christopher Columbus's boat, it was placed in the local church. The basket still survives and is kept in the museum at Calais.

At Versailles, the two aeronauts were received by the King. Blanchard was granted the sum of 12,000 pounds and an annual pension of 1200 pounds. A column, erected in 1787 in the forest of Guines, perpetuates this great event.

The fire on Pilâtre de Rozier and Romain's hydrogen/hot-air balloon, Wimereux, 15 June 1785.

THE FIRST CATASTROPHE

From the middle of 1784, Pilâtre de Rozier was obsessed by the idea of crossing from France to England by air; he dreamed of leaving Paris by balloon and travelling to London. His project received the support of the Minister, Calonne, and he was given an initial credit of 42,000 francs. With Pierre-Ange Romain, who had discovered a means of making material impermeable, he constructed, in two rooms in the Tuileries, a balloon composed of a spherical hydrogen balloon with a small cylindrical hot air balloon fixed underneath, with a gallery for the travellers and a burner.

The principle of the new balloon was described by one of Romain's collaborators, Francois Rever: "By virtue of the gas, the weight of both balloons . . . reached equilibrium in the atmosphere; then, the smoke from the burner gave added lightness; one could move upward at will and, if the lower air currents were unfavourable, go higher up to seek better ones and drift freely."

The balloon was 33 ft. in diameter and was made from fabric coated with a mixture of which the full formula was known only to Romain, but which included strong glue, honey and oil. The outer covering was decorated with painted figures. The balloon was so perfectly impermeable that it remained inflated for two months without a single wrinkle appearing in it. The smaller hot air balloon was a cloth cylinder 25 ft. high sealed at the top with goat's skin.

Pilâtre and the Romain brothers moved in December 1784 to Boulogne-sur-Mer, the place chosen for their departure. Anxious about Blan-chard's preparations, Pilâtre went to England to visit his competitor. A short time afterwards, he witnessed his success and realised the disaster which this implied for him.

Back in Paris, Pilâtre tried to get the project cancelled by Calonne; the Minister received him coolly and would agree to this only if Pilâtre paid back the expenses, which were considerable.

In debt and committed to the project, Pilâtre returned to Boulogne and inflated the balloon several times in January and April, without being able to depart, as the winds were never favourable. There was much criticism of the project, from the papers and in songs of the day. Material problems increased: the balloon was attacked by rats and suffered damage from the cold; it was summarily repaired.

On 13 June 1784, Pilâtre made up his mind to depart; the balloon was inflated and on the morning of the 15th was ready. The winds seemed favourable, at least at certain heights.

The departure took place at 0707; the aeronauts seemed to have forgotten their worries, but the crowd remained silent and subdued. The balloon rose and reached the sea. It had gone just over a league when it was seen to be coming back. Twenty-seven minutes after the departure, the balloon was gliding over Wimereux, when movements of alarm were observed on the part of the voyagers, who hurriedly lowered the burner. An enormous flame appeared at the top of the gas balloon, which deflated in a few seconds. The gallery, the montgolfier and the balloon crashed into the fields at Wimereux, a few hundred yards from the edge of the sea and the river.

Pilâtre, his body shattered, died instantly. Romain survived several minutes, unable to speak.

Several monuments commemorate the memory of this tragedy; a modest "needle" marks the actual spot of the fall at Wimereux, and at the cemetery in Wimille, beside the Calais–Paris road, a tomb covers the remains of the two victims, one of whom was "the first man to leave the earth."

The tomb of Pilâtre de Rozier and Romain, which still remains in the cemetery at Wimille.

Louis-Bernard Guyton de Morveau (1737–1816)

Jean-Marie-Joseph Coutelle (1748–1835)

Nicolas-Jacques Conté (1755–1805)

THE FIRST MILITARY BALLOONISTS

At the instigation of Guyton de Morveau, a man of great foresight, whose role in the creation of military ballooning has been too little recognised, the Committee for Public Safety, on the advice of the Commission for the Study of the Application of Science in the Interests of the State, decided in June 1793 to equip the French armies with captive balloons where "observers, placed like sentinels, hidden in the clouds, would observe the movements of the enemy."

In order to inflate these balloons without using sulphuric acid, a physicist, Coutelle, was ordered to investigate a new method using red-hot iron. On 25 October the Committee decided to supply a balloon to the Northern army and designated the little chateau at Meudon for the construction and testing of the balloon, and for subsequent use as the headquarters of a school of balloonists. Citizens Coutelle, Lhomond and Conté – the

latter a physicist, artist and engineer of great talent – were to be responsible for the work.

On 2 April 1794, the first company of balloonists was assembled and put under the command of Coutelle. Two months later, the first military captive ascent took place near Maubeuge, when Coutelle and Adjutant General Radet went up in the balloon *Entreprenant*.

The balloon was then transported still inflated from Mauberge to Charleroi, and there is no doubt that the observations made by the generals Maison, Morlot and Olivier during the engagement aided them considerably in countering the movements of the enemy, and thereby contributed effectively to the capitulation which took place on 25 June.

The next day, the battle of Fleurus was begun against the Coburg armies. The *Entreprenant* was in the air throughout the entire day, transmitting the observations of General Morlot by signals.

The officers who took part in the ascents showed immediate enthusiasm for this new means of gaining intelligence. Moreover, the

morale of the French troops was noticeably lifted by the presence of this unknown war machine, whilst their enemies, the Austrians in particular, were very much affected by the presence of this globe of which the method of operation was still a mystery to many of them.

Following the movements of the Northern army, the balloonists made ascents in Charleroi, Jumet, Fleurus and Lambersart: on 5 July, at the Battle of Sombreffe, General Jourdan, the Commander-in-Chief, mounted into the basket himself. The value at which he estimated the military importance of the balloon is reflected in the picture of one which he had printed on his writing paper.

This balloon appeared later at the engagements at Liége and Brussels. A second company was formed and at the same time a corps of military balloonists was given official status. In 1795, the first company took part in the sieges of Borcette, Ehrenbreitstein, Bonn and Koblenz; the second company was sent to Pichegru's army near Mainz. The following year, the first company

The construction of balloons around 1793 in a gallery at the chateau at Meudon. Watercolour by Conté.

Military balloonists building a balloon in baudruche. Watercolour by Conté

Head of letter from General Jourdan to Brigadier Dejeau, showing in the letterhead the balloon *Entreprenant*.

was captured at Wurzburg and its balloon still survives as a trophy in the Arsenal in Vienna. The second company operated in Molsheim, Rastadt, Stuttgart, Donauwerth and Augsburg; in three months, they covered more than 200 miles, with their balloon fully inflated and rarely resupplied. This performance provides direct evidence of the excellence of the design, for which Conté must take the credit, and of the workmanship shown in its construction.

A balloon was also sent to the army in Italy and took part in the siege of Mantua; this little known fact is illustrated in the engraving reproduced at the foot of this page.

Unfortunately the new form in which the war was being fought did not lend itself to the use of balloons, which were very difficult to transport, and as a result, in 1797, most of the balloon corps was disbanded. However, Bonaparte ordered the first company to come to Egypt; most of their materials and equipment were in consequence lost at Aboukir.

The activity of the balloonists of the Revolution was to bear fruit later; a new branch of aeronautics had been born.

(Overleaf). The military balloonists' captive balloon at the siege of Mainz (1794). Watercolour by N.J. Conté. (Musée de l'Aéronautique)

The siege of Mantua (August 1796). Italian engraving showing the balloon of the French military balloonists.

Jean-Pierre Blanchard (1753–1809)

Mme Madeleine-Sophie Blanchard (1778–1819)

that period, appears even more remarkable.

It was Garnerin too who launched, on 16 December 1804, a great unmanned balloon for the celebration of Napoleon's Coronation; carrying an imperial crown made from shining glass, it crossed the Alps alone and landed the next day in Lake Bracciano, at the gates of Rome.

Garnerin next travelled across Germany and Italy, then, in 1807, he began a series of nocturnal ascents in an illuminated balloon in the Tivoli gardens in Paris.

On 4 August 1807 he spent the entire night in the air and came down near Rheims; on 22 September 1807 he set off in a violent storm and in seven hours was carried far into Germany, landing with difficulty in a forest in Clausen, near Waldfisbach, in the area near Zweibrucken, which at that time was in the province of Mont-Tonnerre. This voyage was of nearly 250 miles in length and remained the French record for distance until 1863. He made further long flights in each of the three succeeding years, to Broussey-en-Woevre, Aix-la-Chappelle and Simmern, near Frankfurt.

Mme Jacques Garnerin, nee Jeanne-Genevieve Labrosse (1775–1847), was the first woman to pilot a balloon, also the first to make a parachute jump; in fact she is the first female aeronaut, the women who preceded her having done so only as passengers. She carried out many ascents in France, England, Germany and Russia.

minutes, covering 200 miles and landing at Polova, a district of Gisdra. When one considers the situation in Russia at that time, and the difficulties that he was bound to face with transport for the return journey, this great ascent, the record for

At the same period, Mme Blanchard made more than sixty ascents in Europe, until the disaster which took place in Paris on 6 July 1819, when she was killed, falling from her burning balloon.

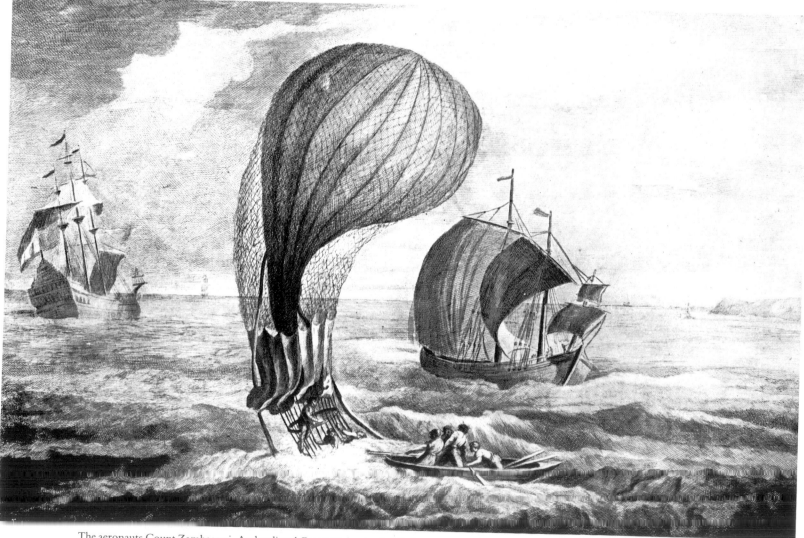

The aeronauts Count Zambeccari, Andreoli and Grassetti, having left Bologna on the night of 7 October 1803, are rescued from the Adriatic.

HEAVIER-THAN-AIR MACHINES AT THE BEGINNING OF THE NINETEENTH CENTURY: GEORGE CAYLEY

The greatest technical genius of the first third of the nineteenth century was undoubtedly George Cayley, the true inventor of the aeroplane and one of the grandest figures in the history of aviation.

Sir George Cayley came from an old Yorkshire family and was born in Brompton on 27 December, 1773. In him were combined all the qualities of his great compatriots and contemporaries who changed the face of the modern world: Richard Trevithick, James Watt and George Stephenson. He was an excellent theoretician who, like these,

George Cayley, the inventor of the aeroplane.

could think in three dimensions; for this reason all the machines which he depicted had realistic proportions and logical dimensions. In 1796, he repeated the experiments of Launoy and Bienvenu with a small bow helicopter, and until the end of his long life he never ceased to be interested in aerial locomotion.

His main works were articles in *Nicholson's Journal of Philosophy* in 1809 and 1810, in *The Philosphical Magazine* in 1816–1817, and in *The Mechanic's Magazine* in 1837 and 1843. In the first of these works, he clearly defines the principles of the aeroplane.

He starts by expressing his conviction that human flight requires less force than might be supposed, and he rejects entirely the idea of using beating wings to produce lift. He declares that "the whole problem is confined within these limits, viz. To make a surface support a given weight, by the application of power to the resistance of air."

Summing up the aerodynamic experiments which he carried out using surfaces fixed to a merry-go-round he defines the angles which the surfaces made with the horizontal which appeared to be most favourable to the production of lift, and, at this early date, concludes that concave surfaces are much more effective than flat surfaces.

He then shows with great clarity the advantage

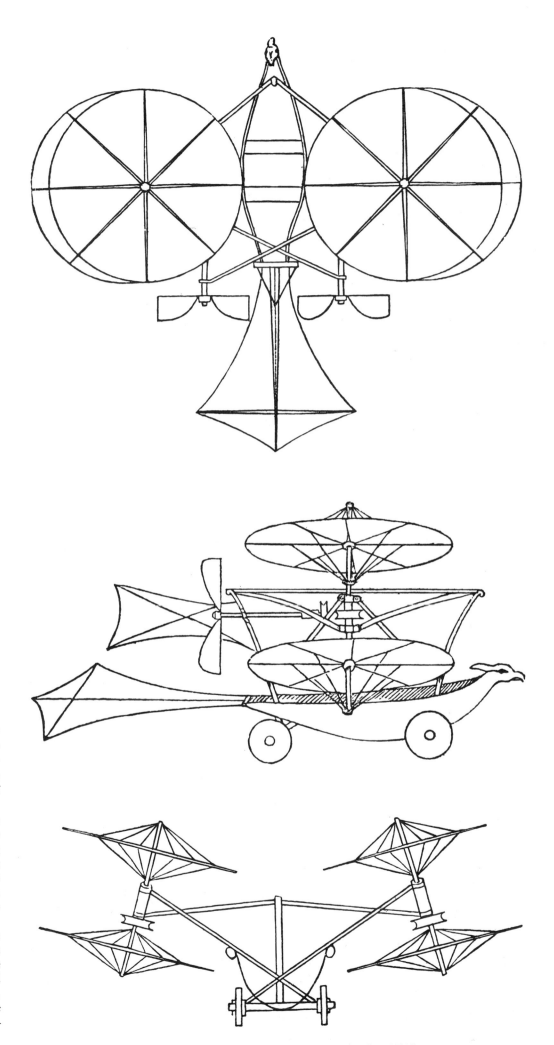

Plan and elevations of Cayley's helicopter-aeroplane (1843).

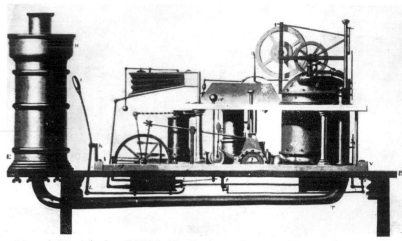

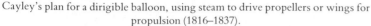
Cayley's plan for a dirigible balloon, using steam to drive propellers or wings for propulsion (1816–1837).

Niepce's "Pyréolophore" (1806). The first internal combustion engine, using lycopod powder as fuel. Original drawing by Niepce attached to his inventor's patent.

of building wings with a dihedral to achieve lateral stability, and the necessity of an "up-and-down" rudder in addition to the "side-to-side" one. To propel the machine, Cayley envisages using either the beating action of a part of the wings which are reserved for this purpose, or a "propeller", which he calls an "oblique flyer".

From the outset he rejects human force as being insufficient, and proposes the use of a steam engine with a light boiler and very thin water tubes, or a gas motor, or an internal combustion engine such as were being built in France at that time (the machine developed by Niepce, using lycopod powder or tar oil).

In short, in 1809, a century before his time, Cayley described every detail of the modern aeroplane.

In 1810, he suggested the use of biplane surfaces braced together as being easier to construct and more solid than monoplane wings; at the same time, he studied in detail the question of diminishing the resistance to forward movement of the fuselage and of streamlining all the various elements of the construction.

Cayley carried out many experiments; before 1809 he built a large glider which could be used for tests with or without a pilot on board. He describes the flights of this machine in the area near his home in Brompton: "It was very beautiful to see this noble white bird sail majestically

from the top of a hill to any given point on the plain below it, according to the set of its rudder, descending merely by its own weight, in an angle of about 18 (8?) degrees with the horizon."

After one experiment in which Cayley had persuaded his coachman to get on board the glider, the coachman refused point blank to continue the tests, begging his master to note that he was employed to drive, and not to fly.

In 1843, inspired by the ideas of Henson, Cayley described a project in the *Mechanic's Magazine* for a helicopter-aeroplane, accompanying the account with the illustrations reproduced here. The circular discs were to ensure the vertical take-off of the machine by rotating, then, when the two propellers had been started, the blades of the supporting discs flattened themselves to form aeroplane wings. The machine included an undercarriage and both horizontal and vertical rudders.

Cayley was a man with a lucidly analytical mind. He realised that aerial travel would be achieved by dirigible balloons sooner than by aircraft; in 1816, he described an airship moved by either wings or propellers, powered by steam. He envisaged that in the future it would be possible to construct rigid dirigibles with a metallic outer covering containing individual bags of gas, and investigated ways of constructing a wooden frame for a small airship. He also examined the potential of glider-balloons, an idea put forward

earlier by Montgolfier.

In 1837, he tried to create a "Society for the Advancement of Aerial Navigation".

Cayley was still publishing essays on aviation in 1852 and 1853, this time in France, in the review founded by Dupuis-Delcourt, and indeed he continued his aeronautical research until his death on 15 December 1857, at the age of eighty-four.

The Niepce brothers' engine, mentioned above, was the first to make use of internal combustion for direct propulsion, using a safe fuel. It was tested in a boat on the Saône, at Chalon, in about 1806, and was patented in 1807, under the name "pyréolophore" by the inventors, after demonstrating the principle at the Academy of Science. The fuel used was lycopod powder, but the inventors envisaged being able to replace this with coal dust.

In 1788, a short time before Cayley carried out his first tests, a Frenchman, General Resnier de Goue, born in Angoulème in 1729, after a brilliant career in the army, published under the pseudonym of *Reinser II* a curious work entitled *The Universal Republic or Rational Humanity*, in which, along with his discussion of social questions, he described and illustrated a plan for a flying machine. This consisted of cane wings covered with fabric, which were attached by ball and socket joints to a kind of corset which went

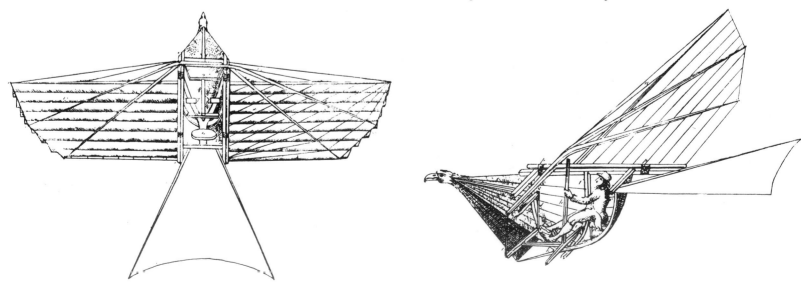
Thomas Walker's flying machine (1810). (Library of the Royal Aeronautical Society of Great Britain)

round the aviator's chest.

At that time he declared that he was too old to test the macine, but he made it clear that he had constructed it. However, having retired in 1801, he returned to Angoulême and built a new machine of a similar type, but this time with feathered wings. Despite his age of seventy-two, on this occasion he did try it out. Throwing himself from the rampart of Petit-Beaulieu, 100 ft. above the ground and 225 ft. above the River Charente, he was able to glide for some way, and land without difficulty in the river, where he was rescued by boat. A little later, in the course of another experiment, he crashed in a field and broke his leg; this did not prevent him from living to the ripe age of eighty-two.

In 1810, Thomas Walker published a short study, entitled *The Art of Flying*, in which the author, unknown elsewhere, analyses numerous anatomical studies of birds from the point of view of artificial flight. He illustrates a flying machine, formed of two beating wings with valves, with a tail to give stability. In a second edition, published in 1830, Walker illustrates small aeroplanes with wings with flexible trailing edges, and a plan for an aeroplane with two monoplane wings in tandem, the first time that this arrangement appears.

From 1806 to 1817, a Swiss clockmaker living in Vienna, Jacob Degen, made a number of trials of a machine with beating wings, which he tested while suspended from a cord connected to a counterweight, which he made lighter as he improved the machine. Later, he replaced the counterweight by a little balloon, and thus carried out a number of ascents – without any attempt at steering – in Vienna, then in Paris in 1812, until a resounding failure in the Champ-de-Mars, when the furious crowd broke the machine into pieces. Nevertheless, Degen flew again in Paris in 1813, and in Vienna in 1817. In 1816 he tested a small helicopter with two propellers which turned in opposite directions.

Several failures also occurred at roughly the same period: in Paris in 1799 Calais jumped from the top of a pole with a little parachute with wings, and fell without doing himself much harm; and in 1811 in Ulm a tailor named Berblin-

Machine with beating wings designed by General Resnier, called Reinser, constructed around 1788.

ger fell into the Danube whilst testing a machine similar to that of Degen. Berblinger's attempt has remained famous in Germany and has been the subject of several novels.

In Italy, during this period, experiments were carried out by a cobbler from Florence, Vittorio Sarti, who was particularly interested in the ap-

plication of propellers to balloons and aircraft. He gave an illustrated description of a remarkable project for a helicopter which, like that of Degen, had two propellers, one above the other, turning in opposite directions; it was, equipped with a sail to prevent the basket from rotating and a sliding counterweight to maintain equilibrium.

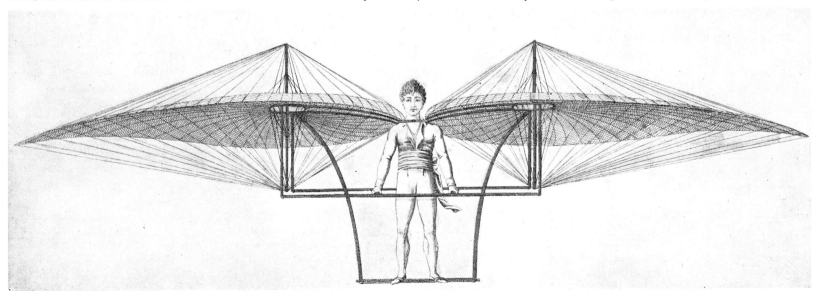

Jacob Degen's machine with beating wings, tested in Vienna, 1806–1811, and in Paris, 1812 and 1813.

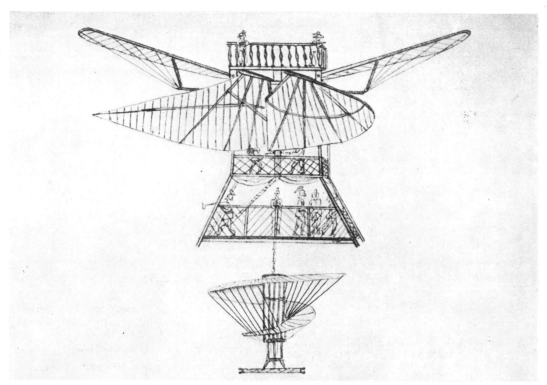

Lambertye's *L'Aerienne*, a machine with beating wings designed for military observations (1818).

Uniforms of airborne troops proposed by Count de Lambertye.
1. Private on guard duty; 2. Private in the "engine-room"; 3. Officer ordering manoeuvres; 4. Light infantryman or boy to climb into the cage or on to the wings.

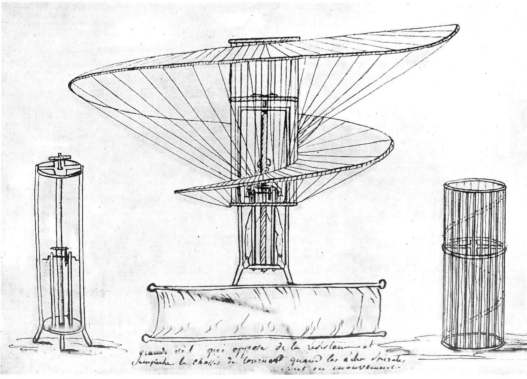

Helicopter designed to ensure communication between *L'Aerienne* and the earth.

MILITARY AVIATION
FROM 1800 TO 1850

After Aboukir there is no record, apart from the invasion propaganda noted above, of any further use of balloons by the French Army until after the end of the Napoleonic period, although in Moscow in 1812 the Russians built a large balloon, designed by a German named Leppich, to bombard the French Army; it was barely finished when the French entered Moscow, and the soldiers crushed the machine underfoot.

However a manuscript of the period, left by Count Adolphe de Lambertye of the French Army, which includes plans for a flying machine entitled *L'Aérienne*. This consisted of a cage with four beating wings, two "flying" wings being placed front and rear to raise the craft while two "steering" wings on its sides propelled it forward. The crew were to actuate the wings by hand cranks.

Lambertye envisaged a small model for one or two people, and a military version, with a crew of nine, including an officer and two "ship's boys". In this the structure has three floors: the "engine-room" in the middle; above, the observation gallery; below, the room where the men would go when off-duty.

To communicate with his airborne fleet, Lambertye planned a helicopter, with a screw propeller, worked by a man using a double crank in a cylindrical cage, inside another cage forming the propeller shaft. A sail stopped the inner cage from turning. The whole was to be made from wood and wicker, covered with fabric and braced by wires. The helicopter would be carried under *L'Aérienne* by a knotted rope providing access between the two.

Apart from an uncomfirmed report of a balloon at Anvers in 1815, the next record of a balloon at war occurs at the French siege of Algiers in 1830.

Jean Margat, a professional aeronaut since 1809, in 1829 demonstrated a balloon to the French Corps of Engineers, and secured a contract to accompany the expedition to Africa with a two-man balloon. The transportation was not without its problems. Margat was nearly shipwrecked four times, and the sulphuric acid to make the hydrogen, loaded in glass demi-johns which broke when the ship rolled, caused the ship transporting it to catch fire. After all this, there is some doubt as to whether Margat actually made an ascent in Algiers.

During the quarrel between the United States and Mexico in 1846 and 1847 the American aeronaut Wise proposed to the American government the construction of an enormous balloon to drop bombs on the citadel of Saint John of Ulloa and the town of Mexico. The plan was not adopted.

In March 1848, the Milanese, under siege from the Austrians, launched paper hot-air balloons carrying printed matter, news and proclamations, while the Austrians during the same siege used balloons to transmit telegraph signals. In the following year, during the siege of Venice, the Austrians launched about a hundred balloons, each carrying a bomb with a timed fuse. The attempt was a complete failure; only one bomb fell near Saint Peter's Square, while most of the balloons, diverted by a cross-wind, exploded their bombs in the Austrian camp.

Mme Margat's flotilla of balloons (1828).

THE GROWTH OF FREE BALLOONING

The art of ballooning spread rapidly both inside and outside Europe during the early years of the nineteenth century; the corollary to this was that it came to be dominated by showmen and public ascents in free balloons rather than by innovators seeking advances in technology. The exceptions to this were France and England, where private ascents became very frequent and where the professionals were often accompanied or replaced by amateurs.

When balloons were first invented, Louis XVI sent to the Emperor of China, as a gift, twelve small balloons and the materials with which to inflate them; at the same time, Lapeyrouse launched hot-air balloons in Chile.

Clarke reports in his *Voyages* the first launch of an unmanned balloon in the Arctic Circle, in the presence of the Lapps of Tornea, in 1816.

E.G. Robertson, who took up Sacharoff of the Saint Petersburg Academy, and was himself the first person to make ascents in Sweden and Denmark during the course of a career which covered almost all the countries of Europe, had two sons who more than any others propagated aerial travel in distant lands.

Eugene Robertson made several "balloon ascent tours" in America: he was in New York and New Orleans in 1825 and 1836; he introduced ballooning to the West Indies and to Mexico with ascents in Havana in 1828, and in Mexico City and Vera Cruz in 1835. He died of yellow fever in Vera Cruz in 1836.

His brother Dmitri Robertson toured widely in Europe, then embarked for India, where he made ascents in Calcutta and Lucknow in 1835. He died in Bombay in 1837.

Other French professionals, Guille, Durant and Michel, made ascents in the United States. The first American aeronauts appeared in 1830 or 1835: Hobart, Clayton, John Wise and Paullin, who was the first man to make an ascent in South America.

Margat too continued his career for a long time after his military venture; it ended only with his death in 1854, at the age of sixty-eight. His wife also made a number of successful ascents.

The first hot-air balloon to be launched inside the Arctic Circle; an ascent in the presence of the Lapps of Tornea, at Enontekis, around 1816. (After Clarke's "Voyages".)

A German aeronaut, Kirsch, made a great number of ascents in France; like his colleagues M. and Mme. Lartet, he used a hot-air balloon which was very strongly heated before the departure and went up without a burner. The ascents were correspondingly brief and, if the danger of fire was avoided, the risks were increased by the violence of the take-off and the uncertainty of the landing. Numerous incidents marked these ascents: on 16 July 1843, in Nantes, Kirsch's hot air balloon broke away prematurely during its inflation, and its anchor lifted away a child of twelve,

Eugene Robertson's ascent in the Castle Garden, New York Battery, 10 October 1826.

Comaschi's ascent in Constantinople at a fête given by Haydar Pasha to celebrate the wedding of H.I.H. The Sultana Adile and H.H. Mehemet Ali Pasha. (Lithograph published in Turkey.)

Left: the accident which befell Kirsch's balloon in the Parc Monceau, in 1844.

Right: Young Guerin carried away by Kirsch's balloon in 1843.

a young boy named Guerin, who was carried for several hundred yards, but came down again without further harm; young Guerin's adventure still remains very popular in Nantes. In the following year, Kirsch's balloon split while being inflated in the Parc Monceau.

An Italian aeronaut, Comaschi, carried out a number of ascents in France and Italy, and in Turkey, where on 8 July 1844, he made a fine ascent, including a maritime crossing between Constantinople and Desmirdje Davasi. In the following year he returned to make a public ascent on 12 June on the occasion of the wedding of the Sultan's daughter to the ageing ruler of Egypt. Two weeks later on 25 June 1845, having gone up once more in Constantinople, he was lost in the Black Sea.

The first person to cross the Alps in a balloon was a Lyonnais, Francisque Arban, whose aerial voyages in France, Italy, Austria and Spain were numerous and remarkably well conducted; he went up from Marseilles alone on 2 September 1849, and landed in the early hours of the following day, near Turin, after having crossed the mountain range.

Arban gave an account of his momentous voyage in the following terms:

"I left from Chateau-des-Fleurs on Sunday 2 September at six-thirty in the evening; at eight o'clock I crossed the forest of the Esterel, at a height of 13,000 ft. It was cold but dry, and my centigrade thermometer read 4 degrees below zero. The wind was blowing from the south-west and was carrying me towards Nice.

For over two hours I was enveloped in thick clouds; my pelisse was not sufficient to protect me from the cold, from which I suffered a great deal, especially in my feet. I resolved nevertheless to continue my journey, and decided to cross the Alps, to which I knew myself to be close, my provision of ballast being sufficient to carry me above the highest peaks.

The cold increased, the wind became regular, and the moon shone out on me like the sun in broad daylight. I was at the foot of the Alps; the snow, the waterfalls, the streams sparkled; the abysses and the rocks formed black masses which cast shadows on this enormous tableau.

The wind prevented my progress from being constant; I was obliged to move down and up in turns in order to cross the peaks which constantly presented themselves. It was eleven in the evening when I arrived at the summit of the Alps; the horizon cleared, my progress became steady, and I was able to think of eating.

I was at a height of 15,000 ft.; I had no option but to continue my journey and reach Piedmont; I could see before me only chaos, and it would have been impossible for me to descend in those regions. After having eaten, I had the idea of throwing my empty bottle in to the middle of the snow so that if one day some adventurous traveller climbed the peak, he would find a sign which would make him believe that someone had explored these uninhabited regions before him.

At one-thirty in the morning, I found myself above Monte Viso, which I knew, having explored it during an early voyage in Piedmont. The Po and the Durance have their sources there. I recognised it by its position and its magnificent

Francisque Arban (1815–1849).

snow-fields. Before this confirmation of my position, a singular effect of mirage, produced by the moon on the snow and the clouds, almost made me believe that I was in the middle of the sea. However, the west wind had not ceased to blow and my calculations showed me that I could not be above the sea. The stars confirmed the evidence of my compass, and then I saw Mont Blanc, towering above the clouds like an immense block of crystal which shone with a thousand fires and whose position on my left indicated to me that I was nearing Turin.

At two forty-five, Monte Viso, which was behind me, showed me for certain that I was very close to Turin. I decided to bring the balloon down, which I achieved without difficulty, still retaining some ballast at my disposal.

I came down near an immense farm; several guard dogs surrounded me, but my pelisse protected me from their caresses. Their barking woke the farmers, who were more surprised than frightened at my presence, and invited me in to the farm-house; they told me that it was two-thirty in the morning, and that I was in the village of Pion Porte, near Stubini, 4 miles from Turin."

Francisque Arban's next ascent was fatal to him. Having left Barcelona on 7 October 1849, in the company of his wife, Arban landed on the beach and put down Mme Arban. Setting off again towards the sea, he disappeared for ever.

His fate was shared by several aeronauts of that period: the Frenchman Ledet disappeared in Lake Ladoga in 1847, following an ascent at Saint Petersburg, and the Italian Tardini, after numerous ascents in Poland and Sweden, drowned in 1851, in the sea off Copenhagen. But none of these aeronauts had the talent or indeed the enthusiasm of Arban, whose performance on his voyage in a balloon from France to Italy via the Alps has only been repeated once, in 1924, by Rene Latu, who was also to die very young following a fall into the sea.

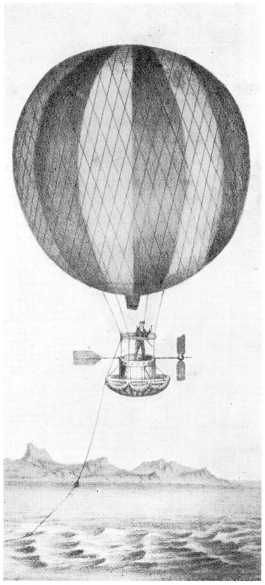

Charles Green's plan for a transatlantic balloon with a propeller and stabilising floats (1840).

CHARLES GREEN

Born in London in 1785, Charles Green discovered ballooning in 1821, and from his first ascent put into practice an innovation of major importance; he inflated his balloon with ordinary coal-gas instead of hydrogen. Green remained faithful to this method, which at that time was easy to implement in England, where coal-gas was already fairly widely used for street-lighting, and in so doing contributed more than anyone else to the spread of balloon ascents. His other major innovation was the use of a ballast rope – a length of heavy rope suspended vertically from a balloon so that its end just trailed along the ground. If the balloon sank, more of the weight of the rope was transferred to the ground and the balloon automatically rose again, and vice versa. This represented an enormous saving of both ballast and gas, the alternate jettisoning of which had up till then been the usual way of controlling height.

Green had the perfect temperament for an aeronaut: he was calm, he was hard-working, he had an ingenious mind and an excellent knowledge of construction, he could charm his passengers with his ease and the sureness of his manoeuvres, and, in the course of the five hundred and four ascents which he made from 1821 to

Charles Green (1785–1870). The earliest known photograph of an aeronaut.

1852, he carried without accident thousands of people, men and women, among whom were some of the greatest names in England. Ballooning as a sport developed enormously under his initiative in Great Britain, particularly after 1836.

It was in that year that Charles Green built a magnificent balloon in red and yellow silk: the *Royal Vauxhall*, the volume of which was over 85,000 cubic ft., an enormous size at that period. It made hundreds of ascents and was still serving nearly forty years after its construction.

On 7 November 1836, accompanied by Robert Hollond M.P. and Monck-Mason, Green left at one-thirty in the afternoon from Vauxhall in London, crossed the Channel, spent the entire night in the air, flying over the North of France, Belgium, the Rhine, and part of Germany, and landing after eighteen hours at Niederhausen, near Weilburg, in Nassau. Nearly 500 miles had been covered and this "great voyage of Nassau" caused a considerable stir, the balloon being re-named the *Nassau* after this flight.

The first long distance aerial voyage: Green, Hollond and Monck-Mason crossing the Meuse, near Liége, during the night of 7 to 8 November 1836.

Disaster of Robert Cocking's inverse parachute, 24 July 1837.

After several ascents in Paris, Green arrived back in London and there pursued his profession with great activity, supported in this by his two brothers and later his son, Charles George Green.

On July 24th, 1837, Green consented to take with him on an ascent the inventor of a parachute in the shape of a reversed cone, Robert Cocking. Above the town of Lee, he cut the cord which joined this new parachute – which was logically conceived but badly constructed – to the *Nassau*. The parachute collapsed and the inventor fell to his death. Green and Spencer, aboard the newly de-ballasted *Nassau*, rose to a great height.

Later, Green made a plan to cross the Atlantic in a large balloon equipped with a rope of floats, which, on the same principle as the ballast rope on land, would keep the balloon at a constant height above the water, and a directional propeller, but the attempt was never made, though towards the end of his career, in 1851, Green made another channel crossing, from Hastings to Neufchatel; his passenger on this occasion was the Duke of Brunswick.

A certain number of Green's many aerial voyages had a scientific purpose, notably the high altitude ascents which he made with Rush, and with John Welsh of the Kew Observatory.

Charles Green died in London in 1870 at the age of eighty-five.

DUPUIS – DELCOURT

Jules-Francois Dupuis-Delcourt, a dedicated aeronaut, a historian of ballooning and the director of the Ambigu, had had from childhood a passion for aerial travel; he made his first ascent in 1824 at the age of twenty-two; he was witness to many famous experiments and incidents; he knew everyone who was involved in aeronautics, and he had the idea of gathering together a definitive collection of books, prints, posters, documents and other objects connected with ballooning. He was also a prolific author and organiser of conferences; he spent his entire life publicising the future form of travel which fascinated him so much.

In 1836, he presented to the Academy of Science a plan for a balloon-kite made from copper, armed with spikes and held permanently in place by means of electrical conductors, which he called the "electro-subtractor", and which was designed to prevent the formation of hail. This study led him to envisage the construction of a free balloon in copper, designed to make ascents. Finding in Edmond Marey-Monge a financial backer, as well as a technician, he completed the construction of this metal sphere in 1844.

The volume of the copper balloon was 18,700 cu. ft. and its surface area was 3765 sq. ft. The covering alone weighed 680 lb.

The difficulties of constructing this ball of thin copper were immense. It was built on a wooden frame which was then extracted while the form of the balloon was maintained by the continuous pumping in of air, lasting for months; it was later refilled with hydrogen, introduced through the top part of the covering while the air escaped from the bottom.

The refilling had not yet been completed when, losing heart at the moment of attaining success, Marey-Monge gave up. Left to his own resources – which were very modest – Dupuis-Delcourt struggled to survive; in August 1844, he transported the balloon, inflated with air and loaded on to a cart, across the whole of Paris to premises

Dupuis-Delcourt (1802–1864), photographed by Nadar.

which he had been lent in the Roule foundry. But faced by ruin, he was forced to renounce his dream of launching the first metal balloon with himself as pilot, and to hand over the debris of the balloon covering to the foundry owner.

In 1847 he assisted Dr Van Hecke to carry out a new kind of experiment in Brussels, a system of propellers with vertical axes designed to achieve, without expenditure of ballast or of gas, vertical movements of a balloon and, in consequence, a form of steering by elevating the balloon to a level where the wind would be favourable.

The experiment, carried out with an unmanned balloon, gave good results, but was not followed up, though the idea of ballast-propellers was taken up again with partial success by Delamarne in 1865, and by Major Beaumont in England in 1874, then much later by Lhoste, Maurice Mallet and Santos-Dumont.

Returning to Paris, in 1849 he made with Regnier a number of demonstrations in the Orangerie at the Luxembourg, of a model of a dirigible balloon made from baudruche. This carried a kind of lattice girder fitted at the front with a propeller with curved blades, at the centre with an elevator, which seems to have been tested in this way for the first time, and at the back with a directional rudder. It was driven by clockwork.

One of Dupuis–Delcourt's most interesting ideas was for the creation of an aeronautical museum, which he expounded in a pamphlet published in 1857 under the title: *Considerations on the Utility of Founding a Ballooning Museum*. It was not until sixty-four years later that the idea was implemented.

Dupuis-Delcourt also created, in 1852, the first ever aeronautical society: the *Aeronautical and Meteorological Society of France*, whose members eventually formed the *French Society for Aerial Travel*, which still exists. This society, intended not for the exploitation of a particular method of aerial travel, but for the study of all questions of ballooning, aviation and meteorology, numbered in 1853 more than 150 members, amongst whom were some of the greatest names in science and of the Parisian world: the Count d'Orsay, Jacques Arago and Count du Roy, George Cayley, the engineers Giffard, Andraud, Franchot, and the inventors Jullien, Vaussin-Chardanne, and Meller. Important works were presented and technical competitons organised. In particular, they studied air resistance, propellers, impermeable materials and the means of mechanically obtaining the upward and downward movement of the balloons. In all, the Society published in 1852 and 1853 four issues of its bulletin, *The Annals of Ballooning and Meteorology*, a precious source of information.

Dupuis-Delcourt died in poverty, in Paris on 2 April 1864, but he left intact his precious collection of aviation history, of which the greater part still exists, divided amongst several collectors and in the Aeronautical Museum.

Dupuis-Delcourt's copper balloon (1844).

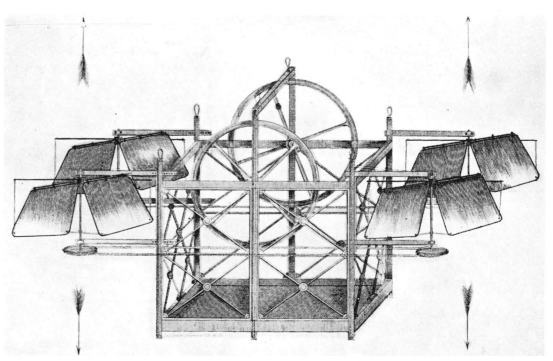

Dr Van Hecke's basket with propellers for ascent or descent (1847).

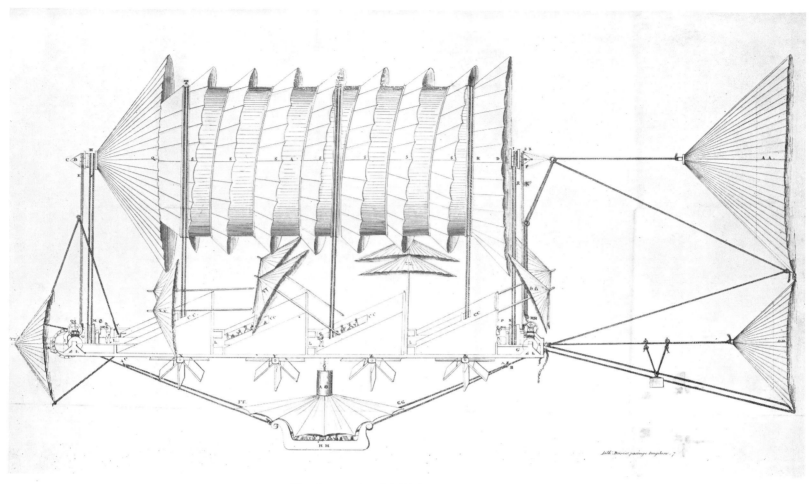

Plan for a rotating dirigible by Pierre Ferrand (1835).

Poster advertising Eulriot's dirigible balloon.

EXPERIMENTS WITH DIRIGIBLE BALLOONS

The period between 1830 and 1850, which saw such a great flourishing in inventions in all the other mechanical arts, included, as might have been expected, a large number of projects for dirigible balloons.

In 1832, Count Lennox and Dr Le Berrier made an ascent at Montmartre with a dirigible equipped with jointed oars which allowed them to achieve enough displacement from the actual line of the wind as to be able, it is claimed, to throw a crown over the column in the Place Vendôme in Paris. After the founding of the Aeronautical Society, they built a new dirigible, which had a volume of nearly 100,000 cu. ft., and was called L'Aigle; it was equipped with paddle-wheels, a little compensating balloon for compressed air, and was supposed to carry seventeen passengers. On 17 August 1834, the net which held the balloon broke; the balloon escaped and was ruptured. After another failure in London, Lennox died from despair.

In 1839, Eulriot made an ascent in the Champ-

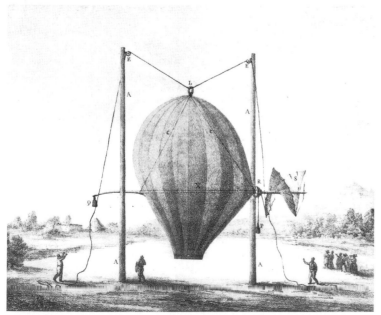

Experiment in Italy on the traction of a propeller.

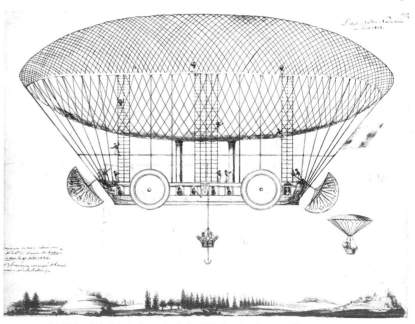

L'Aigle, dirigible balloon built in 1834 by the Count of Lennox.

Monck-Mason's model for a dirigible with propeller (1843).

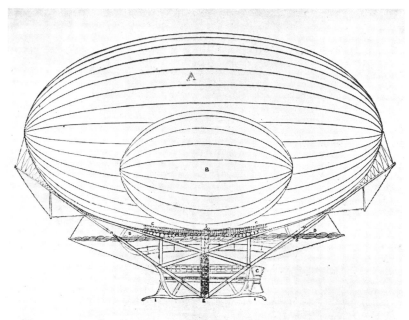

Partridge's plan for a dirigible (1843).

de-Mars in a long, asymetric balloon, with the larger end towards the front, a perfectly rational structure, but he could obtain no result using only the force of his own muscles to turn two paddle wheels with oar-like blades.

Around 1835, a Strasbourg pastor, Kopp, wrote an essay full of interesting ideas for rigid dirigibles with propellers.

In the same year, a rotating dirigible was again suggested by Pierre Ferrand: the outer covering of the gas-bag was itself to serve as the axle of an immense continuous propeller. This impractical idea was often proposed.

On a more empirical note, the trials made in Italy between 1823 and 1828 by Napoléon-Louis Bonaparte, in collaboration with his brother, the future Napoléon III, merit an examination; the prince experimented with the traction of propellers pulling a chariot on a stretched wire; in another series of experiments he fixed his propeller to an air balloon and studied its displacement while suspended from a rope slung between two poles.

The end of the period covered by this chapter, just before the introduction of the motor in aerial travel, saw several interesting achievements, in which the propeller, the use of which was still a subject of controversy at this time when applied to ships, was used regularly by aeronauts.

In about 1840, Green carried out demonstrations with a small balloon with a propeller.

In 1843, Monck-Mason, Green's passenger in the great *Nassau* voyage, demonstrated a model in London which functioned as a dirigible; it was a long balloon, with a rudder and a large propeller moved by a clock mechanism. Inspired by this idea, Partridge described at the same period a dirigible equipped with both a propeller and centrifugal jets which worked by reaction; it had horizontal beams to ensure its rigidity and a small interior balancing balloon.

In 1844, in the Cours-la-Reine, Le Berrier exhibited a model of a dirigible with propellers which were moved by a little steam engine: this was the first real application of a motor to a machine for aviation purposes.

In 1848, Hugh Bell took out an extremely detailed patent for a dirigible balloon and a flying machine, a kind of rudimentary aeroplane. The dirigible, which was described in great detail, was similar in form to that of Partridge. It also was equipped with a small compensating balloon. The basket was suspended from a webbing net that completely enclosed the main gas-bag. The basket carried two side-mounted propellers worked by a hand wheel and a rudder.

Advancing to the stage of experiment, Bell soon built his dirigible, the first elongated balloon to go up in England. He made two ascents in 1850, but with no other force than that of his arms, he could not obtain any satisfactory result as regards the steering. The balloon had a volume of about 17,500 cu. ft.

In 1851, *L'Illustration* published, together with an article by Dupuis-Delcourt, the plate reproduced. This sums up different solutions to the problem of aerial navigation: the balloon-fish of Baron Scott, a project published in 1789 and

Ascent of Bell's dirigible at Vauxhall (1850).

Plans for aerial travel before the use of the motor.

which included, apart from the propulsive oars, little air balloons in front and behind to modify the balance; the dirigible which Pauly tested in 1804 and 1805, with which he obtained some control of steering in the course of the ascents made, and which the inventor reconstructed in 1816 in London; the balloon-glider of Guillé, built in 1814, which failed to go up from the Champ-de-Mars – the forward movement was to have been achieved by angled wings gliding through the air during ascent or descent; Lennox's *L'Aigle*, which has already been described; the project of Dr Van Hecke, including trains of balloons harnessed according to the weight which was to be carried and which upward-pointing propellers could move into favourable air streams; the pro-ject of Mme Tessiore, published in 1845, with the vulture harnessed to it; finally, the multi-ballooned dirigible (1844) of Renous-Grave, a baroque idea conceived by an ignorant inventor.

In this illustration, no balloon has a mechanical motor; it marks the end of techniques that vanished in the face of Giffard's exploit of 1852.

CHAPTER TWO

THE FLYING MACHINES

1843-1900

The period covered in this chapter is a time of research and experiments. It begins with the first applications to aeronautics of the steam engine and ends with those of the combustion engine.

The dates 1843–1900 have been carefully chosen. In 1843, W S Henson published the first complete plans of an aeroplane, an astonishing work for that time. The next year saw the use of the first mechanical motor in aeronautics, the little steam engine which Dr Le Berrier fitted on to his model airship. That same year Henson and Stringfellow constructed a huge model steam aeroplane. Four years later, Stringfellow first successfully flew a model aeroplane, powered by two steam-driven propellers.

Although characterised by experiment, the second half of the nineteenth century gave rise to some important results: a demonstration of aerial propulsion, by Giffard in his huge airship in 1852; a demonstration of control, by the closed circuit of Renard and Kreb's balloon, La France, in 1884; a demonstration of the possibility of flight by heavier-than-air machines by the take-off of Ader's steam aeroplane in 1890: a demonstration of the stability and control of such aircraft, by Otto Lilienthal, from 1891 to 1896.

The attempts to make dirigible balloons were many. After the experiments of Jullien, whose intuition amounted to genius, the achievements of Henri Giffard were of fundamental importance: the first application of steam to aerial navigation. After this, curiously, for over 30 years no experimenter tried to lift a mechanical motor into the air, apart from a limited attempt by Haenlein with a gas machine, until the ascent of the Tissandier brothers in 1883, with an electric motor.

The triumph of Renard and Krebs was due, not only to their understanding of the underlying concepts but also to their technical ability. Part of their contribution was the first solution to aerial locomotion which was accompanied by security, demonstrated by their repeated flights without accident.

The unlucky Wofert remains, in spite of his lack of success, the pioneer of the combustion engine, which he fitted to his airship in 1896, the year in which Lilienthal died. A year later, Schwartz's metal balloon, a prelude of great things to come, made its first ascent. Shortly after, in very different ways, Santos-Dumont and Count Zeppelin began their experiments, which,

after persistent attempts, were to lead to the two forms of modern balloons, rigid and flexible.

Aviation held an important position during this half century; contrary to widespread opinion, the heavier than air problem obsessed the researchers and even the public at this time. Although it was generally assumed that the solution was still distant because of the weight of existing motors, there were nevertheless many plans and experiments; those of Du Temple, Pénaud, Kress, Langley and Hargrave, stand out because of the logic of their concepts and the soundness of their research.

Between 1890 and 1891 two men made simultaneous demonstrations that, although opposed in their approach, had an equal importance in history. Clement Ader built a complete flying machine with an engine, which with him on board skimmed the surface of the ground for some 50 yards. Otto Lilienthal believed that man must first "learn his role as a bird" and made over two thousand glider flights of up to several hundred yards.

Word of their experiments spread, giving birth to modern aviation, through Chanute and the Wright brothers.

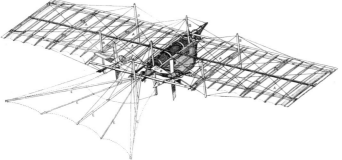

Reproductions from L'Illustration of 8 April 1843 showing details of W.S. Henson's design for a steam-powered areoplane. The key to the drawings on the left hand page reads: A. Frame or wings – BB. Struts carrying iron chains which support various parts of the frame – CC. Longitudinal bar forming outer limit of space reserved for the propellers – DD. The propellers driven by the steam engine – EE. The tail hinged at F – G. The hull containing the steam engine, the cargo and the passengers – H. The rudder.

HENSON'S AEROPLANE

L'Illustration gave up part of one of its earliest editions, No.6, of 8 April 1843, to "Mr. Henson's aerial steam engine". This machine had just been patented in England and its elegant lines had made a great impresion on both the world of engineering and the public at large.

The patent taken out on 29 September 1842 by William Samuel Henson marks one of the most important moments in the history of aviation; it is the first complete description of an aeroplane of which it can be truthfully said that if constructed and supplied with enough power, it would certainly fly. Indeed this machine both in its overall design and in its constructional details was much better conceived than many aeroplanes of the glorious period from 1907 to 1910.

An article, with reproductions of the patent drawings and an impression of the machine in flight, summed up Henson's invention thus:

"The reader should imagine a vast wooden framework, 160 ft. long and 30 ft. wide, which is solid but light, covered in silk or cloth which serves as the wings, although there is no joint or movement, and which moves sideways through the air, the front side higher than the back. A tail, about 50 ft. long and of similar construction is attached to the middle of this lower side; under this tail there is a rudder."

"Finally, hanging beneath the framework is a hull for carrying merchandise and passengers and a powerful but small and light steam engine, that turns two varied wheels similar to windmill sails, each about 23 ft. in diameter and located just under the framework."

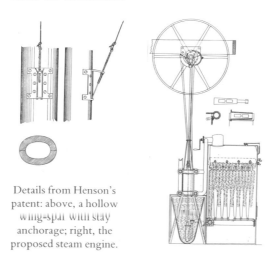

Details from Henson's patent: above, a hollow wing-spar with stay anchorage; right, the proposed steam engine.

For his take-off Mr Henson "has recourse to nature; his machine, once ready to depart, is launched down an inclined plane. As it descends it acquires the necessary speed to keep it in the air for the rest of its voyage. Air resistance slows it down bit by bit; all the steam engine has to do is to make up for this loss of speed . . ."

Amongst the main mechanisms described in the patent are: wings consisting of 3 spars and a leading edge and single and double ribs of curved profile, the whole covered in fabric on both sides, and reinforced by struts and straining wires; the use of hollow wood for the spars; propellors; control surfaces for height and direction together with their controls; sprung landing gear; a cabin enclosed by fabric. The whole structure is conceived in perfect proportion. Finally, Henson completed his description with that of his light steam engine – aviation's first power plant – that was designed to produce twenty horsepower.

Henson had in 1842 made tests on clockwork models, and in 1844 he constructed with Stringfellow who took care of the practical details a large model of the machine as it appears in the patent. This machine was tested without convincing results in 1847, near Chard. It still exists, preserved in the Science Museum in London.

Stringfellow's monoplane of 1848: the first aeroplane to fly using mechanical power.

The boiler and engine of Stringfellow's monoplane.

THE WORK OF JOHN STRINGFELLOW

Henson's colleague, John Stringfellow, was a manufacturer from Chard (Somerset), gifted with ingenuity and an excellent sense of practicality.

He was the first man to make an aeroplane fly using mechanical power. The machine, which was begun in 1846, and which is carefully preserved in the Science Museum in London, was finished in 1848; it was a monoplane with a wingspan of 10 ft., and was 5 ft. 6 in. long, 3 ft. 6 in. of which was the tail. The wing area was 14 sq. ft. Two propellers with four blades, placed in cut-outs on each side of the rear section of the wings, were turned by a small, admirably constructed steam engine with a multiple condenser boiler. The wing was curved in section with a rigid leading edge and a flexible trailing edge. Stringfellow followed carefully the theories of Cayley and Walker and this is very probably the reason for his success.

The whole machine weighed 8 lb., and 8 lb. 9 oz. with the fuel and the water.

Trials took place at the beginning of 1848 in a factory building which was 80 ft. long; the aeroplane was attached to a carriage running along a wire, from which it released automatically. On the first attempt, because the tail was attached at too great an angle, the machine rose abruptly and fell back down with a marked loss of speed. Once repaired, it was launched in a better condition, released itself from the cables, and rose gradually until it hit a piece of cloth hung up at the far end of the hall to catch it, and which it tore because of the speed at which it was going. The trials were continued in the presence of different witnesses, and then were repeated in Cremorne Gardens in London where the machine achieved a flight of about 130 ft.

Stringfellow, satisfied with these attempts, but unable to see success with a full-scale aeroplane immediately possible, abandoned the idea for some twenty years.

The founding of the Aeronautical Society of

Great Britain rekindled his old enthusiasm and for the competition organised by this Society at the Crystal Palace, Stringfellow entered a very beautiful model of an aeroplane. It was a triplane with a wing area of 28 sq. ft., not including the tail, and weighed 35 lb. The power was provided by a small steam engine which produced a third of a horsepower.

At the same time, Stringfellow presented another steam engine, admirably constructed and very light, which won a prize of £100 which the Aeronautical Society had offered for a light motor designed for aviation.

Because of the risk of fire, free flights of the aeroplane were not allowed, and it could only be tested attached to a wire, but its lift could be measured. The motor still exists, in the Air and Space Museum in Washington, where it was taken by Langley who purchased it later.

Stringfellow continued with his research for several years, dedicating the prize money he won in 1868 to his experiments. He died, aged 84, in 1883.

Two views of Stringfellow's steam-powered triplane, photographed in 1868.

Poitevin's equestrian ascent at the Champ-De-Mars, on 14 July 1850.

PUBLIC ASCENTS
1850–1851

The years 1850 and 1851 saw, in France, a major revival of interest in balloons; the newspapers wrote about nothing but balloons, carrying reports of ascents that had suddenly become very numerous, or publishing plans for dirigible balloons.

Arnault, an ambitious manager and director of the Hippodrome, then situated near the Place de L'Etoile in Paris, alongside what is now the Avenue Victor-Hugo, was responsible for much of this resurgence. Having found a first rate performer in the young aeronaut Godard, Arnault organised balloon ascents regularly, on Thursdays and Sundays, from his establishment which was then at the peak of its popularity. The ascents from the Hippodrome were often accompanied by aerobatic stunts: the balloon lifted "the brave Thévelin" on a trapeze, the "Ladies of the Air",

ballerinas attached to a cardboard cloud, or the "Furnished House", a two-storey house, also made of cardboard, surrounding the balloon, not to mention descents by parachute.

A rival organisation, at the Champs-de-Mars, was managed by the aeronaut Poitevin, whose speciality was equestrian ascents. Poitevin made several ascents riding a live horse, or, accompanied by his wife, in a barouche harnessed to two horses, or with a cavalcade of three horses, suspended from a huge balloon. He even went up on a ostrich that was struggling so much that he had to return quickly to the landing area. Mme. Poitevin often portrayed the Rape of Europa, mounted on a bull. The strange thing is that there were never any accidents at any of these bizarre ascents.

At the same time many members of the public took the opportunity to ride in balloons at the Hippodrome, which probably had more far-reaching effects than the popular interest in the staged ascents.

THE WATCHMAKER JULLIEN

"First the facts! Today, 6 November 1850, a balloon of a pleasingly simple shape and totally manoeuvrable has navigated in the wind, against the wind, in accordance with the whims of its inventor . . . and the indications of that master of us all, the public."

It was in this way that the newspaper *Le Siècle* began its account of the demonstration made the day before at the Hippodrome by the watchmaker Jullien from Villejuif.

Pierre Jullien, an ordinary craftsman who became a watchmaker, was a man of rare genius. His passion for aerial navigation, his ingenuity and his instinctive sense of proportions were to place him in the van of the pioneers of aeronautics.

With no fortune, he began his experiments on propulsion around 1845, and it was on the propeller that he focused his research; he measured the speed of little chariots running along wires under the action of varying shapes of propellers driven by clockwork.

He then did tests on a larger scale by sitting on one end of a horizontal beam turning on a central pivot and fitted, at the other end, with two hand-driven propellers. By this means he managed to turn in a circle at a reasonable speed. When considering the shape of his balloon he took his inspiration from fish, and measured the speed and the resistance to penetration, through water, of a number of tapered bits of wood – a perfectly scientific method.

Finally combining his propellers with a fish-shaped balloon made from baudruche he obtained the desired forward movement but with marked pitching; it was then that he had the idea, and was the first to do so, of equipping his balloon with a horizontal fin at the rear, a surface which both steadied the craft and served as an elevator.

A new balloon was demonstrated at the Hippodrome from 6 to 10 November 1850. Julien Turgan describes, in *La Presse*, the first trials:

"M. Jullien carried first into the riding school, then into the amphitheatre of the Hippodrome, a

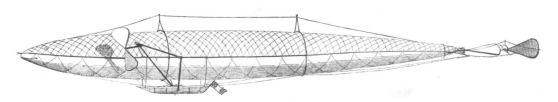

Jullien's model which demonstrated aerial propulsion at the Hippodrome on 6 to 10 November 1850.

small balloon, which was 23 ft. long and of an oblong shape, and having set up a very simple mechanism of his invention, he let go the machine which moved rapidly in the direction which had been previously agreed.

In the riding school there was no wind, so the thing seemed very easy; but once in the amphitheatre our astonishment was great, as we saw the experiment repeated in spite of a fairly strong south-westerly wind. The balloon moved directly into the wind. It was started again in different directions and every time the experiment was successful."

Elegantly constructed, this balloon, with a volume of 13 cu. ft., was powered by two propellers driven by clockwork. The whole thing weighed only 2½ lb.

Arnault, director of the Hippodrome, encouraged the inventor and took out a patent with him, and then helped him to construct a new model nearly 50 ft. long, which was tested successfully at the beginning of 1851.

In the following year, Jullien was able to exhibit a full-size dirigible balloon, in the rue Marbeuf, with the well deserved name of *Precurseur* (*The Forerunner*): 164 ft. long, 26 ft. in diameter, and 36 ft. wide overall, including the two propellers, this balloon was of an asymmetric shape, which was perfectly correct from the point of view of aerodynamics. A net of straps held the balloon with the propellers placed near the centre of resistance. Fins forming both rudders and elevators were provided towards the rear of the gas-bag as was usual in much later dirigibles. Unfortunately, the *Precurseur*, which was moved in November 1852 to the gas factory at Passy, could never be tried out.

In 1858, Jullien made a small aeroplane, 3 ft. long, and weighing only 1¼ oz., powered by two propellers driven by a rubber band. In five seconds this aeroplane flew nearly 40 ft.

Around 1864, Jullien worked on the idea of light electric motors and he would have obtained one horsepower for a weight of only 82½ lb. His final efforts were poured into the development of suitable batteries for this. Unfortunately, no clear documentation remains.

Another of his inventions was the barometer-motor, a machine which perpetually transformed through a mechanism the oscillations of the liquid column of a barometer into circular motion.

Jullien died in 1876, aged 69, poor and forgotten, in the hospice at Sainte-Anne.

BARRAL AND BIXIO

In 1850, two ascents, which caused considerable comment at the time, reminded the public that balloons, besides their use as a spectacle, had a very important role, often forgotten even nowadays, in the acquisition of scientific knowledge. Two scientists, Barral and Bixio, carried out these aerial voyages under the auspices of the Academy of Science of the Collège de France. Neither of them had ever been up in a balloon before. Nevertheless, they made their first ascent from the garden of the Paris Observatory, on 29 June,

The Ascent of Bixio and Barral on 29 June 1850. (Print published by *L'Illustration*.)

during a real storm and with altogether inadequate equipment.

After travelling through a thick blanket of clouds, the novice aeronauts enjoyed a magnificent light above the clouds. Busy with their numerous instruments, thermometers, compasses, and air sampling balloons, they realised too late that the gas-bag had expanded and was pressing down on the basket; causing a rent in it by accident or design they were nearly asphyxiated by the escaping gas; an uncontrolled descent of about 20,000 ft., which they barely slowed down by sacrificing all but their instruments, took them down violently into a vineyard near Lagny.

On 27 July, showing extraordinary courage, they took off again, still in unsettled weather. They reached an altitude of 23,120 ft., where the temperature was down to −39°C, even though at 20,000 ft. it had been only −9.5°C. Around 13,000 ft. they had travelled through a cloud of

tiny icicles in suspension and had observed the rare spectacle of the reflection of the sun on this dazzling cloud. Some pigeons which had been taken up showed a marked reluctance to leave the basket at the maximum height; when pushed, they fell heavily downwards. Barral and Bixio descended near Coulommiers, without further incident other than having a misplacedly zealous rural policeman cut the rope of their anchor with a swipe of his sword.

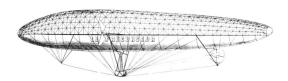

Pierre Jullien's *Le Precurseur*, designed and constructed in 1852, but not flown.

Henri Giffard (1825–1882). Engraving by Dereaux (1863).

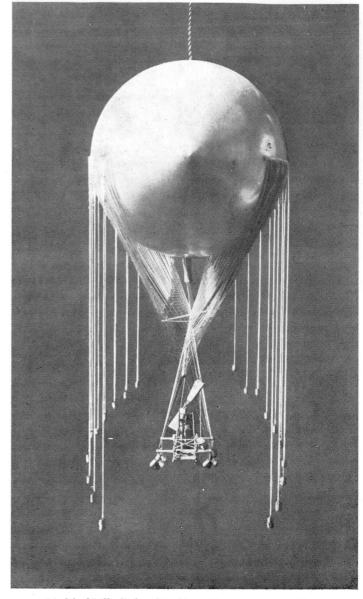

Model of Giffard's first dirigible airship, seen from the front.

THE FIRST DIRIGIBLE STEAM BALLOON

HENRI GIFFARD

Henri Giffard, born in Paris in 1825, was one of France's most renowned engineers. An inventor of great genius and practicality, and a heroic experimenter, his memory is deeply linked to the railway by his invention of the injector for steam engines that still carries his name, and in the field of aeronautics he was the first man to fly with a mechanical motor, and manage, under the power of that motor, to manoeuvre his airship.

After having followed with enthusiasm the beginnings of the railway at Saint-Germain, and himself driven the engines, Giffard became in 1844 the assistant of Dr Le Berrier for his first model of a dirigible airship.

He conscientiously taught himself to manage free balloons with the aid of the Godards, and then constructed in 1852 a huge dirigible airship with a volume of 88,300 cu. ft. assisted by M. David and M. Sciama. This spindle-shaped balloon was 144 ft. long and 39 ft. in diameter. A net

made of straps that went over the gas-bag, which was filled with coal-gas was attached to a 65 ft. boom, designed to maintain the shape of the balloon and to carry the rudder. Underneath was a frame carrying a small platform and the steam engine. This consisted of a vertical boiler with an internal firebox without pipes; the gases from the combustion passed through a case surrounding the boiler, then ran, with the steam, through an exhaust directed downwards. A vertical cylinder turned a three-bladed propeller, 11 ft. in diameter, at 110 revolutions per minute. The machine produced three horsepower and weighed 330 lb. when empty. At take-off it contained an additional 132 lb. of water and coke.

Only one trial took place, at the Hippodrome on 24 September 1852.

Two days later, Emile de Girardin reported in great journalistic style, in *La Presse*, the take-off of the first dirigible airship worthy of this name:

"Yesterday, on Friday 24 September 1852, a man took off, unruffled, sitting on the footplate of a steam engine, lifted by a balloon in the shape of a huge whale . . .

This Fulton of aerial navigation is called Henri Giffard. He is a young engineer whom no sacrifice, no miscalculation, and no danger have been

able to discourage or turn aside from this enterprise . . . It is a great and dramatic spectacle, that of the champion of an idea, confronting with the boldness that his invention has given him, the danger, perhaps even death . . . How can the government . . . not grant credit of 1 million francs to find the solution to the problem of aerial navigation? Is there a more important solution for France?"

Another witness, M. Emile Cassé, later wrote:

"Having been present at this experiment, we love to remember the enthusiasm of the public and the strange feeling that we felt as we saw the brave inventor rise up in his machine to the whistling noise of the steam, replacing in these circumstances the usual waving of a flag as a salute to the public."

Giffard has left us a somewhat clearer and more sober account of his impressions as the first pilot of a dirigible airship:

"I took off alone from the Hippodrome, at a quarter past five. The wind was blowing fairly strongly. Not for a single moment did I dream of struggling directly against the wind, the power of the engine would not have permitted it; that had been thought of in advance and proved by calculations; but I carried out various manoeuvres of

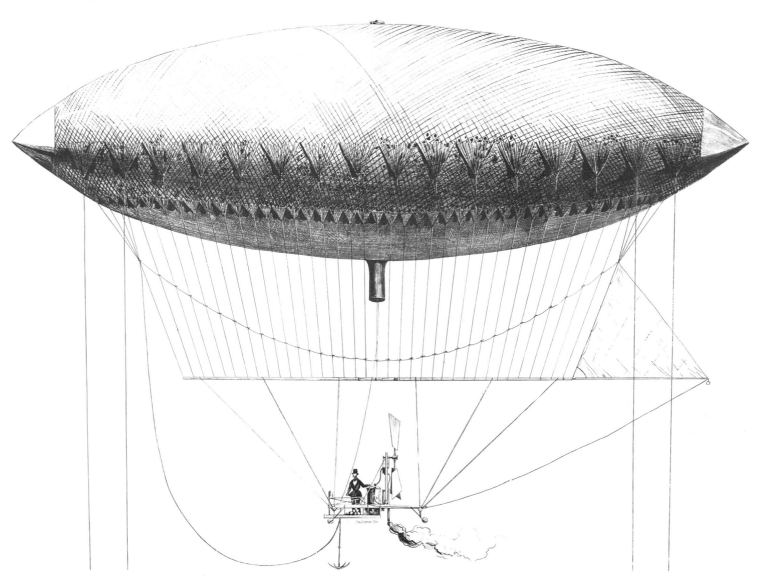

Poster of the ascent of Henri Giffard's first dirigible
steam balloon, on 24 September 1852.

circular and lateral movement, successfully.

The influence of the rudder could be felt immediately, and I hardly had to pull lightly on one of the two steering-lines before I saw the horizon move around me."

M. Cassé confirms having seen the balloon turning in huge circles.

After rising to 6000 ft. Giffard put out the fire, let out the steam, and landed without accident, as night was approaching, at Elancourt, near Trappes.

In August 1855, he took off from the gas factory at Courcelles on board a new steam airship which contained 106,000 cu. ft. of gas and was very elongated as it was 230 ft. long and only 33 ft. in diameter. Very bad pitching developed; the gas-bag slipped inside its net and just as Giffard and his companion, the young aeronaut Gabriel Yon, who had hastened the descent, reached the ground, it escaped completely, split into two pieces and fell back almost on top of the overturned boiler. The flight had been too short to give any meaningful results.

Henri Giffard continued his research into the steering of balloons. To his first and well-known patent in 1851, in which he brilliantly explained the problem and his proposals for resolving it,

under the title *The Application of Steam to Aerial Navigation*, he added in 1855 a second patent describing an airship of 7,800,000 cu. ft. with an eighty horsepower engine and a gas-bag that would retain its shape by being provided with an

elastic belly, an idea which re-occurred later.

Giffard's name reappears in the context of captive balloons. The problems of fixed balloons absorbed him until his premature death, from suicide caused by depression, in 1882.

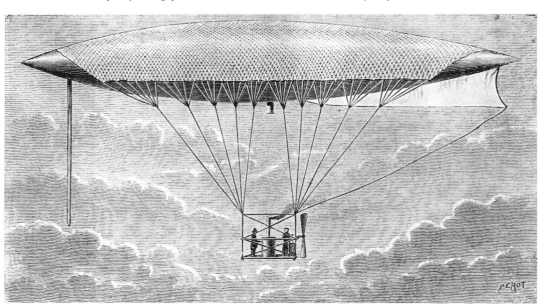

Henri Giffard's second dirigible steam balloon, tested in 1855.

LOCOMOTIVE-AERIENNE-MELLER.

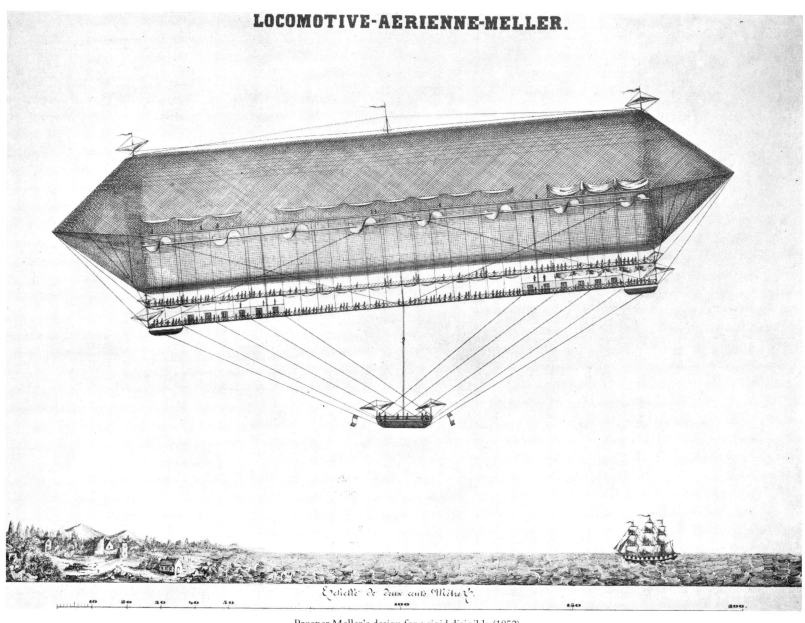

Prosper Meller's design for a rigid dirigible (1852).

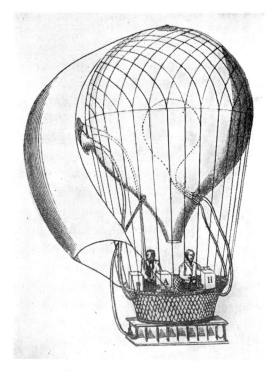

Balloon with sails inflated by bellows.
A proposal of Terzuolo (1855)

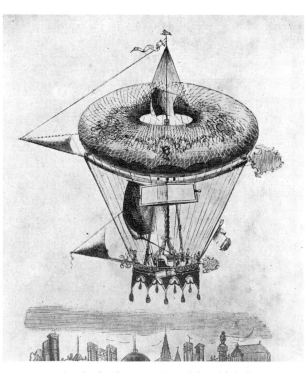

Lassaigne's plan for a ring-shaped dirigible balloon (1851).

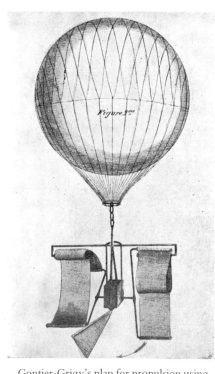

Gontier-Grigy's plan for propulsion using undulating surfaces (1860).

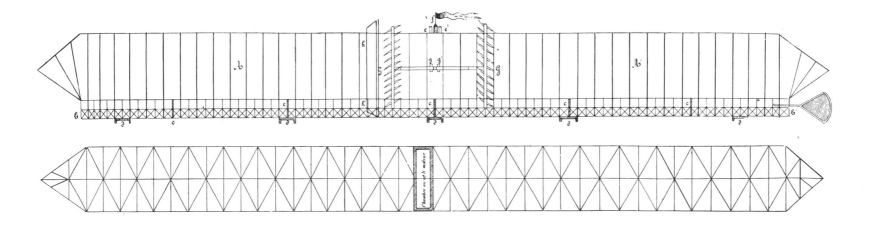

Abbot Carrie, Priest of Barbaste's plan for a rigid balloon with an internal skeleton (1853).

OTHER PLANS FOR DIRIGIBLE AIRSHIPS

Amongst the countless schemes that appeared during this time of passion for balloons around 1850, a few are of interest for showing the origins of devices used in modern airships, others for their curiosity value. The most remarkable is that of Petin, which was completed but could not be tried out; it consisted of four immense balloons that carried inclinable "wings" and a platform carrying steam engines or hand-windlasses (similar to those used by quarrymen) to turn the propellers.

Prosper Meller's plan shows a real rigid airship made entirely of sheet metal or of material stretched over a skeleton. The position of the

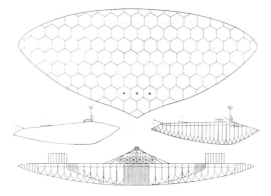

The *Aeroplane*, Joseph Pline's dirigible glider balloon (1855).

propellers and the proportions of this "aerostatic locomotive" bring a zeppelin very much to mind. A short time later, Abbot Carrié also published a

plan for a rigid airship made of copper, also very reminiscent of the zeppelins, although long before their time. Propulsion was obtained from oscillating shutter blades.

In 1855, Joseph Pline proposed a dirigible glider, under, for the first time, the name "Aeroplane", in the shape of a bird, with a framework filled with gas, and fitted with propellers.

In the same year, Terzuolo suggested propulsion using a jet of air which would work, not by reaction, but by blowing on to a sail. In 1860, Gontier–Grigy designed a system of propulsion in which strips of material were alternately folded and unfolded to produce a rowing action. The airships of Meyer and Treille and of Lassaigne were ring-shaped, with sails etc.; they are examples of bizarre ideas that went against the very sound theories of Meller and Abbot Carrié.

Petin's plans for aerial navigation (1850).

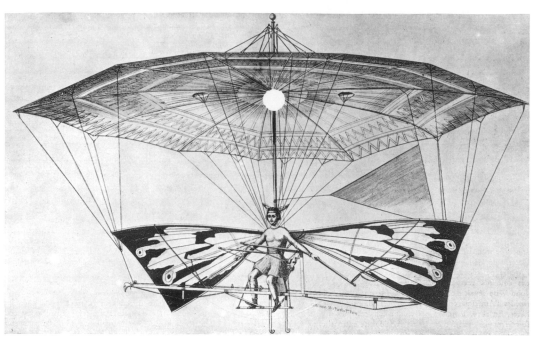

François Letur's dirigible parachute (1852).

FORERUNNERS OF THE AEROPLANE

By 1850 people were as fascinated by heavier-

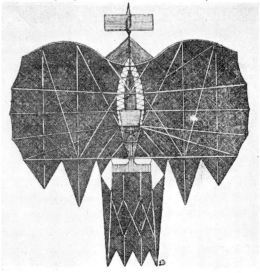

Viscount Carlingford's aeroplane (1853).

than-air machines as they were by balloons.

In 1853 and 1854, François Letur experimented frequently by throwing himself out of a balloon in Paris, Lyon and Rouen, with a steerable parachute that he had invented, which had a tiltable rigid canopy fitted with a handle like a parasol, and two large wings which were supposed to maintain forward movement. The results were not very successful and during a final demonstration in London, he was dragged into some trees, still attached to the balloon, and killed.

In 1851 Auband patented a machine which combined the principles of the aeroplane and the helicopter, having fixed horizontal surfaces, other wings for propulsion, and two propellers for vertical movement.

The first plan of an aeroplane to be published in France was that of a craftsman from Lyons, Michel Loup, in 1853. The body rested on wheels, and was attached to a large horizontal surface in the shape of a bird's wings, but cut out on each side to make room for two enormous propellers. Fins and rudders for controlling direction and altitude completed the machine.

At roughly the same time Viscount Carlingford took out a patent for an aeroplane in England, the first to have a tractive propeller. The inventor contemplated taking off using a chariot running along a cable, a system taken up again by Ferber in France at the beginning of practical aviation.

Also in 1853, Vaussin-Chardanne presented his "dirigible kite", a huge inclined surface on a wheeled chassis, fitted with paddle wheels with articulated paddles for propulsion. Shortly after this time the far simpler idea of the aeroplane as we know it became generally accepted, replacing the countless plans for man-made birds with flapping wings.

THE DU TEMPLES AND LE BRIS

The first complete design of an aeroplane to be patented in France was that of Félix du Temple, the patent being issued to him on 2 May 1857.

Félix du Temple de la Croix, a most original figure and an engineer of great genius, served most of his career as a commander in the French Navy, only being made a general during the Franco-Prussian War. He later became an ardently reactionary member of parliament, and died in Paris in 1890 at the age of 67.

His brother Louis du Temple de la Croix, who was an equally brilliant naval officer, was also promoted to general and placed in command of the Army of the Nièvre in 1870. He had extremely advanced political ideas, was born in 1819 and died in 1889.

Both made their mark in the history of engineering and are considered, Félix especially, among the great forerunners of aviation. Félix and Louis du Temple worked together on aviation problems until disagreements brought about an estrangement. However it was Félix du Temple who was the actual author of this simple and

Felix du Temple de la Croix (1823–90).

rational design, and of the achievements that went with it.

Around the time that this patent was taken out, Félix du Temple constructed "a model of a very light boat; on the upper surface and a little in front of the middle, he placed two wings making an angle of 14° with the horizontal. A propeller, turned initially by clockwork and later by a small steam engine, was located at the front of the boat. Two rudders were fitted to the back; one was horizontal and controlled the angle which the wings presented to the air; the other was vertical, and performed the same function as on a ship. For the take-off, this aerial boat, on a little chariot with wheels, was placed at the bottom of a ramp the angle of which added to that of the wings.

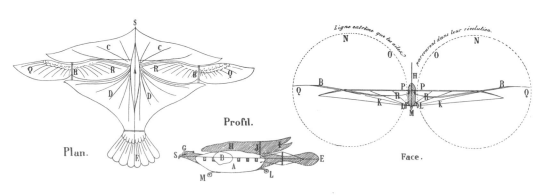

The first French plan for an aeroplane by Michel Loup (1853).

Once the machine was moving, the propeller drove the whole system with enough speed to make the vertical component of the air resistance greater than the weight of the boat. This then rose up into the air, to fall smoothly when the propeller stopped rotating; the wings had the effect of a parachute and it landed on its wheels as a bird lands on its feet."

It was with these words that Louis de Temple described his brother's first experiment: it was the *first flight in which a model aeroplane took off from the ground under its own power*, as well as being the first aeroplane tested in France.

This model weighed 1½ lb. The success of this experiment in miniature led du Temple to complete the memoir, of which the drawings are reproduced here, and to take out one of the most remarkable patents in the history of early aviation, almost ranking with those of Henson, Pénaud and Gauchot.

Having set out the principles of the aeroplane with its two rudders, Félix du Temple then gave a description of the machine.

"A small boat, built from wood, angle iron, or metal tubes, which is solid and light, either open or covered, contains the steam engine or other means of propulsion, and seats for the mechanics, the driver and the passengers.

The wings, with a 56 ft. span, are each made of two pieces of hollow wood, which could be replaced by angle iron or metal tubes, set in the form of a cross. Fixed to the boat, these pieces are lashed together to form a frame to the underside of which light, gummed material is stretched, that can belly upwards like the sails of a windmill.

The tail, constructed in the same way, with two supporting frames, is controlled by a wheel; the rudder is turned by a horizontal bar and ropes.

The machine stands on three wheeled legs of wood or hollow tubes, containing a shock-absorbing device. The undercarriage folds up during flight to reduce air resistance.

The propeller with 12 wooden blades has a diameter of 13 ft."

The motor described is a steam engine but du Temple allows for any form of mechanical power. At the end of the patent, he states:

"The flight of any machine is effected by the forward speed given to this machine by any type of motor. This speed is translated into a force capable of reducing the weight of this machine, by the action of the air on its system of wings and tail."

Finally du Temple puts forward "the idea of using aluminium for constructing machines and crafts destined for aerial travel."

Putting his ideas into practice, Félix du Temple constructed his machine which he fitted with a hot air motor after having thought about a Lenoir gas motor, which had recently been invented. Reverting to steam, he himself invented the famous light boiler with condensor which he produced commercially and which was adopted by the navy. It remains the prototype of all rapid circulation boilers.

Modifying and perfecting over 20 years his machine, which he only ever partially tested, du Temple arrived at wings with a span of 98 ft. consisting of two tubes, each 49 ft. long and 4½

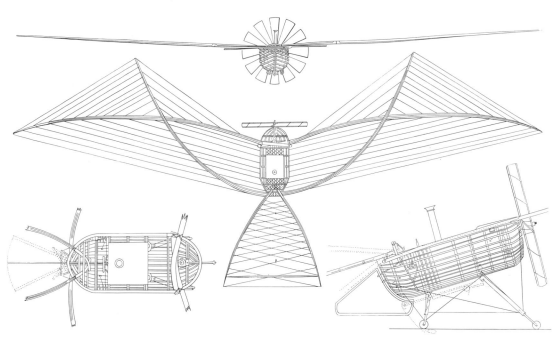

Félix du Temple's aeroplane from the patent of 1857.
Rear and plan views; plan and side-view of hull.

in. in diameter at their point of maximum thickness, curved in the middle and made of rolled up and riveted sheets of aluminium. The steel tubes which made up the body also served as a radiator for condensing the steam from the engine. This last, the boiler and the propeller were placed on adjustable mountings, so that their angle could be altered in order to change the axis of traction.

By a strange coincidence, the region of Brest, at the time that du Temple was constructing his aeroplane, was also the scene of Jean-Marie Le Bris' most interesting experiments.

A captain of coastal navigation and a hero of many rescues, Le Bris built a large glider around 1856, which was designed for experiments in soaring, that is in gliding when the force of the wind maintains the lift. This was a well constructed machine consisting of a body in the shape of a shoe and two large wings with a total span of 49 ft. The inventor could alter the angle of the rear part of the wings during flight.

An experiment was carried out in Tréfeuntec, near Douarnenez, around 1857; the machine was placed on a cart which was pulled against the wind by a horse. The ascent, with Le Bris aboard, went so well that the end of the cable pulled up the seat of the driver of the cart, dragging him into the air. The aeroplane reached an altitude of 300 ft. and landed safely with its impromptu passenger.

During a following attempt, in which it was launched from the top of a mast, Le Bris broke a leg. Le Bris took out a patent of invention for his glider with adjustable wings in 1857.

In 1868 he took up his experiments again with a new but similar machine. He made a successful short flight at Brest, over the merchant port, but the machine was subsequently destroyed during attempts to fly it without a pilot.

Le Bris died, assassinated, in 1872.

The first photograph of a full-scale aeroplane: The Le Bris glider of 1868. (Musée Carnavalet.)

BALLOONING IN AMERICA

The greatest American aeronaut of this time was John Wise: in the number and importance of his ascents he may be compared to Charles Green.

Wise began his career in Philadelphia in 1835. In 1838 he invented the release cord, a string which tore the material of the balloon and which, having been improved into a release panel, has become the usual means of rapid deflation for all balloons, helping to save the lives of countless aeronauts.

Wise also held for many years the record for the longest distance travelled by balloon.

Convinced of the possibility of crossing the Atlantic from West to East, making use of the permanent air-currents, John Wise dreamed of establishing rapid aerial services from America to Europe using huge free balloons. In 1859, he found some partners who formed a society to examine the feasibility of this scheme.

As a first test, a long aerial voyage over land was attempted. On 1 July 1859, Wise left Saint Louis aboard a large balloon equipped with a lifeboat and provisions. He was accompanied by his assistant La Mountain, and Mr Gager and Mr Hyde, the first a partner, the other a journalist. During the course of a magnificent night, the travellers passed over Fort Wayne in Indiana, crossed Lake Erie and flew over Niagara Falls. A terrifying storm then dragged the balloon over Lake Ontario, and it was only after some moments of anxiety that the aeronauts were able to land unharmed in the trees at Henderson, in Jefferson County, in the State of New York. They had covered 802 miles in twenty hours and forty minutes. Their balloon, *The Atlantic*, was carrying mail – the first aerial post – about which Wise said that the American Express Company had wanted to show its interest in the voyage and had asked them to take, towards New York, a transcontinental bag full of mail from the Pacific coast, and letters from the inhabitants of Saint Louis sending regards to their friends in the east, as a declaration of their appreciation of the new method of postal transport inaugurated on this fashion. The bag was recovered from the lake near Oswego and sent on to New York. Among the letters, was one containing a bill for £1000 sterling, according to *The United States Courier*.

Certainly a few balloons had on previous occasions sometimes carried private letters, but *The Atlantic* was the first balloon to be given a sack of normal mail – a little known milestone in the history of aerial post. A short time later, La Mountain and Haddock, in the same *Atlantic*, made another long journey, which ended in the forests of Canada, where they almost died of hunger, after having to abandon their balloon.

After this, a competition was set up to establish a postal service across the Atlantic. Thaddeus C. Lowe, another of the great American aeronauts, entered the competition. He constructed a formidable balloon of over 700,000 cu. ft., called the *City of New York*, designed to make a direct crossing. Very complete equipment was prepared for this attempt which was taken very seriously. As a precaution, Lowe had a large metal life-boat suspended under the basket, with a small hot-air motor. A vertical propeller allowed the balloon to rise and descend as desired. In November 1859, in New York, Lowe tried to inflate the *City of New York*. This operation took several days, at the end of which the balloon was dragged off by a gust of wind, and split open.

On 28 June 1860, Lowe made a successful ascent in Philadelphia, aboard this same huge balloon, rechristened the *Great Western* in honour of the simultaneous inauguration of the giant steamer *Great Eastern*. The balloon, only half inflated, made a short and auspicious trip.

Acting on the advice of the great meteorologist Henry, Lowe made some training ascents; on 20 April 1861, he flew from Cincinnati to the coast of South Carolina. However, the American Civil War interrupted the transatlantic plans.

In 1873, John Wise took up the idea again, and constructed, with Donaldson, a rival 700,000 cu. ft. balloon in New York which suffered the same fate as Lowe's. Wise died in 1879, at the age of seventy-one, a victim of his art: he was lost with his balloon in Lake Michigan, during his 479th ascent.

John Wise (1808–†F1879).

Wise and Donaldson's transatlantic balloon, *The Daily Graphic* (1873).

Inflation of T.C. Lowe's transatlantic balloon in Philadelphia on 28 June 1860.

Basket and lifeboat, with elevatory propeller, on T.C. Lowe's transatlantic balloon (1859–1860).

Eugène Godard (1827–1890)

Louis Godard (1829–1885)

Auguste Godard (1833–1859)

Jules Godard (1838–1885)

Eugénie Godard (1835–1910)

THE GODARDS

During the second half of the nineteenth century the predominant name in European ballooning was that of Godard, a dynasty of aeronauts that carried out the majority of public ascents for over 60 years throughout Europe.

Son of a mason from the Batignolles, Eugène began the career subsequently taken up by all his family with a modest ascent in a hot-air balloon made out of paper, in Lille in 1847. However, once employed by Arnault, the director of the Hippodrome, in 1850, he was successful from the start; on his first paid flight his balloon landed at night near Ostend, and the enthusiastic passengers extolled their journey in the press. The demands for ascents became so numerous that Eugène Godard, in order to meet the requirements, took on all his family as pupils: his elderly father, Pierre Edme, his uncle Abel, known as Fanfan, his brothers Louis, Jules and Auguste and his sister Eugénie. Later several of Abel Godard's six daughters, above all Fanny, also made ascents.

After having covered Europe, Eugène Godard made a tour of ascents in America. Once back in France he took part in the campaign against Italy with his balloon, then during the siege of Paris constructed about 40 message-balloons and in-

structed the sailors who were in charge of handling them. Some of his balloons became famous: the enormous hot-air balloon *L'Aigle* which he built in 1864 measured almost 500,000 cu. ft.

He was made the Emperor's Aeronaut by

Inflation of Jules Godard's balloon at Saint Ouen in 1862.

Napoleon III and appeared on many great public occasions with his balloons.

Eugène Godard's passengers were countless, coming regularly to take part in ascents in the large towns in France, as well as in Brussels, Vienna, Berlin or Amsterdam. Eugène Godard found a loyal clientèle of amateurs, confident of his great skill as a pilot. He was supported by a public that appreciated his trustworthy handling of his balloon and his well made equipment.

Eugène Godard remains an interesting character from the last century. Without bringing anything new to balloon flying, he practised it conscientiously, and the greater part of the aeronauts involved in the siege of Paris were recruited from his many pupils.

His brothers Louis and Jules, constructors and pilots of Nadar's *Géant* were his best disciples. Later, Léon-Eugène, Eugène Godard's son, and especially Louis, Louis Godard's son, were excellent aeronauts. Young Louis Godard was equally famous as a constructor of balloons. He was the last survivor of this large family.

There was another example of a dynasty of aeronauts at the same time in England: the Spencer family who were still represented in active balloon flying in the 1930s by the great grandson of Edward Spencer, who began balloon flying with Charles Green in 1836.

Edme Godard (1802–1873), Fanfan (1808–1867), Jules and Louis.

Basket and burner of Eugène Godard's hot-air balloon, *l'Aigle* (1864). Left to right: G. Yon, Le Guillois, Danduran, Henri de Parville, Busson, Lieux (senior), Eugène Godard.

Fanny Godard (1839–1880) in her ascent gear around 1879.

Louis and Jules Godard's ascent at Saint-Cloud, 1866.

The ascent of *Le Géant* (200,000 cu. ft.) and a balloon with which to compare it (17,500 cu. ft.) from the Champ-de-Mars on 18 October 1863.

HEAVIER-THAN-AIR FLIGHT IN THE 1860s: NADAR

Nadar – his real name was Felix Tournachon – was one of the most curious Parisian characters from the nineteenth century and was the last survivor of the romantic Bohemians. He was a draughtsman and cartoonist, later a photographer he took the world's first recorded aerial photographs from a balloon in 1858; he was known to all the celebrities and gifted with a staggering zest and a selfless enthusiasm which could over-ride all obstacles, and he was always interested in aerial navigation. He made ascents with Godard, enjoying with every pore the infinite and unique delight of the ascent.

Around 1861 Viscount Ponton d'Amécourt took out a patent for a helicopter with two super-imposed propellers. An exchange of ideas with the writer and sailor, Gabriel de la Landelle, and a chance conversation with Nadar, brought together these three very different men. Nadar, full of enthusiasm, began in July 1863 an astonishingly productive campaign by publishing the *Manifesto of Aerial Auto-locomotion*, an impassioned plea for research into heavier-than-air flight. Meetings led immediately to the founding of a society for the encouragment of aerial navigation by heavier-than-air machines and the publishing, by Nadar at his own expense, of the magazine *L'Aéronaute*, of which the first issue ran to 100,000 copies.

Finally, in order to acquire resources for the development of a motor giving "horsepower in a watch case" which would resolve the problem of aerial navigation, Nadar on his own initiative commissioned the construction of a huge 200,000 cu. ft. balloon called *Le Géant* (*The Giant*), whose public ascents would surely raise money.

"It caused a stir" as Nadar said, and indeed a study of the press at that time shows the great interest that the public had in flying in 1863.

Amongst the four hundred and eighteen members of the Society in 1866 were Victor Hugo, Babinet, Offenbach, the painter Stevens, George Sand, Alexandre Dumas, father and son, Hector Malot, Perdonnet the engineer, Edmond About, Emile de Girardin, and Barral. The most active members were La Landelle, Yves Guyot, subeditor of *L'Aéronaute*, Jules Verne, Garapon and Saliwes. Prizes were offered and trials carried out either on Ponton d'Amécourt's remarkable heli-

The house basket of *Le Géant* after being dragged across country at Hanover.

Nadar (1820–1910) photographed about 1866.

copters, small clockwork engines that rose into the air, or with his steam engine, the first mechanical device made of aluminium, or with the flapping wings of Duchesnay and De Groof.

Le Géant made its first ascent from the Champ-de-Mars on 9 October 1863 in the middle of a huge crowd. The basket or car was a wicker-work representation of a two-storey cottage 8 ft. in height by 13 ft. in length, and contained various rooms including a small printing office, a photographic laboratory, a refreshment room, a lavatory etc. Thirteen persons were carried in the car, including one lady, the Princess de la Tour d'Auvergne. Unfortunately the great voyage that had been publicised ended prematurely at Meaux, less than 30 miles from Paris. On 18 October it set off again, carrying nine people: M. and Mme, Nadar, Louis and Jules Goddard, Yon etc. After a magnificent journey of over 370 miles in 16 hours, it landed disastrously at Hanover, the basket being dragged across country for 7 or 8 miles. Most of the passengers were injured and the whole of Europe was aghast at the news. After this Nadar made more ascents in *La Géant* at Brussels, Lyons, Amsterdam and Paris, but they were financially disastrous.

The society for the encouragement of aviation – this word had just been coined by La Landelle to refer specifically to heavier-than-air machines – nevertheless continued its work. Two names stand out among the most loyal members: Louis de Lucy-Fossarieu, a patient observer of the flight of insects and an able experimenter, and Joseph Pine, or Pline, who tested countless paper and aluminium models of gliders that he called his "butterflies", and propellers with a rigid leading edge and flexible wings. In 1868 the group was reorganised in a different way and called itself the *Societé Aéronautique de France (The Aeronautical Society of France)* under Ponton d'Amécourt and later Dr Hureau de Villeneuve. The latter relaunched the *L'Aéronaute*, which continued to be published for 40 years In 1872 the group became the *Societé Francaise de Navigation Aérienne (The French Society for Aerial Navigation)* that still exists today.

A similar *Aeronautical Society of Great Britain* was formed in 1866 with the Duke of Argyll as President and the active participation of Brearey and Wenham. This society, later became the *Royal Aeronautical Society.*

As early as 1868 it organised an aeronautical exhibition at the Crystal Palace, the first to be held, which attracted a number of important exhibitors, mostly supporters of heavier-than-air machines. At the same time it held a competition for light motors which was won by Stringfellow.

One of the most interesting of its first members was F.H. Wenham, a first class technician in love with aviation, who studied in particular multi-winged machines and is the true inventor of the wind-tunnel used universally today.

In France this period around 1864 is marked by the works of the Count d'Esterno in gliding, of M. de Louvrié, who presented a plan for an aeroplane with propulsion by reaction, and of J.J. Bourcart and Guebwiller, who managed in 1868 to obtain lift and even some short flights from a machine with flapping wings based on Besnier's design.

Gabriel de La Landelle
(1812–1886)

Joseph Pline
(born 1828)

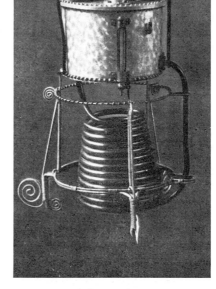

Steam helicopter by Ponton
d'Amécourt (1863).

Yves Guyot
(1843–1928)

L-G de Lucy-Fossarieu
(born 1822)

Clockwork helicopters (1861–1863) by Ponton d'Amécourt. The one on the right has a parachute.

Wilfrid de Fonvielle
(1826–1914)

Albert Tissandier
(1839–1906)

Gaston Tissandier
(1843–1899)

Camille Flammarion
(1841–1926)

Joseph Crocé-Spinelli
(1845–†*F*1875)

SCIENTIFIC ASCENTS

The example of Barral and Bixio was first of all followed in England where Charles Green, who had already made high altitude expeditions with Rush, the American, ended his career with four scientific ascents with Welsh, in 1852.

Ten years later, the British Association for the Advancement of Science paid for thirteen out of a series of twenty-eight ascents, which were carried out between 1862 and 1866 by the great astronomer Glaisher who, despite his advanced age, volunteered to go up as high as possible to carry out meteorological observations. On Glaisher's other fifteen flights he went up as an ordinary fee-paying passenger but was still able to make certain observations. Under the supervision of the excellent English pilot Coxwell, he went up to 26,177 ft. on his first ascent on 17 July 1862. On his eighth, the third commissioned flight, which took place on 5 September 1862, the aeronauts reached a calculated 37,000 ft. which held the record for more than thirty years. Even though they did not use oxygen to compensate for the rarified air, Glaisher and Coxwell resisted altitude sickness remarkably well, but Glaisher fainted at 29,000 ft. when the balloon was climbing at a rate of 1000 ft. a minute, and Coxwell, whose hands were paralysed with cold, had to open the valve

by pulling the rope with his teeth.

Glaisher several times went higher than 23,000 ft., setting a magnificent example of a great scholar launching himself high into the sky to endow science with important observations on such matters as the variability of the decrease in the atmospheric vapour from the ground, the inversion of the fall in temperature with altitude during the night, and the permanence of the atmospheric vapour rays in the solar spectrum observed from a high altitude.

Glaisher also noted that wind strengths and directions at altitude were often very different from those at ground level; during some ascents all the air up to 20,000 ft. was found to be moving in the same direction, during others three or four different air streams moving in various directions might be met with in the same vertical distance.

In France, in 1867, both Wilfrid de Fonvielle and Camille Flammarion independently began a series of scientific flights. Flammarion's, limited in number and piloted by Eugène Godard, were remarkable for their length both in time and distance. The illustrious astronomer left an account, which was widely read, of his journeys from Paris to La Rochefoucauld near Angoulême in 11 hrs 25 min. on 23 and 24 June 1867, and to Solingen, near Cologne, in 12 hrs 30 min. on 14 and 15 July 1867, as well as of shorter journeys spread over two days but broken by stopovers.

Having accompanied all the pilots flying at that time, W. de Fonvielle became a pilot himself, making the last of his numerous ascents, all with scientific purposes, at the age of sixty-seven.

Similarly, Gaston Tissandier and his brother Albert started making meteorological ascents in 1868, from which the former brought back observations and reports, and the latter drawings which popularised balloon ascents.

From 1873 to 1875, the *Société Française de Navigation Aérienne* organised several high altitude ascents with Sivel as pilot, in which the engineer Crocé-Spinelli, in particular, participated. On 23 and 24 March 1875, the balloon *Zenith*, with Sivel, Crocé-Spinelli, the Tissandier brothers and Jobert on board, made a long distance flight: it left La Villette and came down in the Landes after a journey of twenty-two hours and forty minutes.

The following flight was dramatic and has remained famous. On 15 April 1875, the *Zenith* set off on a high altitude ascent, carrying Sivel, Crocé-Spinelli, and Gaston Tissandier who returned alone. His flying companions had died, victims of science, from asphyxiation. The last reading had been taken at 27,950 ft. and the balloon had crashed at Ciron in the Indre. The scientific world was greatly shocked by this catastrophe, which put an end to such ascents for some twenty years.

Jules Duruof's *Michel-le-Brave* at
La Villette in 1874

Henry Coxwell
(1819–1900)

James Glaisher
(1809–1903)

Sivel's *L'Etoile-Polaire* at Leipzig
in 1873

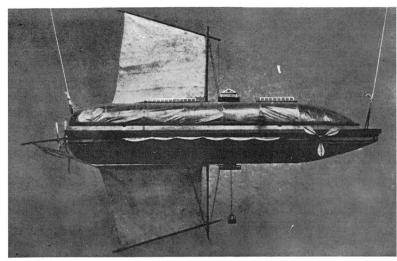
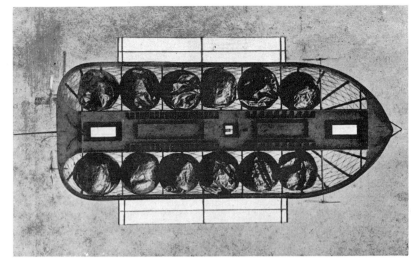

Contemporary photographs of a model of a rigid dirigible by H. Vanaisse (1863).

EXPERIMENTS IN THE
1860s

Fewer dirigibles were tried out during the 1860s than the profusion of publications on this subject would lead one to believe.

In France in 1859, Camille Vert, a prolific inventor interested in both heavier- and lighter-than-air flight, tested in the Palais de l'Industrie a large model dirigible with a steam engine driving two propellers. Having presented his dirigible to Napoleon III in the courtyard of the Louvre, Vert exhibited it in the provinces.

In 1865, an unknown aeronaut, E. Delamarne, built, with the help of Gabriel Yon, a somewhat unusual elongated balloon. The cylindrical envelope, partitioned inside and with a ram at the front, measured 70,000 cu. ft. Two frames, each equipped with a large three-bladed propeller, were fixed by two flexible straps on either side of the gas-bag at its widest point. The basket, with a prow which acted as a windshield, was also equipped with two driving propellers and two elevatory propellers. The muscular strength of three or four aeronauts was needed to drive all these propellers which had blades with raised edges to prevent air loss at their margins. In spite of its rather poor construction, Delamarne's *Espérance* made several ascents in Paris and London in 1865. No positive results were obtained from the steering system, but the *Espérance*'s

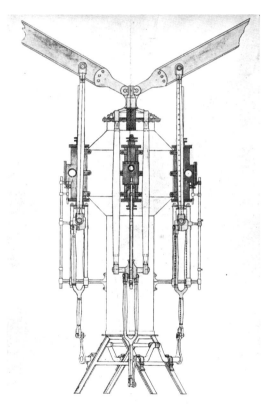

Sketch of a flying machine, by Marc Séguin, made on 26 January 1864 by his son.

elevatory propellers functioned well.

In 1869, Marriott, who had collaborated with Stringfellow, and was then living in America, experimented with a large model dirigible which was 33 ft. long and also equipped with lateral propellers driven by a steam engine. Horizontal planes were fixed to the envelope in order to facilitate vertical movements when the balloon was inclined upwards or downwards by the double rear rudder. Around 1875, Marriott returned to his studies for a heavier-than-air machine but died before completing his work.

Andrews, in America also carried out full-scale tests on a gliding dirigible around 1866.

In France Vanaisse's project, a model of which was shown in 1864, featured a rigid shell filled with separate flexible gas-containing balloons, like the zeppelins later on.

Marc Séguin, a mechanically-minded nephew of Joseph Montgolfier, had been carrying out experiments on heavier-than-air machines for a long time: around 1846 he first tried out a large elevatory propeller, then flapping wings with valves with which he managed to lift a machine with a man on board several centimetres from the ground with each flap. Nadar's campaign in favour of aviation motivated him to publish a memorandum in 1866, and in 1864 he designed an ornithopterous machine with four wings driven directly by four cylinders synchronised by means of cranks placed at the bottom of the machine.

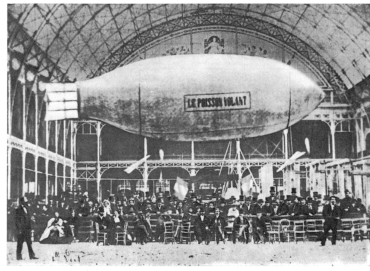

The first known photograph of an aircraft: Camille Verts' model of 1859

Marriott's dirigible experiments in San Francisco (1869)

Durouf's *Neptune*, later the first balloon to leave Paris during the siege,
serving as Nadar's observation balloon in the Place Saint Pierre in Montmartre.

THE SIEGE OF PARIS

Ballooning played an important role during the Franco-Prussian war of 1870. It could even be said that it was thanks to mail-balloons that Paris managed to withstand its siege for more than four months since the balloonists and the carrier pigeons they transported were the only means of communication between the capital and the outside world.

When Paris was threatened at the beginning of September 1870, several aeronauts, including Nadar, Wilfrid de Fonvielle and Eugène Godard, offered their services and equipment to observe the enemy's movements. Three captive balloon posts were installed, in the Place Saint-Pierre in Montmartre, in the Place d'Italie and at Vaugirard. These aerial observatories, which worked day and night, had hardly started operating when Paris was completely surrounded. At a meeting of aeronauts organised by M. Rampont, the post office director, on 17 September, the decision was made to create a mail-balloon service.

It was decided first to use all the existing balloons in Paris while hastily starting to build new ones of 40,000, and later of 70,000 cu. ft. to maintain communication with the provisional government and to provide a postal service.

Nadar organised the first departure from the Place Saint-Pierre: Duruof, renouncing any financial reward he might have obtained had he stayed behind to build balloons, left courageously on 23 September in his old balloon *Neptune*, and came down near Evreux, provoking the anger of Bismarck himself by flying over Versailles.

Two main building workshops were established; at the Gare d'Orléans by Eugène and Jules Godard, and at the Gare du Nord by Yon and Dartois. A total of about sixty balloons were built. Sixty-six manned balloons left, mostly at night. Each balloon carried, along with the pilot, official dispatches and private letters, written on India paper – and uncensored – or on the back of newspapers with tiny print and also on India paper. In addition, a number of passengers on duty or travelling privately left Paris by balloon.

The second balloon was piloted by Gabriel Mangin and inaugurated the return service of carrier pigeons which grew rapidly thanks to the pigeon-fanciers Van Roosebeck, Derouard, Cassiers, Traclet and Thomas. This service was made complete by the use of microphotography, a process perfected by Dagron of reducing photographs to one eight-hundredth of their size on collodian film. By this process 16 pages of text could be recorded on a film measuring 1¼ by 2 in. and weighing one six hundredth of an ounce. On arrival, the films were enlarged and projected on a screen in front of secretaries who transcribed the text. On 21 January, one pigeon transported 21 films containing 38,700 dispatches.

When all the competent pilots, Louis Godard, his father, his adopted brother Mutin-Godard, Trichet, the Tissandier brothers and Fonvielle had left, others had to be found: Eugène Godard trained the sailors and Yon and Dartois the civilian volunteers. This organisation allowed a permanent correspondence to be maintained between Paris and the rest of France with a regularity which certainly exceeded all hopes.

It is remarkable that these numerous night ascents by inexperienced pilots with large, hastily built balloons, during an extremely harsh winter, gave rise to so few accidents. Two balloons were lost at sea with their pilots, the sailor Prince and the soldier Lacaze. Six balloons were taken by the enemy when they landed in Germany or in occupied territory. Many others landed behind the German lines but crew and post managed to escape. There were also a number of very rough landings where people were injured.

The most eventful journey, regrettably causing strategic dispatches to be delayed but ending happily, was that of the balloon *La Ville d'Orléans*, with Rolier and Bézier on board. Carried out to sea during the night of 24 November, the pilots were able to land the next day, after many anxious hours, in a Norwegian forest, near Mount Lid, in the province of Telemark, having covered 875 miles. The balloon got away from its pilots on landing, but was later found intact 200 miles further on. Another balloon swept out over the Atlantic, managed to land, despite a violent wind, on Belle-Ile off the Brittany coast. The injured crew were rescued.

The most illustrious passenger was Leon Gambetta. Head of the provisional government, he was rejoining his regional headquarters by balloon on the *Armand-Barbès*, which left the Place Saint-Pierre on 7 October, piloted by Triquet. He was accompanied by his secretary, Eugène Spuller. The descent went badly and ended on an oak tree in the Bois d'Epineuse, near Montdidier, but the great man was able to accomplish his mission.

The last mail-balloon left Paris with news of the Armistice on 28 January 1871.

In total, 11 tons of mail, representing two and a half million letters, and more than 400 carrier pigeons were transported out of Paris by air. The 66 pilots wer also accompanied by 102 passengers. Nearly all the letters were distributed, but only 57 pigeons returned.

The balloons which had landed in the provinces were collected at Tours and Lille. Fonvielle, Mangin, Dufour, Revilliod and the Tissandier brothers spread themselves out around Paris and, taking advantage of favourable winds, tried to regain the capital. After an attempt at Le Mans, the Tissandier brothers made another ascent at Rouen but it was equally unsuccessful. Mangin prepared a balloon at Amiens and Revilliod at Chartres but neither was able to take off.

Military observations were also carried out by the Germans in 1870 in Strasbourg with an English pilot. On the French side, a company of balloonists was created in Tours, including Mangin, G. and A. Tissandier, Nadar, Bertaux and Duruof. A balloon was attached to the Army of the Loire under the supervision of the last two. Operations,

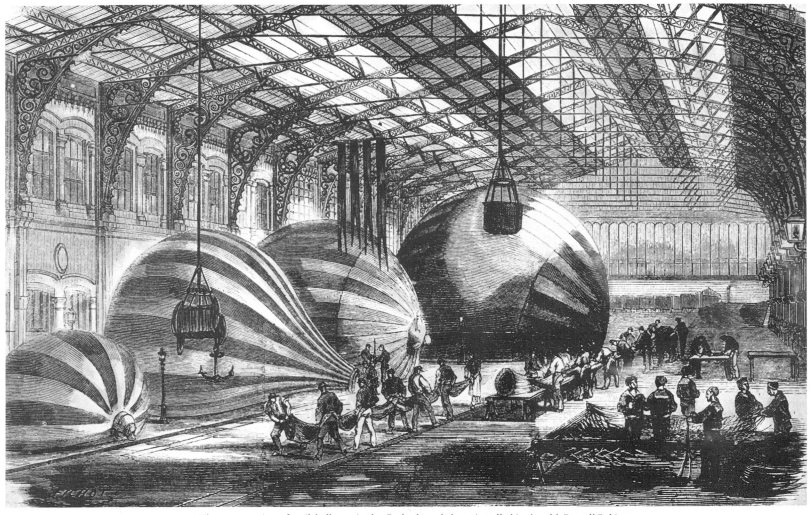

The construction of mail-balloons in the Godard workshops installed in the old Gare d'Orléans.

started in the Orléans area, were interrupted by the Armistice. The Tissandier brothers also tried to carry out observations from a captive balloon near Cercottes, and later at Le Mans, but these attempts failed owing to insufficient organisation, and the confusion of the campaign at the end of the war.

During the second siege of Paris the Commune tried to organise a balloon service under Duruof's leadership, but it never functioned properly, and only a few unaccompanied small balloons carrying proclamations were launched.

The *George-Sand*, inflated by Mangin in Amiens in 1870 to try to return to Paris.

Aeronauts having broken out of besieged Paris regroup at Tours. Left to right: Moutet, T. Maugin, Reginensi, L. Mutin-Godard, Raoul, G. Maugin, Poirrier, Toigneray, Pagano, Ours. Seated: Yahn, P. Marcia Clariot, Surel de Monchamps.

Drama in the Air
"The maniac fell into space!"

Inset: Jules Verne (1828–1905)

Robur the Conqueror
"Through the Rocky Mountains."

Five Weeks in a Balloon
"The *Victoria* towed by an elephant."

Robur the Conqueror
"A ship with thirty-seven masts."

Mme Poitevin (1819–1908)
with Marie Sivel in 1869

Théodore Sivel
(1834–†*F*1875)

Jules Duruof (1841–1898) with his aide,
Barrett, in 1868.

Jean-Baptiste Glorieux
(1834–1905)

Camille Dartois
(1838–1917)

JULES VERNE (1828–1905)

Contrary to popular opinion, Jules Vernes was not an inventor: he was a visionary and his "inventions", though well-researched, were prophetic only because of his vivid imagination. He followed scientific progress closely and joined Nadar's Society, but had no hesitation, where the story demanded it, in openly overstepping the bounds of technical plausibility.

In fact his first novel, *Un Drame Dans Les Airs* (1851), was about balloons. *Five Weeks in a Balloon*, a story of a crossing of Africa, came out in 1863. Balloons also figured, although incidentally, in *Hector Servadac* as a means of passing from a comet to the earth, and in *The Mysterious Island*, in which the heroes, taking off from America, land on the famous island.

Strangely enough, heavier-than-air machines feature little, though in *Robur the Conqueror* (1886) Robur's airship was a helicopter with multiple propellers fixed to masts, an idea of Gabriel de La Landelle. He also portrayed Nadar once, as Michel Ardan in *From the Earth to the Moon*.

Jules Verne only once went up in a balloon very briefly, in Amiens in 1873 with Eugène Godard.

PROFESSIONAL PILOTS

Besides the Godards, numerous other self-trained professional aeronauts emerged in the late nineteenth century.

Mme Poitevin totalled 571 ascents, including an equestrian one from Cremorne Gardens in London (she was prevented by the police from making another on the grounds of danger to the horse). She was followed by her son Duté-Poitevin, and her son-in-law Sivel, who was killed in the *Zenith*. Camille Dartois' career spanned more than fifty years from 1853 to 1904. Jean-Baptiste Glorieux made 641 ascents between 1861 and 1904, mostly in the north of France and Belgium. Gabriel Yon, a colleague of Giffard and Dupuy de Lôme, Jules Duruof, whose wife followed him in his profession, and Gabriel Mangin all figured largely in the siege of Paris.

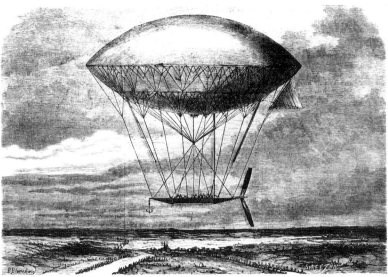

The basket of Dupuy de Lome's dirigible.

Dupuy de Lome's dirigible (1872).

DIRIGIBLES BY DUPUY DE LOME AND HAENLEIN

During the siege of Paris, a number of projects for dirigible balloons were submitted to the National Defence Government, but the only test carried out was unsuccessful and consisted of fitting two hand-driven propellers designed by Admiral Labrousse to the mail-balloon *Le Duquesne*. Camille Vert also started building a full scale version of his steam flying fish at the Cail factory but was unable to finish it.

On 29 October 1870, the government granted a credit of 40,000 francs to the great marine engineer, Dupuy de Lôme, to construct a dirigible for the purpose of leaving and returning to Paris. The construction was however not finished until long after the end of hostilities. Dupuy de Lôme can be seriously criticised for having misunderstood his brief by insisting on perfection down to the last detail, which cost an enormous amount of time, and especially for not having had the courage to apply to his aircraft the steam engine that Giffard had used successfully twenty years earlier; nevertheless, his project showed some technical advances.

His form of suspension provided a more positive connection between the balloon and the basket, even when these were sharply inclined, and he established that the drag created by the ropes and ancillaries was greater than that of the gas-bag itself, a revelation in the matter of aerodynamics.

The fusiform envelope in double thickness rubberised silk had a volume of 12,200 cu. ft. The jacket and the triangulated suspension supported a wicker basket which included a huge windlass, coaxial with the two-bladed 30 ft. diameter propeller, requiring a crew of eight men to turn it. The length of the balloon was 119 ft., the diameter 49 ft. and the total height 96 ft.

The balloon was tested on 2 February 1872 at Vincennes in a strong wind. Dupuy de Lôme, his son-in-law Gustave Zédé, Yon, who had built the balloon, Dartois and the principal collaborators were on board – fourteen in all.

In motion, the propeller allowed various manoeuvres to be made and gave the dirigible a speed of about 6 mph. The balloon's performance and stability were excellent, but as a method of transport it was a failure, as might have been foreseen.

At the same time, a German, Paul Haenlein, was experimenting in Austria but the value of his work has remained largely unrecognised.

As early as 1865, Haenlein had taken out a patent for a dirigible with a small compensating balloon and fitted with a gas motor based on Lenoir's recent invention. He formed a committee in Vienna which undertook to pay the expenses for a large scale test.

Haenlein's dirigible was a cylinder with a cone at either end. It had a volume of 85,000 cu. ft., a length of 165 ft. and a diameter of 30 ft. The basket took the form of a long framework extending under the envelope to maintain its shape and distribute the tractive effort. The gas engine, which was fed from the gas in the balloon itself, was fixed to this frame. Haenlein, to his eternal credit, was the first to use this type of engine which consisted of four cylinders horizontally opposed, and produced 3½ horsepower at 90 rpm. The ignition was by Ruhmkorff coil.

The engine weighed 513 lb., not counting 242 lb. for the radiator and 165 lb. of water. The balloon was inflated at Brno with town gas under difficult conditions. Partial tests were carried out on 13 and 14 December 1972. All the ballast had to be removed because of the lack of lift; it was not thought wise to test it as a free balloon and it was restrained by ropes.

Several five-minute tests were made; the balloon moved forward so quickly that the soldiers bravely kept the ropes up with it by running.

At this stage the financial crisis reached Austria, regrettably putting an end to the trials.

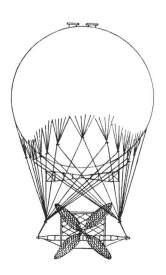

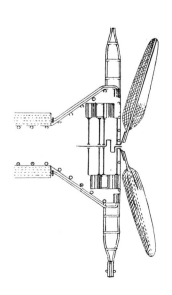

Rear view

Haenlein's dirigible balloon (1872).

Gas engine and propeller

The death of Vincent de Groof, 9 July 1874.

Multiple kites about
to land by J. Simmons (1876).

SOME FAILURES AND DISASTERS

On 9 July 1874, a Belgian by the name of Vincent de Groof was taken up from Cremorne Gardens in London by a balloon to which was fastened a flying machine which he had invented. Some minutes later he freed himself from the balloon, but almost immediately his machine seemed to turn over, the wings folded up and the aviator came crashing down with his aircraft in a street in Chelsea. De Groof died a short time later in hospital. He had spent many years building and testing his machine on the ground. It consisted of a vertical frame in which he stood up, at the top of which there were two very large flapping wings fixed by hinges. The pilot operated these wings which were lifted up again by springs. The machine was completed by a tail which was intended to act as a stabiliser. After two unsuccessful attempts in Belgium, de Groof went to England. On 29 June 1874, he and his machine were carried up by a balloon but the apparatus was not released. The following experiment was the fatal one.

The pilot who had taken him up, Joseph Simmons, was nearly a victim of this accident too;

having been swept up suddenly to a great height by the sudden loss of weight, he fainted and only regained consciousness as his balloon was about to land on a railway line in front of an approaching train.

Simmons later devised a string of kites destined for military observation; these kites had a triangular form when in action and were easy to store when not in use since the three main struts were independent and the kite only took shape with the force of the wind. Partial tests were carried out in Aldershot in 1875 but only one kite managed to take off, while the others were damaged. Simmons tried to demonstrate his string of flying kites at Brussels the following year but no ascents could be made owing to the lack of wind. He died in 1888 from injuries received during an accident while landing his balloon.

Among other incidents during the same period, the famous descent in the middle of the North Sea of M. and Mme Duruof should be mentioned; they left Calais on 31 August 1874 during a professional ascent made in unsuitable weather in order not to disappoint their public, and were picked up in the Skagerrak, between Denmark and Norway, by an English fishing boat which brought them back to Grimsby after a disappearance of several days.

Public ascents gave rise to a certain number of accidents of various sorts: the younger Triquet was killed by being dragged across country on landing in 1876; Braquet in 1874 and Navarre in 1880 and a number of others let go of the trapeze of hot-air balloons which had no basket; Brest, d'Armentières and Eloy were lost at sea; others died when their hot-air balloons caught fire; Petit, Julhès and Toulet forgot to open the release vent of their balloon; but most of these catastrophes were caused by the negligence of the victims, and were due either to faulty equipment or to a disregard for the most elementary rules of navigation. In a slightly different category was the unfortunate slave who in Bangkok, in 1874, at a party for a sovereign when there was no competent aeronaut available, was released alone in a balloon which headed for the sea, and was never seen again.

The fact remains that many of the more successful professional pilots made literally hundreds of flights without untoward incident. The page reproduced opposite appeared in a French periodical shortly after the Zenith disaster; the really interesting fact about it, however, is the scarcity of the accidents it depicts, as evidenced by their dates, and even then it will be noted that many of the accidents shown were not fatal.

LES ACCIDENTS DE L'AÉROSTAT. 170.

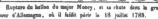

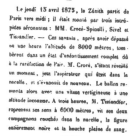

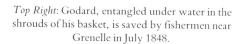

CATASTROPHE DU ZÉNITH.

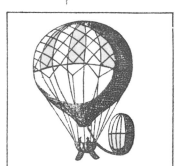

Imagerie de P. DIDION, à Metz.　　Déposé

Reproduction of page from French periodical published shortly after the *Zenith* disaster in 1875.

Top Left: The failure of Major Money's balloon and his descent into the North Sea, in which he was nearly drowned, on 18 July 1785.

Top Centre: The fall from a burning balloon of Mme Blanchard, who set out from the Tivoli and fell to her death on the roof of No. 16 Rue de Provence, on 6 July 1819.

Top Right: Godard, entangled under water in the shrouds of his basket, is saved by fishermen near Grenelle in July 1848.

Centre Left: After an equestrian ascent at Bordeaux, Lt Gallé landed at Cestas. The balloon, relieved of the weight of the horse, carried the aeronaut up again. He was found the next day, 14 September 1850, horribly mutilated.

Centre Right: Fatal ascent of Olivari at Orléans, in the Loiret, on 25 November 1802.

Main Picture: THE *ZENITH* DISASTER. On Thursday 15 April 1875 the *Zenith* left Paris about noon, manned by three intrepid aeronauts: MM. Crocé Spinelli, Sivel and Tissandier. These scientists, after climbing in an hour to more than 26,000 ft. became totally unconscious as a result of the rarefaction of the air. M. Crocé, waking for a moment, knocked overboard the breathing apparatus which was in the basket, and passed out again. The balloon went up again at a terrifying rate, to an unknown height. At three o'clock M. Tissandier, recovering his senses at 20,000 ft. discovered his two companions stretched out in the basket, their faces entirely black, and with blood coming from their mouths. He managed to bring the balloon down until it impaled itself on some trees near Ciron in the department of Indres. After having vainly called to his companions, and having attempted to revive them, he was forced to accept that they had been completely asphyxiated. The two bodies were taken back to Paris by M. Tissandier, on 18 April. On 20 April the funerals took place amid a distinguished and attentive crowd; the Academy of Sciences and all the learned societies were officially represented and the two unfortunate victims of their dedication to science were accompanied all the way to the Père Lachaise cemetery.

Bottom Left: Ascent of Robert and the Duke of Chartres (Philippe-Egalité) at St Cloud on 15 July 1784, which was followed by a perilous descent.

Bottom Centre: The ascents of Salder (James Sadler) from Bristol and Dublin in 1810, at the end of which he had to be rescued from the Irish Sea.

Bottom Right: Harris, leaving London on 29 September 1824, loses the gas from his balloon, which descends so rapidly that he is killed on the spot.

PÉNAUD

Alphonse Pénaud is one of the most engaging and moving figures in the history of aviation. Gentle, modest, lucid and full of good sense, a pioneer in all that he undertook, as perfect a technician as he was a skilled theoretician, he died very young, leaving behind him work of genius.

The son of Admiral Pénaud, he was born in Paris in 1850, and had intended to go into the Navy when he was struck down by an illness which left him disabled for life. It was during his incapacity that he decided to devote his undoubted intelligence to research into aviation.

In April 1870, Alphonse Pénaud invented the "engine" of twisted rubber bands which has been used in most subsequent aircraft models, and which remains the classic method for small-scale experiments. He first applied it to a helicopter with two propellers, one of which was free, the other being fixed to the chassis. It was very lightly built and easily went up to the ceiling and stayed there before coming down. Modified by Dandrieux, the Pénaud helicopter became a flying toy which amused children for many years. Pénaud was a perfectionist and this can be seen in the helicopters which he subsequently had built by Breguet, the clockmaker-engineer: the tiny metal pieces were made in aluminium and the propeller blades were of gilded paper to reduce their thickness.

On 18 August 1871, Pénaud flew a little aeroplane in public in the Tuileries gardens; it was a planophore, a monoplane with the propeller driven by twisted rubber and fitted with a stabilising tail at the back. This experiment first demonstrated the possibility of sustained flight by an aeroplane. Pénaud repeated it many times in front of the Société Française de Navigation Aérienne, which had just been formed and where he was to become an organiser and the most assiduous and most ingenious of members. The planophore, built with either a pusher or a traction propeller, allowed Pénaud to study the laws of longitudinal equilibrium in aeroplanes. To compensate for the rotational reaction of the propeller, he twisted the aerofoils on one side or loaded the opposing wing with a light weight. Flights of 200 ft. were made with a machine weighing little more than half an ounce. As well as the joys of invention, Penaud knew the joys of discovery in "dusty tomes" and always acknowledged the work of his precedessors, particularly Cayley and Pline.

Alphonse Pénaud (1850–1880)

In September 1871, Pénaud first flew a little mechanical bird, powered as always by rubber springs, which he had made himself. It travelled 10 to 15 yards and rose as high as 16 ft. above the take-off point. Copied as a toy, Penaud's bird was

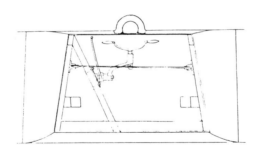

Single control for elevator and rudder of Pénaud and Gauchot's aeroplane (1876).

never improved on. In 1872 and 1873 he published a treatise on movement through the air and proposed a method for studying air resistance. He then developed his theory of gliding and, in 1873, advocated the use of a zoetrope – an early version

of the stroboscope – for studying the flight of birds, and that of instantaneous photography through a succession of shots which was used shortly after by Marey. At the same time he analysed the influence of the proximity of the ground on flying machines, the importance of balancing aeroplanes and the division of the bird's wing into lifting and propelling parts.

In 1875, the French Academy of Science awarded him a prize for his theory of flight. In the same year he defined the three main obstacles to human flight: air resistance, the high weight/strength ratio of most materials and the lack of a lightweight engine. He applied himself in particular to the first two, trying to find a way of making use of air resistance while eliminating its harmful effects, while testing materials, he studied fabric, metal and wood, and their assembly.

He was as familiar with the problems of ballooning as he was with research into the instruments of navigation and piloting. But where Pénaud put his greatest effort was into the design of an aeroplane which he outlined as early as 1873 and patented with the builder-mechanic Paul Gauchot in 1876. There is no other document of that period in existence as complete as this on a feasible project.

The aeroplane was an amphibious, tailless monoplane, of the "flying wing" type with two "puller" propellers. Pénaud and Gauchot built into their design: a metal or wooden wing with an exterior covering which contributed to the strength of the structure; the eventual elimination of shrouds and, in the meantime, the use of flattened or streamlined cables; a folding undercarriage with shock-absorbers of rubber or compressed air; a watertight fuselage-hull; floats at the ends of the wings; variable pitch propellers with a guard to avoid contact with the ground; elevators and a rudder worked by a single control, handlebars which could be turned and inclined with one hand; assistance to be given to the pilot by balancing and spring-loading the controls; a rear tail skid; a vertical stabilising fin. The wings were thick, but streamlined. The ribs were covered on both sides by fabric, metal or plywood. The longerons were of box-section or of I-section with open webs.

The engine was not specified but Pénaud expressed his overriding faith in the hydrocarbon engine. The surface of the hull and of the wings could be used as a condenser. The patent also described the following details: a windscreen, a streamlined headrest, a liquid clinometer, ane-

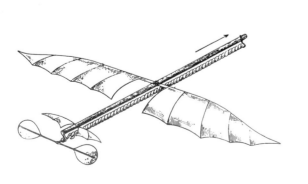

Pénaud's "planophore" aeroplane (1871)

Pénaud's helicopter (1870–1874)

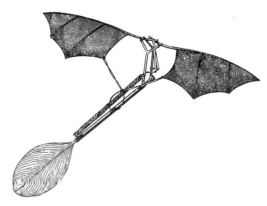

Pénaud's mechanical bird (1874)

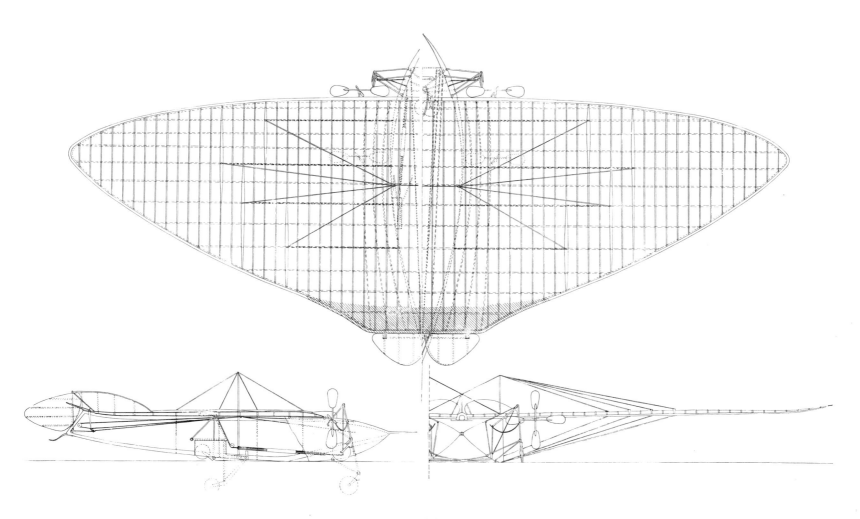

Pénaud and Gauchot's amphibuous aeroplane from the drawing of the patent of 1876. Plan, front and side views.

mometric airspeed indicators, air pressure gauges on the wing, a process for the automatic electrical control of the elevator. Increasing the slenderness by appropriate means to facilitate the movement of the wing through the air was carefully thought out, as was a launching catapult.

In his efforts to put this project into practice, Pénaud, who had no fighting spirit, came up against material obstacles. His became morose and he broke off with the Societé Française de Navigation Aérienne. After having solicited Giffard's help in vain, he put his designs in a little coffin, dropped it off at Giffard's house, went home and committed suicide. This was in 1880. Alphonse Pénaud was only thirty years old.

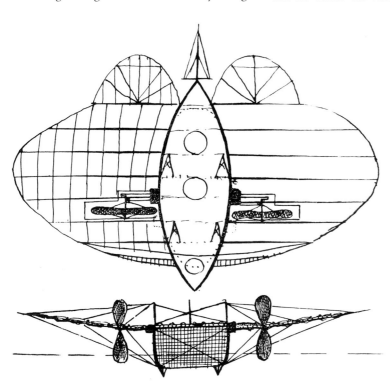

Pénaud's first project for an amphibious aeroplane.

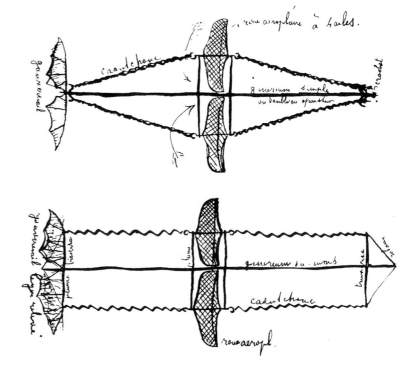

Sketch of Pénaud's aeroplanes with revolving wings (1874).

Tatin's mechanical bird (1875).

Tatin's model aeroplane powered by compressed air (1879).

TATIN AND OTHERS

Victor Tatin was a friend of Pénaud's and his principal emulator. His long life enabled him to see their common dream achieved, for he died in 1913, when aviation was developing rapidly.

A very skilful clockmaker-mechanic, Tatin started his aviation work in 1874 by presenting a mechanical flying bird, inspired by those of Pénaud and of Hureau de Villeneuve, to the Société Française de Navigation Aérienne. He described his system in these terms:

"My apparatus is very small and consists of a wooden frame, at the front of which there is a little machine whose purpose is to transform the circular movement into two lateral to and fro movements. To accomplish this, a crank receives the couple from the twisted rubber and moves an articulated connecting rod on a guide sliding between two columns; this guide transmits its rising and falling movement to two little steel arms moving around a common horizontal axis by means of two little connecting rods . . . The leading edges of the wings are made from the shafts of trimmed feathers bent to the shape of rackets; the surface of the wing is of cloth . . . A wire leading from the main wing rib passes above the cloth and is fixed to the body at the rear edge of the wing; it accompanies the wing in its movement and maintains it on a nearly horizontal plane when it is going down, but the cloth is completely free when it is going up. A peacock's tail feather is placed at the back and serves as a tail. The whole thing weighs less than ⅓ of an ounce which includes one twentieth of an ounce of springs. The wingspan is 9½ in.

In spite of its miniscule dimensions, this beautiful machine could fly for a distance of 15 to 20 yards on being released from the hand.

After numerous flying tests with different machines of this type, with weights varying between ¹⁄₅₀ of an ounce and 3¼ lb., and after carrying out other experiments on lift with flapping wings driven by steam, under the supervision of Marey at the Ecole Pratique des Hautes Etudes, Tatin ended up, like Pénaud, by completely rejecting wings with alternating motion,

Charles Renard's decaplane glider (1873).

and from then on only considered the aeroplane.

His first aeroplane, which still exists at the Musée de l'Aéronautique, in Paris, is an admirable construction, made entirely by himself.

The body was a reservoir formed by a steel strip rolled in a spiral and fixed by 1,800 rivets. This reservoir contained compressed air which fed an oscillating cylinder which drove, via a transmission system, two propellers with horn blades. The flat wings, spanning 6 ft. 3 in., were fixed on the top of the body. The total weight, with the three wheels and 3 ounces of compressed air, was just under 4 lb.

Tests took place at Chalais-Meudon in 1879. The machine, attached by a wire to a post in the middle of a large platform, took off and flew in a circle for several seconds, over the heads of the spectators; however, no free flight was attempted.

Twenty years later Tatin collaborated on the design of the Santos-Dumont dirigibles and even designed some manned aeroplanes towards the end of his life. He also tackled numerous other aeronautical problems, inventing a recording aneroid barometer in 1880. This device was tried out as an altimeter in 1882.

In 1872, Second Lieutenant Charles Renard, whose name will always be remembered for his work on dirigibles, started his aeronautical career while stationed at Arras by building a model of a decaplane glider. In the centre of the rather heavy tapering body there was a mast to which were fitted ten planes laid out in the manner of a Persian blind. At the rear was a stabilising tail. Also included however, was a new and little-known device, a small horizontal aileron on each side of the fuselage. These two ailerons were connected in such a way that they turned in opposite directions when activated by a pendulum. Renard's idea was that if the machine heeled over and started to turn, the action of these ailerons, one lifting up inside the turn and the other pressing down on the outside, would flatten out the machine and restore it to a straight line.

A trial was made at the Tour de Saint-Eloi in 1873. The machine glided well enough, but spiralled: the pendulum had functioned perfectly correctly but had obeyed the centrifugal force generated by the first turn; instead of that of gravity, so that the movement of the ailerons and the man-

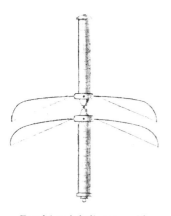

Dandrieux's helicopter with double springs (1879).

Mechanical birds of Jobert (1873) and Hureau de Villeneuve (1872)

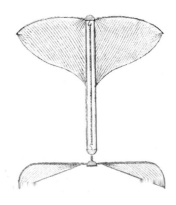

Dandrieux's butterfly-helicopter (1879)

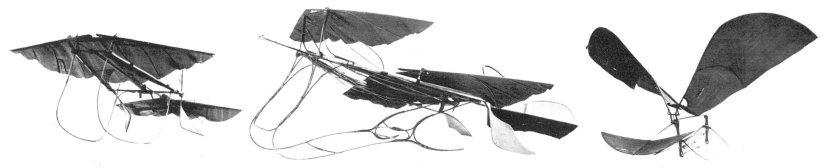

Wilhelm Kress aeroplane, models: left, the *Aérovéloce*, (1880); right, the 1877 model with buffer in front.

Mechanical bird by Kress (1888).

oeuvre executed were the exact opposite of those planned by the inventor.

About this time Jobert and Hureau de Villeneuve also presented their mechanical birds to the Société Française de Navigation Aérienne. Jobert made both two- and four-winged models.

In 1877 the Austrian engineer, Wilhelm Kress, after making several tests with helicopters, reinvented the aeroplane, which he was astonished to learn had been in existence for a long time. He

Enrico Forlanini (1848–1930)

made several models of single or tandem monoplanes, equpped with two propellers driven by twisted rubber. These machines flew very well and were able to take off unaided.

A little later, a toymaker by the name of Dandrieux, who was fascinated by the idea of aviation and had made some large machines with flapping wings, commercialised and popularised helicopter-butterflies and other flying toys that worked by twisted rubber, and were derived

from those of Pénaud.

The first helicopter to fly with a true steam engine was made by the Italian engineer, Enrico Forlanini, in 1877, although as early as 1842, in England, W.H. Phillips, the inventor of fiee extinguishers, had succeeded in making a machine take off which had two vertical propellers driven by reaction, the propeller blades containing tubes which allowed the combustion gases from a similar mixture to that used for extinguishers (coal, saltpetre, and gypsum to create steam) to escape circumferentially from their tips. The helicopter took off suddenly to a great height, crossed two fields, then crashed down; the propeller blades were flung a long way away.

The Forlanini helicopter consisted of a 9 ft. diameter propeller fixed to a frame carrying a tiny, very cleverly constructed two-cylinder steam engine. The transmission, via two crown wheels drove a smaller upper propeller 6 ft. in diameter which was sufficient for take-off, after which reaction drove the lower propeller also. The boiler was a metal sphere slung below the machine on the end of a tube and served as a counterweight to maintain the balance. The boiler contained superheated steam and had no firebox, this being separated from the machine and only used for heating before take-off. The total weight of the machine was 7¾ lb., of which the engine weighed 3½ lb. and the boiler, when full of water, 2½ lb. The surface area of the propeller blades was 2 sq. ft. and the machine developed between a quarter and a third of a horsepower.

Forlanini's helicopter succeeded in taking off freely on 29 June 1877 in Alexandria, then shortly after in Milan. It went up more than 40 ft. into the air and stayed there for twenty seconds. This remarkable machine is still in existence and is kept in Milan. Forlanini died in 1930, at a very advanced age, after a long career in aeronautics.

Around the same time in France, M. Castel

built a helicopter which ran on compressed air; a vertical frame on four wheels supported a horizontal arm at each end of which was a propeller with eight blades. The propellers on each side turned in opposite directions and could be independently tilted during their rotation to allow the aircraft's movements to be controlled in flight. The whole machine weighed nearly 50 lb. and each propeller had a diameter of 5½ ft.

The compressed air reached the cylinder

Victor Tatin (1843–1913).

through a rubber tube. Tests were intended to have been made with the machine held captive, but at the first trial the helicopter broke loose, flew violently into a wall and broke.

In 1879, Emmanuel Dieuaide made a stream helicopter with two propellers, placed one on top of the other, of a similar design to Ponton d'Amécourt's. The propellers were large and each had three blades. The machine broke up before giving any worthwhile results.

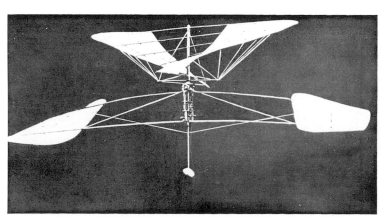

Forlanini's steam-powered helicopter (1877). Overall view.

Detail of mechanism.

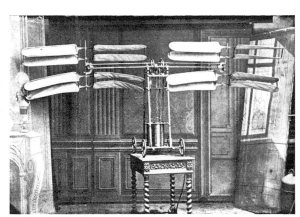

Castel's helicopter using compressed air (1879).

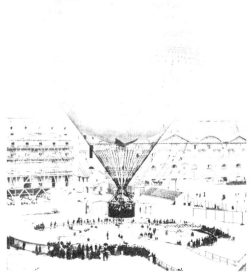

Giffard's great captive steam balloon in the courtyard of the Carousel (1878). On the left of the right-hand picture, the ruins of the Tuileries.

CAPTIVE BALLOONS

Henri Giffard was the chief promoter of public captive balloons which for forty years were the classic attraction at exhibitions and which allowed tens of thousands of people to be "baptised in the air", an often fruitful initiation.

His first 175,000 cu. ft. captive balloon with a steam winch, installed at the 1867 Exposition, was an immediate success and the Empress herself insisted on going up in it.

In 1868 and 1869, he installed two captive balloons in London of 370,500 and 423,500 cu. ft. respectively. The first later made a free ascent in Paris in 1869 under the name of *Pole-Nord* and thus became one of the largest free balloons to take to the air.

Finally, the "star turn" of the 1878 Exposition was the colossal captive balloon that Giffard placed in the courtyard of the Tuileries; this

balloon still holds all the records of size for a gas balloon. It contained 882,000 cu. ft. of pure hydrogen; it had a diameter of 118 ft. and a total height of 180 ft. The envelope alone, formed of seven thickensses of fabric and rubber, weighed over 11½ tons. The basket, which had a diameter of 20 ft., could carry 50 passengers up to a height of 1600 ft. at each ascent. From 10 July to 4 November, the great balloon carried 35,000 people. It was still in use in 1879 until it was split open by a hurricane when on the ground.

Afterwards, numerous balloons of the same system, but with volumes of 85,000 to 150,000 cu. ft., figured in exhibitions all over the world under the supervision of balloonists such as Yon, Louis Godard, Lachambre, Mallet, Surcouf and Lair.

The idea of applying the principle of the kite to captive balloons, to avoid the swings and falls caused by the wind, is an old one.

In 1844, Transon proposed equipping a balloon

with a sail in the form of a parasol, the angle of which could be regulated. Shortly after, in 1847, Marey-Monge revived an idea of Guyton de Morreau for an elongated captive balloon, where the position of the cable attachment would regulate its angle. In 1851, Prosper Meller designed a captive balloon where the sphere was divided into sections, forming a plane which acted as a kite.

The first detailed studies of kite balloons were, however, made by Alphonse Pénaud and Charles Renard.

In 1874, Pénaud presented a design for a military or meteorological captive balloon; it was an elongated symmetrical balloon, covered with a suspension jacket edged with triangulated shrouds attached to a rope ellipse to which the cable was also connected. The shape of the gasbag was maintained by a small compensating balloon fed by a pump, though later he favoured Giffard's idea of a flexible belly.

In December 1878, Charles Renard proposed an elongated balloon also covered with a jacket carrying the handling ropes with the suspension attached to a system similar to the one he had invented for spherical captive balloons, two mutually perpendicular bars joined by fans of rope, the lower bar carrying both the freely swinging basket and the trapeze of the cable.

Neither of the two designs was actually built.

In France, in 1874, military ballooning became a permanent fixture for the first time and was considered a new and necessary arm, attached to the Engineers. Lieutenant Renard was entrusted with the entire new service and, in 1877, created the Chalais-Meudon laboratory and a workshop, from where all French military ballooning material was produced and where so much important scientific work was done.

The French military captive balloons, with articulated suspension and steam winches made in Chalais, took part in most of the manoeuvres from 1880 on and were used in several campaigns, in Tongking (North Vietnam) in 1884, in China in 1900 and in Morocco in 1907.

Great Britain followed the example in 1879 by

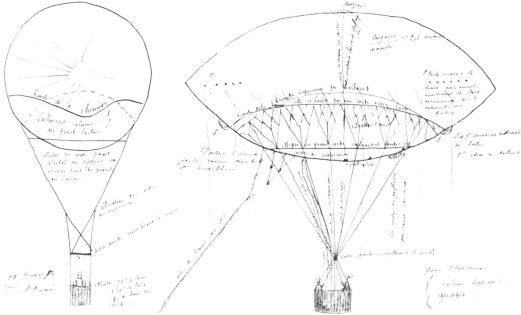

Original sketch of Pénaud's kite balloon, presented to the Société Française de Navigation Aérienne (1874).

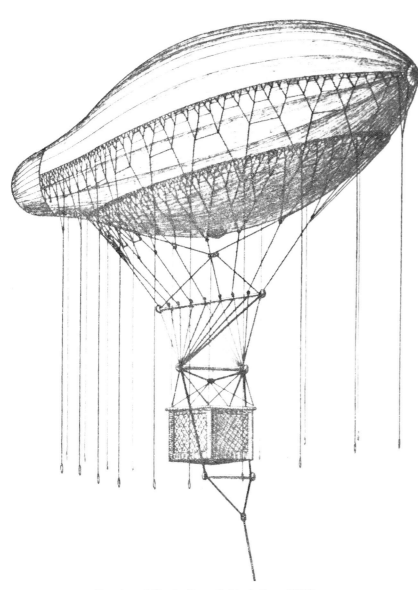

Drawing of Charles Renard's kite balloon (1878).

Captive balloons at the fall of Hong-Loa in Tongking, 1884.

opening establishments at Chatham and Aldershot. In 1885, English balloonists took part in the Bechuanaland and Sudan campaigns. It was on these occasions that cylinders were used for the first time to transport compressed hydrogen. In 1899 and 1900 several captive balloons were used for operations by both sides during the Boer War and, in 1900, balloonists were attached to the expeditionary corps to China.

The Italians began military ballooning in 1885 with French material made by Yon and L. Godard and used their balloonists in 1887 in the Abyssinian campaign, at Massawa and Saati. The gas cylinders were carried by camel.

Most nations founded corps of military balloonists, nearly always starting with French material furnished by Yon and Godard or by Lachambre. The dates of creation of some of these corps were: 1884, Russia and Spain; 1886, China, Holland and Belgium; 1889, Denmark; 1890, Austria and Japan; 1893 Bulgaria and U.S.A.; 1897, Sweden and Switzerland.

A ballooning corps functioned regularly in Germany from 1884 but was not used in action until the Great War. The German balloonists can take credit for first regularly using kite balloons or "drachen balloons".

Italian military ballooning force during the Abyssinian war in 1888. Transport of gas cylinders by camel.

Mouillard's aeroplane, in Cairo.

MOUILLARD

Louis-Pierre Mouillard holds a very specific place in the history of aviation. Neither a mathematician nor an inventor, nor even really a builder, he nevertheless had an immensely inspiring effect on his fellow pioneers. A patient, reliable and extremely logical observer, a draughtsman, a poet and a lively warm, and uplifting writer, he left a short but unforgettable collection of writings which had the merit of inspiring both Chanute and the Wright brothers. They paid him the highest homage, saying that at the blackest moments of their careers, when they were discouraged in their research and were in danger of losing faith in what they were trying to do, it was by reading Mouillard that they found the courage and hope to continue and successfully finish their work.

Mouillard was born in Lyons in 1834, and was attracted to flying from childhood; when he was still very young he had the idea of measuring and weighing birds exactly.

His life took him to Algeria and Egypt where he gave himself passionately to the study of the flight of birds, both of flapping flight and more particularly of gliding – that is to say the soaring flight of large birds, as they rise in never-ending circles, their wings immobile in the wind.

As an experimenter there is not much to show: his first machine, built in Lyons in 1856, was abandoned. Two experiments followed in Algeria, the second in 1865. One of them failed because the machine was too fragile. In the other, the glider, which had movable wings, took Mouillard up in spite of himself. He covered 46 yards skimming the ground, but this unexpected success seems to have rather frightened him. During another experiment, the machine folded up, and he dislocated one of his shoulders.

Later, Mouillard built another large aircraft in Cairo but he had become crippled and never tried it out completely. On the other hand, he tested numerous small scale models, of which one had the very interesting distinction of having a vane automatically controlling two ailerons which were intended, like those of Renard and Pénaud, to act as steering controls and keep the aeroplane going in a straight line.

In 1881, Mouillard published *L'Empire de*

Louis Mouillard (1834–1897).

L'Air, Essai D'Ornithologie Appliquée á L'Aviation, a magistral work. Ten years later he wrote *Le Vol Sans Battement* (*Flight without Movement*) which was not printed until long after his death.

Mouillard was an enthusiast, a dreamer, and totally without personal ambition. He died in Cairo in 1897, alone and almost penniless. A few passages from *L'Empire de L'Air* will give an idea of his character.

Flying is undoubtedly the most beautiful way of moving that nature has given her creatures."

" . . . Nothing is so beautiful as the flight of this enormous bird [the vulture]; one cannot see one go by without stopping and contemplating the majesty of its movement . . . It is the model par excellence of the study we are working on . . . He who has seen [an oricou] in flight for five minutes and who has not realised the possibility of air transport does not have an analytical frame of mind . . . to say the least."

"I waited for years to see this movement. Finally, one day in Africa, two mating eagles gave me this spectacle. One of them . . . was lifted up by a gust of wind and took off like this, directly, slowly . . . and without flapping its wings once. One can't see such demonstrations every day, one has to look for them persistently; one has to be fired with enthusiasm for this study and one has to be drawn to it by something inexplicable so that certain movements just make your heart beat faster."

"One has to want to see a lot and do what has to be done in order to see properly; gather facts, work them out if one can, and normally one can with intelligence and good sense."

"I must observe well today. . . . I must get the exact measurements and the precise weight of an animal, in the wild, and in perfect health."

"I must . . . understand the movements, processes and evolution of birds; know all their manoeuvres, and especially understand them; otherwise, I'll never get there."

" . . . But when one bothers to go and find one, when one sees this enormous animal [the griffon vulture], as large as a sheep, taking off, with difficulty at first, with the great flaps of its wings making a hissing noise that can be heard 300 yards away in the silence of the desert; then when one sees it circling endlessly and effortlessly one has an interesting spectacle in front of one's eyes: every human being is nailed to the ground, even the Arab. We discovered in that bird a way of moving one would never have dreamed of; it has in it something of the majesty and singularity of a moving train."

"Forward then, you lucky, healthy ones; to your task! You only need to build; the work is all prepared."

Biot's glider with articulated blades (1879–1880)

BIOT AND GOUPIL

Several little known but interesting attempts at aeroplanes were made around this time. In 1879, Biot, a modest researcher who had invented an ingenious conical tailless kite around 1861 and who, as early as 1868, is said to have made a short ascent suspended from an enormous kite, produced a monoplane glider whose wings were made of individual blades, rather similar to bird feathers, the angle of which could be modified before each experiment. Biot made several successful glides near Clamart with this machine which is preserved at the Musée de l'Aéronautique and which must be the earliest full-scale aircraft still in existence. Biot also collaborated with Mouillard and with Dandrieux in making gliders and flying machines with flapping wings.

In 1883, A. Goupil, an engineer who has left some remarkable work on aviation, built and tested a monoplane aeroplane with a wing area of 290 sq. ft., weighing 110 lb., and having a wingspan of 20 ft. and an overall length of 26 ft.

Goupil's steam aeroplane, seen from the front, with its regulating ailerons.

Held against a wind of about 12 mph at an angle of 10 degrees, this machine was capable of lifting two men from the ground. With the data acquired, the following year Goupil published a project for a steam aeroplane which included some remarkable mechanical devices: a streamlined body with a propeller in front and resting on elastic skids supported two concave wings which had a small span but were very wide at the roots. The aircraft was equipped with a horizontal mobile tail and a rudder at the rear and with what the inventor called the "regulator" at the front. This consisted of two rigid ailerons controlled either by hand or automatically and whose movements were synchronised so that when one went down the other went up. Goupil stated clearly, and for the first time, that these ailerons were instruments for the *directional control of the machine*. Besides this, in the event of longitudinal tilting, the simultaneous action of the two ailerons in the same direction could put the machine back on the horizontal line. The automatic control was achieved by a balance mechanism, the weight being provided by the pilot himself sitting on a swinging seat, and the movements being transmitted to the ailerons.

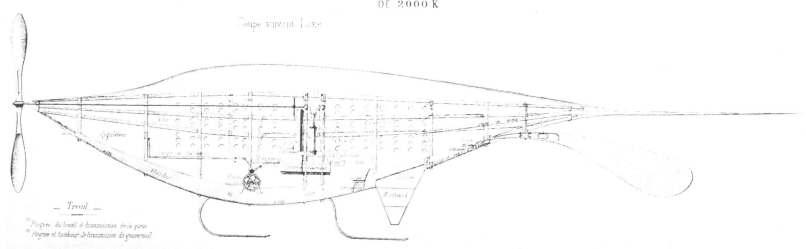

Longitudinal section of the body of the steam aeroplane designed by Goupil (1884).

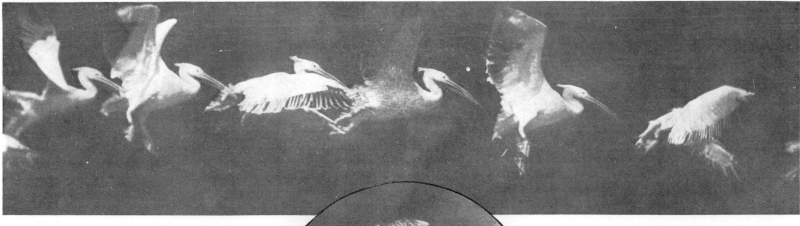

Side view of the flight of a heron (1889) –

MAREY AND THE FLIGHT OF BIRDS

The first scientific studies of the movements of living creatures were made by Etienne-Jules Marey, perfecting techniques which he later used for research into the flight of birds.

• Between 1860 and 1880, he tried out various kinds of apparatus for measuring the movements of limbs, most of them based on his pneumatic "drum" which transmitted the movements to a recording stylus. During this period he also carried out research into the synthesis of wing movements. In 1882, taking up one of Pénaud's inventions and using a chronographic camera with a fixed plate and occulting disc, Marey was the first to make successful photographic sequences of birds in flight, obtaining successive im-

Etienne-Jules Marey (1830–1904).

ages as close together as fifty per second or spaced out and disassociated by means of a revolving mirror. Using three cameras, in 1887 Marey obtained three simultaneous pictures on a black

chronographic images produced by a revolving mirror. background: a side view, a view from above and a three-quarters view.

In 1882 Marey invented the photographic gun with a circular moving plate. Then, in 1888, he replaced the fixed plate of the chronographic camera by a band of sensitive paper which moved periodically in a manner synchronised with the appearance of the slits in the occulting disc. In 1889 and 1890 Marey further improved on this camera by changing to sensitive bands of celluloid, which was transparent, and in 1892 he projected the series of photographs he had taken on a screen. The invention of cinematography indeed was to a large extent a sequel to Marey's work on chronographic photography.

Towards the end of his life, Marey studied by means of smoke produced from polyporus tinder the eddies set up by different bodies or shapes when placed in a moving airstream.

A duck landing (1882).

Phases in the action of a gull's wing.

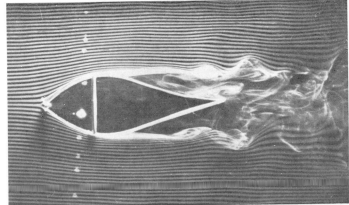

Deformations in an air stream, shown by tinder smoke, in contact with a curved surface and with a tapering body (1900–1901).

The first electric dirigible balloon, built by the Tissandier brothers, leaving Auteuil on 8 October 1883

THE TISSANDIER AIRSHIP

In 1881, Gaston and Albert Tissandier tested and then presented at the famous Exposition d'Electricité at the Palais de l'Industrie a model of a dirigible balloon, the propeller of which was driven by a little electric motor built by Trouvé, the power being provided by Planté accumulators.

Moving on to a full-scale experiment, the brothers had a fusiform balloon made for them by Lachambre which had a volume of 37,400 cu. ft., a length of 92 ft. and a diameter of 30 ft. The balloon was covered with a webbing suspension jacket and had a bamboo basket. Two rigid bars reinforced the centre of the balloon.

The basket was equipped with a propeller designed by Tatin, 9 ft. 4 in. in diameter and driven by a motor of 1⅓ horsepower. The electric battery was composed of 24 cells containing bichromate of potassium. Simple but ingenious devices allowed the liquid to come into contact with the zinc and carbon elements. The engine and the batteries together weighed 616 lb. Gaston Tissandier had been in charge of this side of the operation, while his brother Albert had concerned himself with the design and construction of the balloon. The Tissandier brothers had also made a

The basket of the first electric dirigible: left, Gaston Tissandier; right, Albert Tissandier

special machine for the rapid and large-scale production of hydrogen.

On 8 October 1883, the world's first electric dirigible went up with its inventors on board from their private balloon workshop in Auteuil. With the power of the 24 battery cells, the balloon could stand up to the wind for about twenty minutes above the Bois de Boulogne but the experiment could not be carried further owing to a lack of lateral stability. The landing took place without untoward incident at Croissy-sur-Seine.

On 26 September 1884, the Tissandier brothers, accompanied by M. Lecomte, made a second ascent. The rudder had been improved and fitted with a rigid keel. The batteries and the bichromate solution had been modified to give the motor a power of 1½ h.p.

The balloon crossed Paris, stemming a wind of 7 mph, several times for quite a long while. The rudder functioned satisfactorily. The descent went off well at Marolles-en-Brie.

Unfortunately the experiments had to be discontinued as the Tissandier brothers lacked a hangar in which to wait for calm weather. Also, on 9 August 1844, the first trial had taken place of a dirigible balloon with a far more powerful motor, with the resources of the French Army, behind it. The experiments of the Tissandier brothers had so far been at their own expense, and they no doubt felt that the time had come to bow out gracefully. Nevertheless they deserve great credit for being the first to demonstrate the practicality of electricity for air navigation.

Adrien Duté-Poitevin (1844–1900)

Charles Renard (1847–1905)

Arthur Krebs in 1884

Paul Renard in 1907

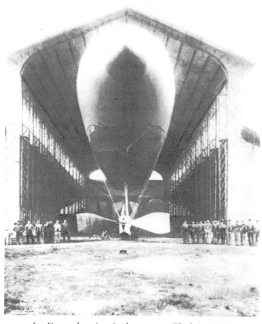

La France leaving its hangar at Chalais (1884)

THE FIRST AERIAL CIRCUIT
THE DIRIGIBLE *LA FRANCE*

France, which had led the world in air navigation with the first manned ascent by Pilâtre de Rozier, now achieved the first aerial circuit in a balloon.

First electric engine for *La France* built by Krebs.

This important event took place from the Chalais-Meudon Park on 9 August 1884; the dirigible *La France*, manned by its inventors Captain Charles Renard and Captain Arthur Krebs, took off, went on a journey and came back to land at its starting point.

Charles Renard, who was born in 1847 in Damblain, was an outstanding theoretician and practician in all that he approached; he devoted most of his time to aeronautics but he was a man of wide knowledge who left his mark in other fields as well.

He created the Chalais-Meudon establishment for the French Army and it was there that he made the world's first truly dirigible balloon that he named *La France*. He was personally responsible for the aerostatic and the electrochemical side, that is to say the design of the aircraft and of its batteries, while the mechanical side was entrusted to Captain Krebs, who had collaborated with him from the start. The actual construction of the balloon was supervised by Lieutenant Paul Renard, Charles Renard's younger brother, and by Duté-Poitevin, the establishment's civil pilot. *La France*, an elongated asymmetric balloon with a gas-bag of varnished cloth restrained by a jacket to which the ropes supporting the basket were attached, had a volume of 65,800 cu. ft., a length of 165 ft. and a diameter of 27 ft. 6 in. at its widest point. The compensating air balloon had a volume of 15,500 cu. ft. The bamboo basket, which was covered with canvas, was unusual in being 108 ft. long. It had a very large propeller at the front and at the rear a steering rudder and an elevator which served above all as a stabiliser.

The electric motor, designed by Krebs, was a multipolar engine producing 8 h.p. for a weight of 211 lb. at 3,600 rpm. Reducing gears transmitted the motion to the propeller, which turned at 50 rpm. The engine ran on a light battery made up of cells the size of lamp glasses containing chromic and hydrochloric acid. Each cell contained a positive tubular electrode of platinised silver and a pencil of zinc.

The battery weighed 880 lb. and was capable of providing 16 h.p. for 1 hour and 39 minutes. It was the lightest generator of electricity yet to have been produced.

The first ascent was described in the following terms by the pilots in their note to the Académie des Sciences:

"At four o'clock on a particularly calm afternoon the balloon, set free and having a very low

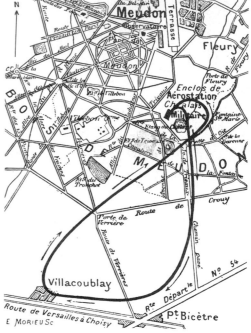

The first aerial circuit (9 August 1884).

ascensional force, rose up slowly to the height of the surrounding plateaux. The engine was put into motion and soon, under its impulse, the

The basket of *La France* with its second engine (1885)

96

The first dirigible balloon to fly a closed circuit: the *La France*, of Renard and Krebs, in the Chalais-Meudon park (1884)

balloon increased its speed, faithfully obeying the slightest action of its rudder.

At first we kept to a north-south route, heading for the Châtillon and Verrières plateaux; when we were level with the Choisy-Versailles road we changed direction so as not to go over the trees and put the balloon on course for Versailles.

Above Villacoublay, finding ourselves about 2½ miles from Chalais and entirely satisfied with the balloon's performance, we decided to come back and try to land at Chalais itself, despite the lack of open space between the trees. The balloon executed a half-turn to the right with a very narrow angle (about 11°) being given to the rudder. The radius of the turn described was about 500 ft.

The dome of the Invalides, which was our land-mark, showed Chalais to be slightly to our left.

When we were level with it, the balloon ex-ecuted, with the same facility as before, a change of direction to the left; and it was soon gliding 1000 ft above its departure point. At that point its tendency to descend was accentuated further by manoeuvring the valve. During this time we had to go backwards and forwards several times in order to keep the balloon over the landing point. At a height of 250 ft. we dropped a rope which was seized by men on the ground and the balloon was brought back to the same meadow from where it had left."

A journey of 4¾ miles had been covered in twenty-three minutes.

At the next outing on 12 September, the bal-loon stood up against quite a strong wind for ten minutes or so but the engine over-heated and had to be turned off. The landing took place at Velizy.

On 8 November, *La France* made two new ascents, again manned by Renard and Krebs, with landings at Chalais.

In 1885 the engine was replaced by a bipolar Gramme motor producing 9 h.p. The balloon was lightened to allow for a third pilot.

On 25 August 1885, piloted by the Renard brothers, *La France* went up for an hour but the wind forced them to land at Villacoublay. On 22 September, Duté-Poitevin accompanied the two officers: the balloon headed towards Paris, turn-ing at Point-du-Jour. The onward journey lasted forty-seven minutes and the return took eleven minutes. The dirigible's actual speed was 13½ mph. The experiment was repeated the next day over a similar route.

Five times out of seven, the dirigible had returned to its point of departure.

The basket of *La France* being transported by barge from Meudon to Paris for the 1889 Exhibition.

Pompeien Piraud's flying machine with articulated wings (1882).

FURTHER EXPERIMENTS

A certain number of researchers had tried to obtain propulsion or lift, and often the two together, by means other than the propeller: the solutions which were contemplated or tested varied enormously. Since most of them consisted of the alternating movement of large pieces of equipment, they were not successful, but it is interesting to review these attempts.

Beating wings, inspired by those of bats, were much studied by Pompeien Piraud. This inventor, whose skilful creations were more interesting than his ideas, started experimenting in 1879 at Grand Camp, near Lyons, with a machine with flapping articulated wings driven by a steam engine, until this exploded. He renewed his tests in 1882 but obtained no concrete results, and did not manage to complete a larger machine that he had been counting on trying out initially on his elongated balloon *l'Espérance*.

Various experiments were tried, using the old solution of wheels with valves or articulated paddle wheels. Some inventors, such as M. Hérard towards 1888, tried out large-scale wheels to which a number of frames were fixed in such a way as to remain always vertical. These frames

Hérard's machine with rotary wings and automatically feathering blades (1888).

were equipped with venetian or louvred blinds which opened during parts of the rotation and closed during others under the action of a cam. The lifting wheels of Pichou's *Auto-aérienne*, on which tests were carried out from 1872 to 1912, were like a sort of slatted roller in which the slats could be tilted by gears at varying angles to the tangential during different stages of each rotation of the roller, in order to provide a net thrust in a given direction. In the same spirit, but infinitely more scientifically, Professor Wellner, of Brno in Moravia, tried out a model and developed a project for lifting rollers for an enormous flying machine which was nearly built around 1893. In the place of simple flat slats, Wellner contemplated using aerofoil sections which had an efficient aerodynamic profile. This idea was based on Armour's work of 1873.

In 1890, Victor Tatin and Professor Charles Richet tested a large model steam aeroplane, a monoplane weighing 73 lb. with a wingspan of 21 ft. 8 in. and a surface area of 86 sq. ft. Tatin was quite logically concerned with reducing the effort necessary to produce the required lift and tried to eliminate useless drag; in consequence all the mechanism was enclosed in a cloth-covered body allowing only the propeller axles to project at the front and the rear. The steam engine weighed 24

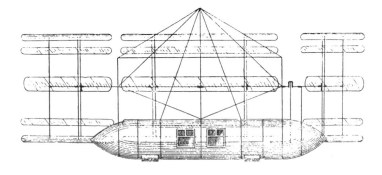
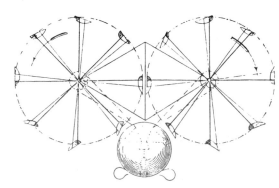

Wellner's project for a flying machine with rotary lifting surfaces (1894).

Victor Tatin and Charles Richet's steam aeroplane without its canvas covering (1890).

lb. with the accessories and had a power of 1 h.p. The aircraft was tried out at the Cap de La Hève in 1890, the launch taking place on an inclined runway 46 yards long which sloped up at the end. The flight started well, but the tail deformed in flight and the machine crashed at the foot of the cliff. It was repaired and tried out again in 1896 and 1897. Three flights took place above the Giens harbour; a maximum distance of 150 yards was achieved but each time the unmanned aircraft went into a classic "stall" situation and fell into the water.

In 1894 Sir Hiram Maxim, an American living in England, and the inventor of the Maxim gun, after numerous tests on a carousel and in a wind-tunnel, which he was one of the first to make use of, tried out an exceptionally large aeroplane which consisted of an octagonal surface area prolonged by inclined lateral wings. Four horizontal tiered planes could also be added on each side which, together with the two elevators, gave it a total surface area of nearly 600 sq. ft. The wingspan, with all extensions fitted, was more than 100 ft. A remarkable boiler, which had a gas-burner with 7,650 jets, provided the steam for the two compound engines, each of over 180 h.p. and extremely light, which independently drove two propellers with diameters of nearly 18 ft. All up the aircraft weighed just over 800 lb. Experiments took place on a railway track which had been specially set up. Maxim had, it would appear, an obsession not to let his aircraft fly freely, at least during its early tests. The machine, therefore, was first tried out with an underframe with deliberately heavy wheels but the front of the aircraft nevertheless left the track and it was damaged; it was then tested between two superposed railway lines, the upper one (of 3in. by 9 in. Georgia pine) being to limit the flight or at least stop the machine rising from the ground; after travelling some 1000 ft. the aircraft broke the top rails in an effort to rise, went off the track again and broke up, which put an end to the tests that had cost Maxim several thousand pounds. In spite of this considerable disbursement, Maxim's efforts did not contribute greatly to the progress of aviation.

Maxim's colleague Horatio Phillips built one of the earliest wind-tunnels and was one of the first to demonstrate the importance of stream-lining solid bodies as well as the provision of curvature in wings. Around 1893, Phillips tried out a large-scale steam-powered multiplane aircraft which had forty superposed shallow but wide surfaces. This aircraft rose up easily while maintaining contact with the ground by means of a large wheel connected to a carousel. As with Maxim's, it will never be known how stable this aircraft would have been in free flight.

Maxim's aerodynamic tunnel.

Maxim's aeroplane: the lateral wing extensions are not in place (1894).

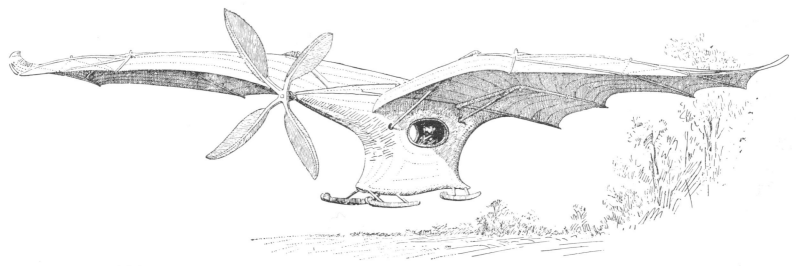

Ader's *Eole*, the first aeroplane to leave the ground with its pilot (9 October 1890).

THE FIRST MANNED FLIGHT

On 9 October 1890 a man, for the first time, flew in an aeroplane which left the ground under the power of its engine alone. This first take-off was very brief and the flight could not be sustained; it was nevertheless a very great event, the credit for which is entirely due to Clément Ader.

A self-trained engineer, born in Muret in 1841, Ader was an inventive genius and came to Paris to exploit his ideas. He is remembered for his work in perfecting the telephone and for the installation in around 1880 of the first French telephone lines.

He had always been interested in aviation and, after several youthful experiments, in 1873 he made a large bird with wings of goose feathers with which he tried out the power of lift against the wind, the machine being held captive with its inventor on board. He displayed this machine in Paris in Nadar's workshop in 1874.

Around 1882, the financial rewards from his inventions enabled Ader to begin building a large steam aeroplane, which mechanical progress had made possible. This aircraft was finished in 1889.

On 19 April 1890 Ader patented a very detailed description of the principal specifications for this aeroplane, which was extremely complicated but admirably conceived. Drawing his inspiration essentially from nature, Ader had studied the flight of storks and bats. His conclusions had been in favour of the aeroplane solution, that is to say a non-flapping surface, appropriately curved, spir-

alling from front to back, which he called the universal curve. But curiously enough, although he had adopted the principal of the gliding bird, the form of his aircraft was completely derived, down to the absence of a tail, from a mammal

Clément Ader (1841–1925)

with flapping wings – the flying fox. For this machine, he invented the word *avion*. The wings, of hollow wooden spars covered in silk, could be moved in many ways; mobility at the shoulder joint allowed them to move bodily forwards or backwards while they were also capable of partial folding during flight as necessary for speed or

movement, independent warping for each wing and variation in the amount of curvature. Combinations of these movements were to suffice for all manoeuvres. There was no elevator. Owing to the elasticity of the materials the surface area had an equal tension in all flying positions. Furthermore, the whole surface area could be folded when not in use. The machine rested on a frame with wheels, the back ones being attached to the rudder. A fourth wheel, in front, was a protection against the risk of overturning.

A propeller, with four feather-like blades of bamboo, was driven by an admirable light steam engine, with two vertical steel cylinders and a boiler with little undulating tubes heated by liquid or vaporised fuel burners. The aircraft was named *Eole*. Its principal dimensions were: wingspan 46 ft.; length 21 ft. 4 in.; surface area 300 sq. ft.; total weight, including the engine, 386 lb. The engine had a power of 20 h.p. With 66 lb. of water and 22 lb. of alcohol and a pilot on board, the *Eole* weighed a total of 650 lb., i.e. around 2 psf. and 33 lb. per h.p.

Tests took place in October 1890, out of the reach of prying eyes in the seclusion of the grounds of Mme Isaac Pereire, at Armainvilliers, where a well-levelled "manoeuvring area" had been specially prepared. Besides the accounts given by Ader's employees and a few gardeners, there remains from this first flight a document in the form of unsigned minutes which Ader kept:

"On the ninth of October one thousand eight hundred and ninety, at five minutes past four in the afternoon, in the grounds of the château of

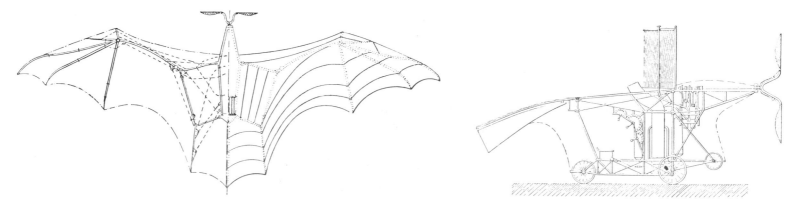

Plan and elevation of the *Eole* from details given in Ader's patent.

Left: The 30 h.p. steam engine of Ader's *Eole No. II* (1891–1893). *Right*: Ader's *Avion No. III* tested at Satory in 1897.

Madame Pereire, at Armainvilliers, near Gretz (Seine-et-Marne) a conclusive air navigation experiment took place.

The aeroplane No. 1 named *Eole* and manned by Monsieur Ader, its inventor, left the ground and kept itself in the air by its wings, skimming the ground over a distance of about fifty metres under the power from its motor alone. The manoeuvring area was 220 yards long and 27 yards wide on hard rolled ground."

In 1893 the *Revue de l'Aeronautique* published a detailed memorandum by Ader on the *Eole*, preceded by an identical account of the experiment but with the following addition:

"Unfortunately, the aircraft was not sufficiently stable and it would have been rash to continue this attempt the results of which, although far from negligible, showed the need for further studies."

On 12 October 1890, Ader sent Nadar a very interesting letter: "My dear Nadar, I have solved the problem at the expense of much work, fatigue and money; the aircraft I have used for my final studies is called *Eole*; it has just made its first flight, with me inside, over a distance of 55 yards; this distance could not be longer because the manoeuvring area is too short. The experiment took place at Gretz-Armainvilliers, in the grounds of Mme Pereire who was gracious enough to give me hospitality. I feel it is my duty to tell you about it, since you have been so interested in the matter, in case you would like to see the *Eole* which will be here for a few more days."

On 20 June 1891, *L'Illustration* published a drawing of the *Eole*, a sketch made clandestinely, but substantially correct. The article was optimistic – a bit too much so considering the results obtained; it began with these words: "Nobody saw anything, nobody knows anything: but *L'Illustration* has friends everywhere . . . "

There is no doubt about the results obtained; they are in any case not surprising and it is important to understand their real meaning.

Ader himself always considered this first take-off to be a very important event but limited in that it was an experiment that could not be carried further with the existing equipment. He considered himself very lucky to have achieved what he had done and had not hoped for more. Moreover, he immediately modified the *Eole*, fitted it with a new boiler and took the aircraft to Satory where, in September 1891, it would appear that he "almost flew". The *Eole* hit some wagons and was damaged. Once repaired, it was publicly displayed in Paris. The War Minister and

President of the Council, M. de Freycinet, saw it and there and then resolved to have the tests continued by the War Department. A laboratory-workshop at Auteuil under military jurisdiction was set up for Ader, to whom a part of the Henri Giffard legacy was also allocated to repay him for the costs which he had already incurred.

A new aircraft, named *Avion No. III* was finished in 1897. This was very similar to the *Eole* but had a wingspan of 52 ft. 6 in. and a weight when empty of 568 lb. In working order, with a pilot, it weighed a little less than 880 lb. The *Avion No. III* had two independent steam engines of 20 h.p., each driving a four-bladed propeller, but fed by a single boiler. No mechanical difficulty was too great for M. Ader; he seemed to enjoy solving all the problems which arose, and this time he counted on very rapid results with a flight from Satory to Vincennes to conclude the trials. These took place at Satory after detailed and extensive laboratory tests where the steam engine ran for several weeks and the wings underwent static tests. A circular runway 1600 yards long was prepared at Satory.

There are two conflicting accounts of the tests which took place on 12 and 14 October 1897: Ader's version states that on 12 October he went round the runway "flying intermittently" during which time "none of the wheels touched ground" and that on 14 October he covered 165 yards on the runway by short flights, then made an "uninterrupted flight" of 330 yards, during the course of which the *Avion No. III* was carried off the runway by a strong wind and turned over on landing, breaking a wing, the front wheels and the propellers, but not injuring its pilot.

This account, accompanied by a sketch, was repeated so often that it was believed. It should be noted, however, that M. Ader only published it nine years after the experiment, when Santos-

The *Avion No. III* with its wings folded.

Dumont was making his first flights, and that his earlier communications were much less positive.

The second, official, version is contained in the detailed report concluding in favour of continuing the experiments which was written on the spot and sent to the War Minister by General Mensier and General Grillon, delegates of the Commission, who formally witnessed Ader's test.

Of the test on 12 October the report says:

"The wheel marks left on the ground, although this was not very firm, were hardly noticeable; it was clear that part of the aircraft had been held up by its wings although the speed was only about a third of what it could have been if M. Ader had used all the engine power . . . "

The attempt on 14 October is described thus:

"At departure, which took place at 1715 hrs, the aircraft, with the wind behind it, ran smoothly at a steady speed; it was however easy to note later from the wheel marks that the rear of the aircraft had frequently lifted and that the rear wheel which formed the rudder had not remained constantly on the ground.

"As the aircraft approached Point B, the two members of the commission saw it suddenly go off the runway, do a half turn, fall on its side and finally come to a halt . . . "

In 1906, General Mensier and M. Binet, who had also witnessed the tests, wrote an account of their recollections to M. Ader but were unable to state that they had *seen* flight themselves. M. Binet stated that he had found traces of wheels and noticed their disappearance, from which he concluded that "the *Avion No. III* seemed to possess all that was needed to fly."

Later, General Mensier, at over eighty years old, went back on his statements but the facts had been established.

The War Minister did not accept the Commission's recommendation to continue the tests. Ader, no longer bound by military secrecy, tried to find support but, deeply discouraged, suddenly destroyed the *Eole*, all his studies and his whole laboratory, only sparing the *Avion No. III* which he offered to the Conservatoire des Arts et Métiers where it has been religiously kept.

Much later Ader, who was a real prophet in military aviation, published a complete plan for the organisation of aerial observation and bombardment. Indeed, in his famous work *L'Aviation Militaire* he foresaw squadrons of reconnaissance planes or bombers, aviation schools and airfields and drew diagrams of special darts and bombs.

Honours came with time and after a long life Ader died in Toulouse on 3 May 1925.

Otto Lilienthal (1848–†*F*1896)

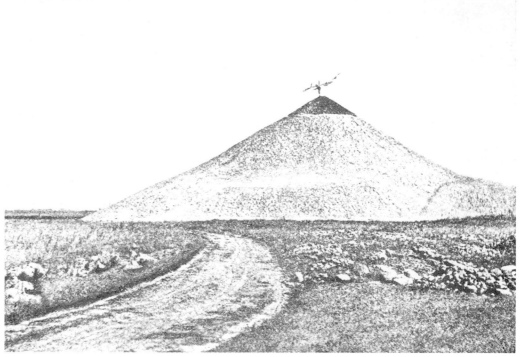

Otto Lilienthal's hill (1893)

OTTO LILIENTHAL

Otto Lilienthal was the true father of modern aviation.

Even if he did not invent the aeroplane, he was the first man to control a flying machine heavier than air, and he laid down the principles which led directly to the Wright brothers' success.

Born in Anklam in Pomerania on 24 May 1848, Otto Lilienthal was fascinated from childhood by aviation: when he was twelve he and his brother Gustar tried out large rudimentary gliders, at night, then machines with flapping wings.

He became an engineer and in 1889 published an important work on aviation based on the flight of birds, and two years later built his first real glider. He was among the first to realise the significance of the curvature of the wing.

Selfless, scientific and practical, a skilful constructor and a courageous, determined and sound experimenter, he established the techniques both of gliding and soaring, realising how easy the transition would then be to the motor aeroplane. He defined his method in these terms:

"When gliding in the air, the designer is confronted with a great number of phenomena that

The aviator has thrown his legs back to balance his machine.

are not found elsewhere; in particular, those relating to the wind must be taken into consideration in the construction and use of flying machines. The manner in which we will be subject to the variations of the wind when gliding in the air can only be learned when one is actually in the air . . .

The only way which will lead us to a rapid solution of human flight is by practising systematic and vigorous experiments on actual flight. These experiments and flying exercises should not be carried out only by scientists, but by all those who would like to find an exciting pasttime in the air, so that the flying machine and the handling of it can, by habitual use, rapidly reach the highest degree of perfection . . . One can fly over long distances with a very simple machine with no undue effort and this sort of gliding flight, moving safely through the air, gives more pleasure than any other sort of sport."

Lilienthal's flying machines were many and varied, but between 1891 and 1895 they were all monoplanes with a span of about 23 ft., in bamboo and cane, covered in cotton and weighing about 45 lbs. The experimenter held on to the machine by his elbows and his forearms. Running down a hill, against the wind, he rapidly left the ground and glided, bending his knees and his body in order to restore the balance.

Lilienthal made more than two thousand glides over distances of up to 330 yards. Several times he succeeded in rising higher than his point of departure and in making turns. His tests took place in Werder, Steglitz, Lichterfelde and Rhinower.

Following a natural progression, he started using a carbonic acid motor to work paddles on the ends of his wings, for Lilienthal did not have much faith in the propeller.

To reduce the wingspan, Lilienthal built a biplane which gave good results, but, on 9 August 1896 in Rhinower, the upper plane broke off. Thrown to the ground, Otto Lilienthal was picked up unconscious and died the following day.

Lilienthal is the first man to have been photographed in flight: this was just one of the reasons for the enormous influence he exercised on all the researchers of his time and later, and by means of which he inspired hesitators with confidence in the future of aviation. A witness to his flights has left the following impressions:

"I had read numerous articles on Lilienthal and had seen many photographs of him in the air, but I had no idea of the perfection to which he had carried his invention, nor of the precision with which he guided his machine . . . From all that I have witnessed, nothing can be more thrilling nor arouse such admiration and enthusiasm as the tremendous and daring speed of Lilienthal in the air. The sight of a man supported by large white wings, moving over you at a great height with the speed of a racehorse, while the wind makes a strange droning noise in the guy-ropes, gives an impression one can never forget."

In the 1894 edition of *L'Aéronaute*, M. E. Veyrin spoke of Lilienthal in these words: "The word 'conquest' is not exaggerated in the present case. I do not see how one can look at and reflect upon these photographs without feeling the calm enthusiasm that comes from tremendous hope in the future."

A monoplane glide around 1895: the aviator in a normal flying position.

Otto Lilienthal's biplane in 1896.

The end of a glide by Otto Lilienthal.

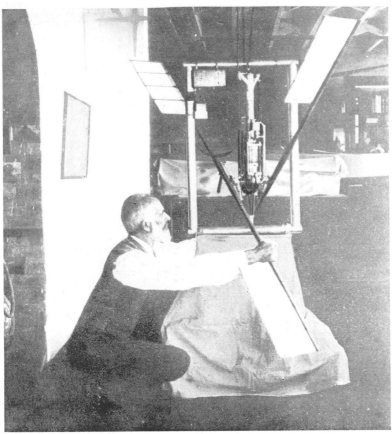

Lawrence Hargrave (1850–1915) experimenting with flapping wings.

Hargrave's quadruplane with propellers driven by compressed air (1889).

HARGRAVE AND LANGLEY

One of the most methodical and inspired researchers of this period was a modest but talented Australian from Sydney, Lawrence Hargrave, an engineer and a scholar. He is remembered in particular for his invention of the box-kite, an invention that transformed the design of kites for meteorological and scientific purposes and had a notable influence on the general development of aviation.

As can be seen from the diagrams, Hargrave studied many new kite forms and researched lateral stability by making the surfaces dihedral and by channelling air into the round or quadrangular cells, and longitudinal stability by separating the surfaces into two elements placed in tandem; he also conducted research into aviation and, as well as tests on flapping wings, created some very strange aeroplane models: his tailless monoplane, whose surface was longer than it was wide but nevertheless had excellent stability, deserves special mention. This machine was equipped with an engine running on compressed air

which drove not a propeller, but two driving flapping wings, like a pair of sculls. Other machines, like the quadruplane, were fitted with a propeller driven by tensioned rubber bands, a small steam engine or a motor running on compressed air.

Hargrave was a remarkable mechanic and created minute steam engines, notably an extremely light model with three star-shaped cylinders. He also carried out extensive work on wing profiles, on soaring using captive gliders, and on the automatic stabilisation of aeroplanes.

A profound believer in the future of aviation,

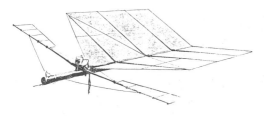

Aeroplane propelled by flapping wings (1892).

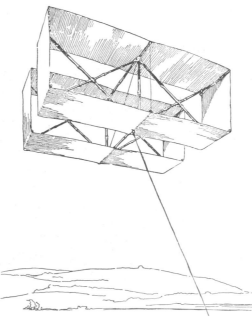

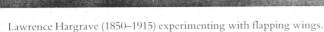

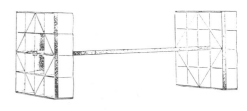

Hargrave kite with square cells.

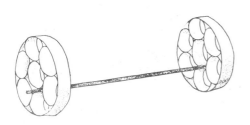

Hargrave kite with round cells.

The Hargrave box-kite (final model).

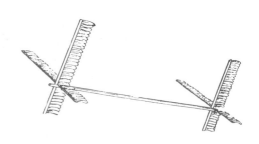

Hargrave kite with feathered wings.

Hargrave said that it was useless to try to convince the sceptics while waiting for success. He preferred to build, experiment, make his results known to all and invite their repetition. He expressed himself thus:

"One must get out of one's head that by hiding the results of one's work one will become rich; annual payments on a patent are a waste of money. The flying machine of the future will not be born ready made and capable of flying 1,000 miles. Like everything, it will evolve gradually. The first problem is to obtain something that flies at all. When that is achieved, a complete description ought to be published to help others. Excellence of design and execution will always defy competition."

Samuel Pierpont Langley, secretary of the Smithsonian Institute in Washington, did valuable work on the exploration of the infra-red parts of the solar spectrum before devoting the end of his life to aviation.

Langley began his researches in his new field by attempting to define the basic principles of flight by testing various elements on a steam-driven carousel or "whirling table" which he built at Allegheny, and which was capable of circumferential speeds of up to 70 mph.

Later he built a series of small-scale models powered by twisted rubber bands of diverse forms – biplanes, monoplanes with curved-back wings, then with paired wings in tandem. Although they had already been invented by Walker and Brown, the last named machines have kept the name "Langley type", in recognition of the considerable importance that Langley gave to

the study of this configuration, and to the fact that he devoted himself almost exclusively to it for the next ten years.

Langley built a steam powered aeroplane, which he called *Aerodrome No. 5*, the engine of which he constructed himself. With this machine he made a decisively important experiment on 6 May 1896: the first sustained flight of over one minute and over a long distance obtained with a

Samuel Pierpont Langley (1834–1906)

mechanical aeroplane which then landed without incident. Two pairs of wings in tandem with spans of between 12 and 13 ft. sustained a body approximately 16 ft. long. A two-cylinder 1 h.p. steam engine, heated by burning refined petroleum, drove two propellers placed between the pairs of wings. The total weight was about 30 lb.

To provide impulse for take-off, Langley resorted to a catapult mounted on a barge moored in the Potomac river; like Tatin, he carried out his tests over water in the justified hope of reducing damage at the end of the flight.

When the signal was given, the *Aerodrome* left from a platform 20 feet above the water and at first rose up directly against the wind, moving all the time with remarkable stability then making large turns about 100 yards in diameter and rising constantly until there was no more steam when, after about one and a half minute's time and at a height estimated at between 80 to 100 feet, the propellers stopped turning and the machine, deprived of their help, glided down so slowly and calmly that it touched the water without the slightest shock and was, in fact, immediately ready for a new test.

This second experiment was almost identical to the first, the aircraft flying for one minute thirty-one seconds and landing about 300 yards from the point of departure after having covered an actual distance estimated to be more than half a mile.

The tests took place in the presence of another scientist, the inventor of the telephone, Alexander Graham Bell, who afterwards commented: "No one who witnessed the extraordinary spectacle of a steam engine flying with wings in the air, like a great soaring bird, could doubt for one moment the practicability of mechanical flight."

On 28 November 1896 a new test was made with the *Aerodrome No. 6*, which was nearly identical to the *No. 5*. The flight lasted one minute forty-five seconds during which time more than 1300 yards was covered.

Langley's *Aérodrome No. 5* projected by its catapult.

The first sustained flight of a model steam aeroplane (16 May 1896).

Pilcher's monoplane glider *Bat* (1895).

A flight by Pablo Suarez in Argentina (1895).

THE FOLLOWERS OF LILIENTHAL

The photographs of Lilienthal's flights were a revelation, and profoundly impressed aviation researchers. In France, the reaction was mainly one of keen curiosity with no thought of imitation. Only the Comte de Lambert bought a glider from Lilienthal and started making a few tests near Versailles, but these were not followed up owing to the lack of a suitable testing ground. Even in Germany, Lilienthal had no followers.

In Britain, Percy Pilcher, after visiting Lilienthal, tried out his first flying machine in Glasgow in 1895. In all he made five types of gliders based on the German machine.

Having practised taking off from a hill, Pilcher had himself hauled into the air by horses, as had Le Bris before him. Modifying his machine after each test, Pilcher obtained encouraging results, gliding for around twenty seconds.

While building the rest of his gliders Pilcher created a small company with M. W. Wilson with a view to making a business of aviation once the problem had been solved. He also tried to procure for himself a light combustion engine for his fifth glider, the *Hawk*, but being unable to obtain one he designed and built an engine himself in 1898. In the meantime, he devised a new way of taking off using a rope strung between two hills which enabled him to achieve glides of about 250 metres. His last glider, the *Hawk*, was fitted with wheels with shock absorbers.

There had been no incident to cloud the experiments, carried out over four years, when, on 30 September 1899, near Market Harborough, the tail of his monoplane broke off in flight. Pilcher died two days later.

In Argentina, Pablo Suarez started testing in 1895 with a copy of Lilienthal's glider. His were the first real attempts at heavier-than-air flying in South America. He made a number of glides by throwing himself into the wind.

But Lilienthal's greatest follower was the engineer Octave Chanute. Born in France in 1832, and becoming a citizen of the United States, where he spent his life, Chanute was one of aviation's most sympathetic characters.

He came to aviation in 1891 and made himself one of its leading figures through his sound judgment, engineering skills and excellent methods; he was also one of the most generous, endowing poor researchers, publishing numerous and excellent works and always being ready to pass on his knowledge and give wise advice. Selfless and full of concern for others, he was adviser to the Wright brothers and Ferber, among others.

Too old to go up himself on the many and various gliders that he built after 1895, Chanute chose two young assistants, Herring and Avery, who carried out all the tests under supervision between 1896 and 1901, and helped him to set up his final testing ground on the dunes on the shores of Lake Michigan.

A glide on Chanute's biplane (1896).

The Chanute glider with three rows of biplane wings.

Chanute's glider with four swinging superposed wings.

Checking the impermeability of the OErn.

Salomon-Auguste Andrée (1851–†F1897)

The departure on 11 July 1897.

THE ANDREE POLAR EXPEDITION

Around 1892, Salomon-Auguste Andrée, a Swedish engineer, conceived a plan to reach the North Pole, by means of a free balloon which would leave from the Arctic regions, and was able to mobilize generous support. He had a balloon, of 159,000 cu. ft., made in France by Lachambre which was supposed to be able to stay in the air for thirty days. The basket contained a bunk, provisions and all the instruments. The pilots used it only for resting. They were normally on a platform over the basket. Between the balloon and the ring supporting the basket there was a canvas cone with pockets containing the equipment for the return over the ice field: sledges, a folding canoe, food for four months and arms.

Following experiments in Sweden, Andrée hoped to be able to obtain some directional control over his balloon by means of a steering sail which would function because heavy guideropes trailed across the ice would both slow down the balloon sufficiently to allow a relative wind to fill the sail and also act as a fulcrum against which it could work.

To avoid magnetic disorders, nothing was made of iron. All the details had been studied with great care, but the explorer had not thought of the overall picture: his equipment was too heavy and left room for only a very small amount of ballast; also, he and his companions lacked

experience in flying and in arctic conditions.

The expedition went to Spitzbergen in 1896: a hangar was built on Danes' Island but the wind remained unfavourable and they had to give up.

In 1897, Andrée made another attempt. His companions were two young scientists, Nils Strindberg and Knut Fränkel. At 1350 on 11 July 1897 the balloon, the Œrn, left its hangar, which

The expedition canoe found on White Island in 1930.

had had to be dismantled to let it out, for there was quite a strong wind blowing from the south. A moment later the balloon was blown down by the wind and the basket touched the water. Some of the guide ropes broke off unexpectedly. The balloon went on its way, rose up and disappeared.

A carrier pigeon, killed in Spitzbergen, brought the following message: "13 July, 1230. Lat. 82° 2'; Long. 15° 5' E. Good E. course, 10° South. All

well on board. Third message by carrier pigeon. Andrée." Buoys were later found with news of 11 July. Then there was silence for thirty-three years.

On 6 August 1930, the crew of the Bratvaag, hunting seals, found the wreck of the expedition on White Island, to the east of Spitzbergen. They found the canoe, the sledges, a number of implements, the bodies of Andrée and Strindberg and the bones of Fränkel. The most moving part was that Andrée's log-book and Strindberg's notes and letters were found in perfect condition, and the camera as well, complete with Kodak films that could be developed a third of a century later.

The air journey had lasted sixty-five hours, until 0730 on 14 July. Travelling freely and quickly for thirteen hours, the balloon had passed 82° 15' latitude when the wind dropped. It then drifted for twenty hours towards the west before coming immobilised for thirteen hours. During this part of the journey, the basket was frequently in contact with the ice. Heading off again towards the pole, the Œrn, after a difficult end to the journey, air navigation interspersed with sledging, finally stopped on 14 July at 82° 55' 7" latitude north and 29° 32' longitude, that is to say less than 300 miles from Danes' Island and nearly 500 miles from the pole.

The return over the ice field had begun on 21 July; it was difficult and the route had to be changed several times. On 2 October the heroes reached White Island and set up a winter camp there. Their last note is dated 17 October 1897.

The balloon on the ice field, 14 July 1897.

Andrée, Frankel and Strindberg pushing the canoe on the ice.

These two photographs were taken in July 1897, and developed in 1930 after being recovered from the expedition's last camp.

Wolfert's dirigible *Deutschland* at Tempelhof, 14 June 1897.

The first Zeppelin, side view (1900).

Schwartz's dirigible at Tempelhof, 3 November 1897.

DIRIGIBLES IN GERMANY

In 1896 Germany took the lead in developing the airship, when Dr Wolfert made the dirigible *Deutschland*. The basket, the top of which was in direct contact with the balloon, contained a Daimler 8 h.p. engine, *the first petrol motor to have been applied to an airborne machine*. This achievement placed Wolfert among the dirigible's leading pioneers. He went up from Berlin on 28 and 29 August 1896 and on 6 March 1897 without incident, though without much success with the navigation. On 14 June 1897, Wolfert and the mechanic Knabe took off from Tempelhof. Several minutes later, the *Deutschland* caught fire and crashed. Wolfert and Knabe were the first victims of power-driven flight.

The first entirely metallic rigid dirigible, built by the Austrian engineer Schwartz, took off from Templehof; the envelope, which had a volume of 130,500 cu. ft., was *entirely in sheet aluminium*, eight thousandths of an inch thick, on an aluminium frame. A Daimler 12 h.p. engine drove

The frame of the *Zeppelin No. 1* without its covering.

three propellers. It took off on 3 November 1897 with the mechanic Jaegels Platz on board. It circled several times, then descended very rapidly. Platz was unhurt but the balloon broke up.

Around 1873, General Count Ferdinand von Zeppelin started studying a system for a rigid dirigible on which he took out a patent in 1898. His design was for an airship consisting of supple and independent balloons in a rigid frame covered with an envelope.

In 1900 the rigid balloon became a reality with the *Zeppelin No. 1*. Its frame of aluminium angle sections was 420 ft. long. Its seventeen internal balloons had a total volume of nearly 400,000 cu. ft. There were two gondolas, each carrying a Daimler 15 h.p. engine.

Zeppelin No. 1 went up three times, with increasing success, on 3 July and on 17 and 21 October on Lake Constance. It was replaced in 1905 by *Zeppelin No. 2* which was slightly smaller but had two 85 h.p. engines, and was wrecked in a gale. *Zeppelin No. 3* made a successful debut in October 1906, and was replaced in 1908 by *Zeppelin No. 4*.

The first Zeppelin in its floating and moveable hangar in Lake Constance, and in the air, at an altitude of 1300 ft.

Departure of the first Santos-Dumont dirigible from the Jardin d'Acclimatation in Paris (20 September 1898).

Below: The basket, the engine, the propeller and the pump of the *Santos-Dumont No. 1*.

SANTOS-DUMONT IN FRANCE

In 1898 a young rich Brazilian of French descent came to Paris to build dirigible balloons.

After practice with free balloons, notably with the *Brazil*, the smallest manned balloon so far built, which had a capacity of less than 400 cu. ft., he had a small dirigible made by Lachambre, of only 6350 cu. ft., very elongated, made for the first time in extra lightweight Japanese silk which included – also an innovation – a suspension using eyelets, in other words eyed flaps in the actual fabric of the envelope, to which the cables car-

rying the basket were directly attached. The basket held a modified Dion-Bouton engine.

After an initial failure, the first ascent took place on 20 September 1898 at the Jardin d'Acclimatation in Paris. All went well until the descent when the balloon lost its shape due to the incapacity of the pump to keep the compensating balloon full-folded in two, and crashed down in the gardens of the Bagatelle without serious damage.

One year later, the *No. 2* came out. It ended in the trees and also folded up. The *Santos-Dumont No. 3*, which followed immediately, had a different shape, more ovoid and much shorter. This balloon made several successful ascents but never managed to return to its departure point.

The *Santos-Dumont No. 3* in flight (1899).

The *Santos-Dumont No. 2* folded after its accident (1899).

Louis Godard junior in 1891.

François Lhoste (1859–†*F*1887).

Henri Lachambre (1846–1904).

Louis Capazza (1862–1928).

Henri Hervé (died 1922).

FREE BALLOONING IN FRANCE AT THE END OF THE NINETEENTH CENTURY

The free balloon developed rapidly after 1879. On 9 September 1883, ninety-eight years after Pilâtre de Rozier's ill-fated attempt, Lhoste accomplished the first air crossing from the continent to England, from Boulogne to Rucking near Ashford in Kent, a performance which he repeated in 1884 and 1886; on 12 and 13 September 1886, the engineer Hervé made the first air journey of more than twenty-four hours, from Boulogne to Yarmouth (24 hr. 10 min.); Capazza and Fondère succeeded, on 14 November 1886, in making the first balloon crossing from Marseilles to Corsica on 19 and 20 October 1897, Louis Godard (the younger) and seven passengers left Leipzig and landed after a flight of 24 hr. 15 min; in 1892 Mallet made a solo flight of 36 hours with a stopover and in 1894 a journey (with stopovers) that lasted 6 days. Lachambre, Jovis and Mallet took hundreds of passengers up in balloons, one of the best known being Guy de Maupassant.

In 1893, Hermitte and Georges Besançon started launching meteorological balloons carrying recording instruments which went up to 50,000 ft. and more to provide information on atmospheric physics. The Aéro-Club de France, the first amateur air organisation, was founded.

At the 1900 Exhibition in Paris, fifteen competitions were held, the main prizes being won by the new Aéro-Club pilots, most of them pupils of Mallet, the great balloon maker. On 16 to 18 September 1900 J. Balsan stayed in the air for 35 hr. 9 min., and went up to 28,000 ft. on 23 September. The Comte de la Vaulx made the first solo air journey from France to Russia on 30 September, landing at Brest Konyaski (768 miles); the last competition on 9 October was crowned by the record of the Comte de la Vaulx and the Comte de Castillon de Saint-Victor in the *Centaure*, who covered 1195 miles in 35 hr 45 min. landing at Korostychev near Kiev.

Maurice Mallet (1861–1926)

A balloon rally at the Aéro Club de France

The *Horla* at La Villette (1887): with Guy de Maupassant, Jovis and Mallet.

Winners of the 1900 competitions: the Comte de Castillon, G. Hervieu, J. Balsan, Jacques Faure, the Comte de La Vaulx, G. Juchmès, L. Maison.

Releasing a meteorological balloon at Chalais-Meudon, 31 March 1893.

CHAPTER III

THE AIRSHIP AND THE AEROPLANE

1900–1914

The first fourteen years of this century were of the utmost importance to aviation. They included moreover almost all the "years of innocence" which separated man's first flight from his application of this new art to war or to commerce.

This short but eventful time could also be called the era of the petrol engine, as in fact this type of engine was used in all the successful dirigibles and flying machines from 1900 to 1914.

In 1903 the Wright brothers in America, with patience and determination, by skilful deduction and with a clear sense of directing experiments towards a great ideal, after innumerable tests on kites and gliders, evolved the first aeroplane to function in all its details. With this machine Wilbur and Orville Wright made the world's first sustained powered flights. The following year a new aeroplane enabled them to accomplish turns and closed circuits. One year later, the flying time of half an hour was exceeded. Aviation was really born.

In the immediately succeeding years, however, France was to become, more than any other country, fascinated by power-driven aeronautics. Alongside the first real air journeys, achieved by the Lebaudy airships from 1903 on, flying, supported by the efforts of the disciples of Ferber and Archdeacon and demonstrated practically by Santos-Dumont, was given a tremendous impetus in that country in the years after 1906,

owing to its extremely favourable reception by a trusting public.

To Santos-Dumont, in 1901 and again in 1906, fell the immense honour of "launching" and popularising the two main instruments of air travel, the airship and the aeroplane. The name of this inspired and ingenious Brazilian who himself tested the machines he invented, will conjure up for all those who lived during these years fond memories of his enthralling achievements.

At the same time, ballooning became a great sport with the advent of the free balloon and the visions of great journeys in the future opened up to those who "believed" in zeppelins.

The first closed kilometre of Henri Farman and his first journey over the countryside, Blériot's crossing of the English Channel, and the displays and records of Wilbur Wright at the camp at Auvours were the great events of this period.

There is no doubt that the visit of Wright, more advanced then than his rivals in the search for the solutions, and unquestionably possessing "secrets of flight" which European researchers had not yet discovered, contributed much to the brilliance and effectiveness of events at this time. On the other hand, the acceptance by the world at large that Wilbur Wright came to France to seek was of decisive importance, as much for himself as for aviation. It was in France moreover that, starting with Gabriel Voisin, the construction of aero-

planes first became an industry and the technical methods were determined that were to prevail for a long time.

There was a heavy price to pay in human life for all this progress. An insufficient knowledge of aerodynamics, groping and empirical methods of piloting and the fact that research was still misguidedly directed towards lightness at all costs, caused most of these losses. It was therefore necessary to explore new fields on all levels – scientific, technical, human and material; an exploration made even more delicate by the fact that its remarkable instrument – the light aeroplane – was already subject, by the very nature of the principles of flight, to the same basic weakness that today's aeroplane has not yet eliminated. At least, in these early days, aviation "forgave" much, thanks to low landing speeds and to the lightness of the craft involved; as a result, methods of handling were possible which would have been inconceivable with the aeroplanes of, say, 1932, so much heavier and faster.

Although the advantage of relative safety due to slow flying speeds was somewhat negative, it did not stand in the way of long journeys; witness the amazing voyages achieved by the great pilots of 1913 – Garros, Brindejonc des Moulinais, Pourpe, Bonnier and Gilbert, all of whom were to be victims of the imminent war, and Vedrines, who was not to survive them for long.

The dirigible *Santos-Dumont No. 6* leaving the park of the Aéro Club de France in the Coteaux de Saint-Cloud (1901).

The dirigible *Santos-Dumont No. 4*: the inventor is
sitting on a simple bicycle saddle (1900).

The dirigible *Santos-Dumont No. 5* during its first trials
at Saint-Cloud (July 1901).

SANTOS-DUMONT WINS THE DEUTSCH PRIZE

M. Deutsch de la Meurthe created a Grand Prix of Ballooning in 1900 at the Aéro-Club de France, offering 100,000 francs to the first aeronaut who, taking off from the Aéro-Club park at Saint-Cloud and circling the Eiffel Tower, returned to the starting point in less than thirty minutes. Several competitors entered for this race but only Santos-Dumont actually took part.

In 1900 Santos-Dumont installed a hangar in the Aéro-Club park where he made numerous but restricted tests on his airship *No. 4*. In this machine a single long boom supported a 9 h.p. engine which drove a traction propeller, and the aviator sat, without a basket, on a bicycle saddle. Shortly after, Santos-Dumont transformed his machine into *No. 5* with a more powerful engine of 16 h.p. weighing 215 lb., built by M. Buchet. At the same time, Santos-Dumont himself made a lattice girder of triangular section containing a little wicker basket. For the first time in ballooning, the suspending cables were made of "piano wire", greatly reducing the drag.

On 12 July 1901, the *Santos-Dumont No. 5* made three flights from Longchamp, first round the Hippodrome and then a trip around the Eiffel Tower. A problem with the rudder necessitated a stopover in the Trocadero gardens. The next day, "Santos" carried off the round trip Saint-Cloud – Eiffel Tower – Saint-Cloud in forty minutes, but a breakdown forced him to bring down his balloon on the trees in the Rothschild park.

On 8 August he had just gone past the Tower when a hydrogen leak forced him to land on the houses in the Trocadero. The balloon was torn to shreds but the aeronaut stepped out of the basket, which was left hanging from the walls, amazingly

The accident of the *Santos-Dumont No. 5* (8 August 1901).

unscathed. Work on the *Santos-Dumont No. 6* was started the same night; it was ready in twenty-two days.

Finished on 6 September, the *No. 6* handled well but suffered a series of accidents during its trials until on 10, 11 and 14 October, Santos-Dumont had several successful outings, even stopping off for lunch at the waterfall at Long-champ.

Eventually, on 19 October, at 1442, Santos-Dumont left Saint-Cloud, turned at the Eiffel Tower at 1451 and at 1511 and 30 seconds passed the guide rope at the Aéro-Club park, landing at 1512 and 40 seconds. In spite of a few protests, he thus gloriously won the Grand Prix – a just reward for his efforts.

Santos-Dumont has been criticised for not having been scientific enough in his experiments. Although he certainly neglected the problems of stability and jumped somewhat haphazardly from one model to another, his technical work remains important as he was responsible for using new materials and mechanical devices which were adopted by all his successors. But the most interesting aspect of his efforts was the public display over Paris of the possibilities of air locomotion. Santos-Dumont set a wonderful example by his lack of self-interest and by his courage in always carrying out his tests himself; the considerable popularity he so rightly enjoyed encouraged numerous imitators. He played this role twice: for the dirigible in 1901 and for the aeroplane in 1906. It is an unequalled triumph which places him amongst the greatest figures in all the history of aeronautics.

The *Santos-Dumont No. 5* rounding the Eiffel Tower.

The accident of the *Santos-Dumont No. 6* at Longchamp
(20 September 1901).

The Buchet engine for the *Santos-Dumont No. 5*.

Augusto Severo (1864–†*F*1902)

Severo's dirigible *Pax* (1902)

Ottokar de Bradsky (1866–†*F*1902)

TWO DISASTERS

The success of Santos-Dumont stimulated other inventors, but the results were not always felicitous: 1902 saw two catastrophes in Paris.

On 12 May the *Pax*, a balloon of 70,500 cu. ft. containing some interesting innovations, in particular a support frame which passed through the gas-bag and carried a large propeller at either end, and which was equipped with two engines and two steering propellers, took off from Vaugirard. It was carrying its inventor,

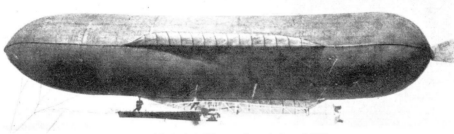

Bradsky's dirigible seen from below (1902).

the Brazilian deputy Severo, and Sache the mechanic. Several minutes later the *Pax* caught fire, exploded and came down across the Avenue du Maine.

On 13 October the *Bradsky* dirigible with Ottokar de Bradsky, its inventor, and Morin the engineer on board left Vaugirard and crossed Paris without turning. Above Stains the basket, inadequately suspended, suddenly broke away and crashed to the ground with the crew.

M. Roze's *Aviateur*, a rigid double balloon, both heavier and lighter than air, tested in 1901, was unable to take off.

The debris of the *Pax* across the Avenue du Maine (13 May 1902).

The basket of the *Bradsky* which fell at Stains (13 October 1902).

The *Aviateur-Roze*, front view, with its two rigid balloons, each of 47,650 cu. ft. and their propellers; on the right the basket-cabin and the inventor.

Wilhelm Kress (1836–1913)

Kress's seaplane with floats at Tullnerbach (1901).

THE KRESS SEA-PLANE

The earlier contributions of the Austrian inventor Wilhelm Kress have been noted. Fulfilling his pipe-dream, the modest piano-maker made himself an engineer, enrolling himself in 1893, at the age of fifty-seven, as a mature student at the Polytechnic School in Vienna; by 1898 he was able to begin construction of a full-scale aeroplane.

The machine consisted of three pairs of wings in tandem, at different elevations so as not to use the same air stream, and with a total surface area of just over 1000 sq. ft. The entire structure of the machine, except for the wooden ribs of the wings, was of light steel Mannesmann tubes: it was a remarkable construction for that time, with excellent components, judiciously chosen, which are admired to this day by modern technicians who have been able to study them.

Kress had envisaged taking off on either snow or water. With this in mind, the machine was supported by two long floats made of aluminium sheets whose lower keels could be used as runners on the snow.

At the back there were three rudders, one to steer with, one an elevator and the third for use on the water. These three rudders were actuated by a horizontal "one-handed" lever. Kress had understood, like Pénaud, the importance of having one single, instinctive control.

Two large propellers provided the thrust. Kress's seaplane was also designed to have great natural stability.

In spite of the perfection of his work, finished as early as 1899, Kress suffered dreadful setbacks for reasons beyond his control.

The engine he had specified was to have an output of 40 h.p. for a weight of 440 lb. Several suppliers backed down. Some experiments were nevertheless made with an engine of only a few h.p.

The Mercedes engine, finally supplied in 1901, provided – in spite of the maker's undertakings – only 30 h.p. and weighed 840 lb.; it was a disaster, for the machine ended up by weighing 1870 lb. instead of 1410, which sank the floats up to the gunwhales and destroyed the stability. Moreover, the power was now insufficient.

In October 1901, Kress himself – despite his sixty-five years – began testing on the Tullnerbach lake.

After practising keeping straight on the water, the inventor started speeding up: "The speed and the lift increased rapidly", he wrote. "Water spurted up in front and the floats were already emerging considerably from the water . . . " At this moment when, in spite of all, he seemed to be reaching definitive success, Kress saw before him a stone groyne. He stopped the engine and turned sharply, the machine rocked and, the wind catching it under its wings, turned over. The old inventor got out in time and clung to one of the floats until the machine disappeared. It was more than twenty minutes before the unfortunate Kress could be picked up by a boat.

The wreck of the seaplane dashed all his hopes; fished out in bits and pieces, the machine was put together again in 1902 but, due to lack of funds, could not be finished. Wilhelm Kress died in 1913 and had some consolation in seeing others achieve his hopes of a life-time; he is assured, however, of an important place amongst those true pioneers of air navigation who came close to finding the solution to the great problem.

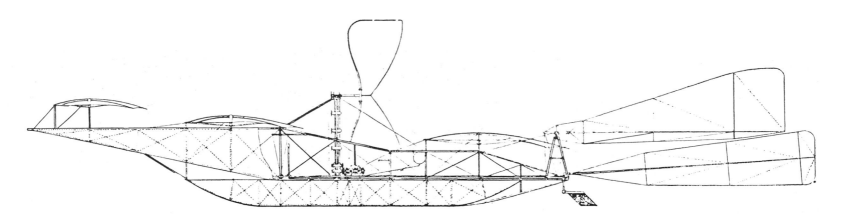

Elevation of Wilhelm Kress's seaplane with floats, tried out in 1901.

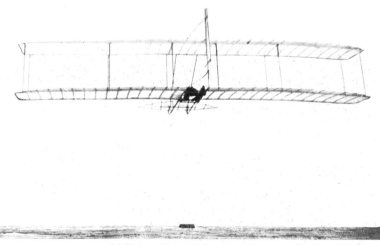

A successful flight of the 1902 *Wright* glider at Kill Devil.

The Wright brothers' camp at Kitty Hawk during a visit by Octave Chanute.

THE WRIGHT BROTHERS' FIRST EXPERIMENTS

It was Wilbur and Orville Wright who first achieved the goal of a power-driven aeroplane which could take off with its pilot for a continuous flight.

The Wright brothers were the sons of the Protestant pastor Milton Wright of Dayton (Ohio); Wilbur was born in 1867 and Orville in 1871.

They had an austere and simple upbringing and their characters were marked by their father's spirituality and his practical mind. Honesty, loyalty, the ability to work methodically, creative minds, and good judgement combined to lead them to their magnificent success; they triumphed where all their predecessors had had to admit defeat.

Their interest caught in childhood by an elastic-powered Pénaud model, they had arrived simultaneously at the idea of aviation as a practical proposition in about 1896. By reading Means' Aeronautical Annuals, the works of Chanute and Langley and by studying the work done by Mouillard and Lilienthal they realised what still needed to be done. In 1900 they built their first glider with which they wanted, first of all, to study the question of equilibrium in flight; a question which they, like Lilienthal, judged to be essential.

The machine was composed of two equal planes, with an elevator in front. There was no vertical control surface, but the ends of the wings could be bent to maintain lateral equilibrium. The

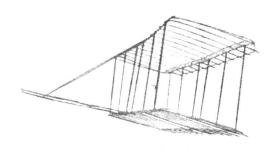

The 1900 *Wright* glider being tested as a kite.

experiments took place on the deserted dunes at Kitty Hawk in North Carolina.

The tests, which started in October 1900, consisted at first in flying the glider like a kite, without a pilot, to check the stability and to measure the lift and drag; later manned glides were carried out from the top of a sand dune. The Wrights were the first to use the lying position for the pilot in order to diminish the air resistance.

A new glider was tested in 1901. The spruce struts, the ash ribs, the shrouds of piano wire and the fabric which completely covered the structure, were still to be found in most aircraft of thirty years later. With this glider, the Wright brothers travelled 55 yards. Chanute helped with the tests and gave precious information to the Wright brothers who had, nevertheless, invented their machine and their method before knowing him. The 1902 glider permitted glides of up to 220 yards.

More than a thousand glides were made in 1902, alternating with a series of methodical experiments. Coming to aviation as to a sport, the Wrights trained themselves to very scientific research.

In 1903, they started testing again with a system of directional control achieved by varying the curvature of the wings. Headed into the wind, the machine flew for seventy-two seconds and advanced only 30 metres.

This result gives an idea of the sophistication of the machine and the skill of its operators. The Wright aeroplane was only awaiting its engine and its propellers.

Carrying the glider back up the dune (1902).

The end of a glide (1901).

First flight of the *No. 4* glider (7 December 1901).

Ferdinand Ferber (1862–†*F*1909).

The *Ferber No. 6* on the pylon at La Californie (December 1902).

FERBER'S EARLY WORK

Captain Ferber was the greatest forerunner of practical aviation in France. He was the first Frenchman to build life-size gliders and to test them methodically; he attempted to catch up – without their rigorous experimentation but following the same principles – with Lilienthal, Chanute and the Wrights in the experimental cycle which was to lead to power-driven aviation.

Ferdinand Ferber was absolutely selfless, giving his leisure, his fortune, and eventually his life to his experiments. He always shared his results, lending his documentation as well as his time to those who were interested.

Ferber learned of Lilienthal's work in 1898.

After having built three monoplane gliders with no tail which gave discouraging results, in 1901 Ferber started more advanced tests at Nice on his glider *No. 4*, inspired by Lilienthal's machines. This machine weighed 66 lb. and had a wing area of 161 sq. ft. Taking off from some 16 ft. high scaffolding, Ferber stayed in the air for 24 seconds, and advanced 50 ft. This glide took place on 7 December 1901. It was followed by several other tests, but the stability remained uncertain and the flying captain went on to build a biplane glider in bamboo, of the same configuration as the Wrights'. In tests at Beuil (Alpes Maritimes) and then at La Californie near Nice between June and September 1902, he covered distances of 25 to 50 yards, but the last flight ended with a hard landing owing to inadequate controls.

A new biplane was tested in 1903 at Conquet (Finisterre) with lateral stabilisers forming a keel. Captain Ferber was at last able to acquire a basic understanding of how to control an aeroplane. In the meantime, he had had built at Nice, on the grounds of La Californie, an interesting testing tower consisting of an iron pylon, 60 ft. high, carrying on a pivot a 100 ft. cross beam. This device enabled a machine to be held up to the wind at a certain speed, and was also used for testing the traction of propellers.

As early as December 1902, Ferber had equipped his sixth glider with a small engine driving two coaxial, counter-rotating traction propellers which later provided him with much valuable information for the design of his power-driven aeroplanes.

Ferber experimenting at the forage store at Nice, 15 January 1902.

Captain Ferber running against the wind at Nice with his *No. 4* glider.

Launching the *Ferber No. 5* on the beach at La Californie at Nice in September 1902.

Captain Ferber gliding in his *No. 5* at Conquet, 3 September 1903.

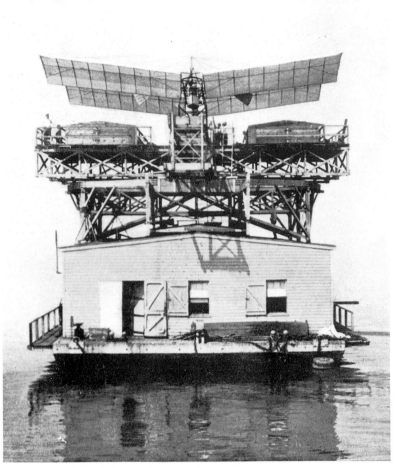

Langley's aeroplane on its launching catapult on top of
its boat-hangar moored in the Potomac river.

The accident of 8 December 1903; the rear planes folded up and the
aeroplane reared up vertically before plunging into the Potomac.

LANGLEY'S FULL-SCALE AEROPLANE

Professor Langley's full-scale aeroplane was tested twice in 1903 but both tests were regrettably failures. The aeroplane, which was beautifully constructed, was similar in most respects to the 1896 model: the two planes in tandem, totalling 1033 sq. ft., were joined together by a chassis carrying two lateral propellers between the wings and a cruciform tail at the back. The combustion engine, a 5 cylinder radial, gave 52 h.p. for a weight of 340 lb. and worked perfectly. The design, remarkable for that time, was the work of the engineer Manly.

The first launch took place on the river Potomac, at Widewater, by means of a catapult placed

The 52 h.p. petrol engine built by Manly for Langley's
1903 aeroplane.

on a house boat, a complicated and tricky procedure. After innumerable difficulties, the test took place on 7 October. Manly acted as pilot. As soon as it was launched the machine dived and fell into the water, without much damage. The accident was attributed to a stay catching in the apparatus of the boat.

On 8 December a new test was attempted under the same conditions. This time, the machine broke up completely on take-off, the back planes collapsed and the aircraft reared up vertically before crashing into the water. Manly was extricated with great difficulty. The aircraft was unusable and the funds had completely run out.

Bitterly discouraged, Langley died on 28 February 1906. Manly's engine is now preserved in the Air and Space Museum in Washington.

The *Langley* aeroplane, launched by its catapult, diving
down towards the Potomac (7 October 1903).

The wreck of the *Langley* aeroplane in the Potomac
(7 October 1903).

The basket of the *Lebaudy* with Rey and Juchmes.

Georges Juchmès (1874–1918)

The *Lebaudy* landing on the Champs-de-Mars, 12 November 1903.

THE LEBAUDY AND SANTOS-DUMONT AIRSHIPS OF 1902–1907

The current interest in dirigibles prompted two major French industrialists, Paul and Pierre Lebaudy, to realise the grand ideas of one of their engineers, Henri Julliot. The dirigible took the name of its owners, the *Lebaudy*, and was popularly nicknamed *Jaune* (yellow).

The envelope, made for the first time with two skins of rubberised fabric, was attached by guy-ropes to a platform of steel tubes, a ballooning first, from which was suspended a boat-shaped basket, also of steel tubes and very solidly built. A 40 h.p. Mercedes engine drove two metal propellers at 1,200 rpm. Stabilising planes and a rudder completed the airship whose ends, involuntarily turned down, gave it a very strange aspect.

Successful trials were carried out at Moisson, near Mantes, in November 1902. During a second series of ascents in 1903 the *Lebaudy*, manned by the pilot Juchmès, and Rey, the mechanic, accomplished a journey of 23 miles over the countryside on 8 May, which was the first cross-country flight of a power-driven machine. On 24 June, it covered 61 miles at an average speed of 22 mph; finally, on 12 November it accomplished the journey from Moisson to the Champs-de-Mars (39 miles). In 1904, it made a new series of flights, marked by the first female ascents (by the Mmes Lebaudy), the first photographic shots, and the first night ascent, to be made by a dirigible.

The 1905 ascents were made under military control and included trips to Moisson, Meaux and Chalons, where a storm tore apart the dirigible which had no hangar. The *Lebaudy* moved to Toul, where the War Minister, Monsieur Berteaux, took part in an ascent. Offered by Messieurs Lebaudy to the army, the *Lebaudy* enjoyed a long career as a training balloon.

The work of Julliot, the engineer, and the piloting of Juchmès contributed greatly to its progress. The robustness of the construction permitted numerous experiments on a scale hitherto unapproached. Until the Second World War many of the mechanical devices inaugurated in 1902 on the *Lebaudy* were to be found on all non-rigid or semi-rigid dirigibles.

The various designs of Santos-Dumont are known by their numbers, which themselves give an idea of their multiplicity; they met with varying success, but were never without interest.

Among the best-remembered were: the *No. 7*, a very fast balloon, destined for the Saint-Louis races in 1904 but destroyed by vandals; the *No. 10* of 1903, designed to hold 10 people but never completely tested; the *No. 13* of 1905, a hot-air balloon; the *No. 14*, also of 1905, which had two forms – a very slender cigar and then an almost ovoid one; and finally the *No. 16*, of 1907, a little heavier than air, and destroyed on its first trial.

The *No. 9* of 1903 is of special interest; this little balloon of 9,200 cu. ft., with a 3 h.p. engine, was very popular and made many successful outings, flying over the 14 July Parade at Longchamp, and allowing its owner to make visits to the centre of Paris, to the Champs-Elysées and the Avenue du Bois-de-Boulogne.

The *Santos-Dumont No. 7*, a "racer", 1904.

The *No. 9* at Saint-Cloud (1903).

The *Santos-Dumont No. 10*, an "Omnibus-Balloon", 1903.

The first shape of the *Santos-Dumont No. 14* (1905).

The *No. 14* on the beach at Trouville (1905).

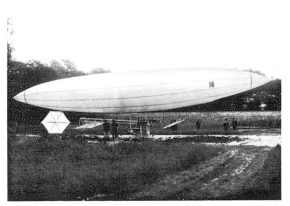

The *Santos-Dumont No. 16*, a composite machine (1907).

The first sustained flight of a power-driven aeroplane: the historic flight of Orville Wright at Kitty Hawk, on 17 December 1903.

MAN'S FIRST SUSTAINED FLIGHT

17 December 1903 was the greatest day in the history of aviation. The Wright brothers carried out, one after another, four sustained flights with their power-driven aeroplane. This definitive victory took place on the Kill Devil dune at Kitty Hawk, between Manteo and Norfolk in North Carolina.

Alongside their practical work on gliders the Wright brothers had carried out a series of theoretical and laboratory experiments using a wind tunnel to verify the work of their predecessors, to correct their errors and to formulate new ideas on the flight of aeroplanes. On top of this, they successfully constructed a petrol engine, which provided about 12 h.p. for a weight of 240 lb.

Now in possession of all the necessary components, both tangible and theoretical, and having correctly analysed the problem in the light of their unequalled experience, the Wright brothers arrived naturally and inevitably at the solution which had eluded so many for so long.

Their aeroplane of 1903 was similar to the 1902 glider, had a wing span of approximately 40 ft., a length of 22 ft. and a surface area of about 500 sq. ft. The pilot, lying on his stomach, controlled an elevator at the front, a rudder at the back and a mechanism for differentially warping the wings. The two geared-down propellers were driven by bicycle chains.

A first test on 14 December was only a partial success. Launched down a slight slope, because the wind was light and the launching track short, Wilbur Wright, who had won the toss to be first pilot, pulled up too sharply and stalled the aircraft, which sank gradually to the ground, still canted upwards at a high angle. It landed on one wing and swung round, breaking a skid and damaging the front elevator. The flight had lasted 3½ seconds and had covered a distance of 105 feet.

The machine was repaired by midday on 16 December but there was no wind, so the trial was postponed until the following day, when the brothers woke to find a strong wind blowing. Orville Wright later wrote:

"We laid the track on a smooth stretch of ground about one hundred feet north of the new building . . . By the time all was ready J.T. Daniels, W.S. Dough and A.D. Etheridge, members of the Kill Devil Life Saving Station; W.C. Brinkley of Manteo, and Johnny Moore, a boy from Nag's Head, had arrived . . .

Wilbur having used his turn in the unsuccessful attempt on the 14th, the right to the first trial now belonged to me.

After running the motor a few minutes to heat it up, I released the wire that held the machine to the track, and the machine started forward into the wind. Wilbur ran at the side of the machine, holding the wing to balance it on the track. Unlike the start on the 14th made in a calm, the machine, facing 27-mile wind, started very slowly. Wilbur was able to stay with it till it lifted from the track after a forty foot run. One of the Life Saving men snapped the camera for us, taking a picture just as the machine had reached the end of the track and had risen to a height of about two feet. The slow forward speed of the machine over the ground is clearly shown in the picture by Wilbur's attitude. He stayed along beside the machine without any effort. The course of the flight up and down was exceedingly erratic, partly due to the irregularity of the air, and partly to lack of experience in handling this machine . . . The machine would rise suddenly to about ten feet, and then as suddenly dart for the ground. A sudden dart when a little over a hundred feet from the end of the track, or a little over 120 feet from the point at which it rose into the air, ended the flight. As the velocity of the wind was over 35 feet per second and the speed of the machine over the ground against this wind ten feet per second, the speed of the machine relative to the air was over 45 feet per second, and the length of the flight was equivalent to a flight of 540 feet made in calm air.

This flight lasted only 12 seconds, but it was nevertheless the first in the history of the world in which a machine carrying a man had raised itself by its own power into the air in full flight, had sailed foward without reduction of speed and had finally landed at a point as high as that from which it had started.

At twenty minutes after eleven Wilbur started on the second flight. The course of this flight was much like that of the first, very much up and down. The speed over the ground was somewhat faster than that of the first flight due to a lesser wind. The duration of the flight was less than a second longer than the first, but the distance covered was about 75 feet greater.

Twenty minutes later, the third flight started.

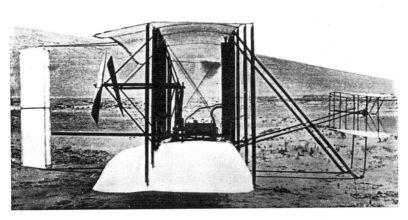

Orville and Wilbur Wright

The Wright aeroplane at Kitty Hawk, 17 December 1903, sideview

A rear view of the engine

This one was steadier than the first one an hour before. I was proceeding along pretty well when a sudden gust from the right lifted the machine up twelve to fifteen feet and turned it up sideways in an alarming manner. It began a lively sidling off to the left. I warped the wings to try to recover the lateral balance and at the same time pointed the machine down to reach the ground as quickly as possible. The lateral control was more effective than I had imagined and before I reached the ground the right wing was lower than the left and struck first. The time of this flight was fifteen seconds and the distance over the ground a little over 200 feet.

Wilbur started the fourth and last flight at just 12 o'clock. The first few hundred feet were up and down as before but by the time three hundred feet had been covered the machine was under much better control. The course of the next four or five hundred feet had but little undulation. However, when out about eight hundred feet the machine began pitching again, and, in one of its

darts downwards, struck the ground. The distance over the ground was measured and found to be 852 feet; the time of the flight 59 seconds."

Fully satisfied by this expected success, the two brothers, knowing that the age of flight had at last arrived, went back to Dayton for a family Christmas and to build a more solid aircraft which was tried out at Simms Station in 1904. The most important results of the one hundred and five flights of this series were: the first turn on 15 September, and the first closed circuit, which was also the first flight of more than 1 kilometre, on 20 September. Wilbur Wright piloted these two flights. On 9 November the machine flew round the airfield four times (2.85 miles) in 5 minutes and 4 seconds.

A third aircraft, with a 25 h.p. engine, was built and tested in 1905. It accomplished around 50 flights of increasing length at Simms Station. On 6 September, the 1904 record was broken; on 5 October Wilbur Wright flew over 24 miles in 38 mins., 3 secs. All these flights were made in a

circle, returning to the point of departure, with no accidents. Contrary to later allegations, they were conducted on absolutely flat ground, mostly using propeller thrust only, although during the course of the 1905 tests, the Wright brothers made a pylon-catapult, to facilitate take-off in calm weather.

Having conducted all their experiments at their own expense, with all the risks that entailed, and convinced of the value of an invention which was totally theirs, from conception and construction to thorough testing, the Wright brothers, in the interests of commercial confidentiality, stopped their tests until their business agreements had been concluded, and only took up their experiments again at Kitty Hawk in 1907. By this time, numerous discussions had taken place between the French government or individuals and the Wright brothers for the sale of their discoveries, but these all broke down when a group, with Lazare Weiller and Hart O. Berg at its head, was formed and acquired the Wright licence for France.

The flight on 16 November 1904 at Simms Station.

20 miles in 33 minutes at Simms Station on 4 October 1905.

The hangar at Simms Station, Dayton, in 1905. The aeroplane is taking off with a catapult for the first time.

At a height of 25 metres during the flight of 4 October 1905.

Wright Cycle Company

Established in 1892

1127 West Third Street

Dayton, Ohio. Dec. 28, 1903.

Major Ferber,
17th Alpine Battery,
Nice, France.

Dear Sir:

Your letter in regard to the Scientific American came while we were away at Kitty Hawk, North Carolina, and was not forwarded to us. We thank you for the compliment paid us in writing to the Scientific American, and feel proud to have one so prominent among aeronautical experimenters call himself our pupil.

As we informed you in our last letter a short time before leaving for the South, we this year built a much larger machine than any we had used heretofore, and prepared to apply power to it, if we found it sufficiently controlable. While the new machine was under construction, we carried on some practice with our last year's glider, and succeeded in raising our former record of 26 seconds to one minute, eleven and four-fifth seconds. We made quite a number of glides of over one minute in duration. However, we have found this slow gliding in which we remain sometimes for a number of seconds without descending the hill at all, much more difficult and dangerous than that in which the speed over the ground is greater.

On the 17th inst. we took our new machine out for trial. It was equipped with engine and propellers, so we decided to make our trials from the flat sand instead of starting on a hill as in others. A cold gusty wind of a little over 20 miles per hour was blowing from the north. We had arranged to have the machine run on small wheels on a track until the propellers had given it sufficient speed to rise from the ground. Starting in this manner, we made four successful flights during the morning, the longest of which was 59 seconds in the air with a speed of 11 miles per hour over the ground against a wind of 20 to 25 miles. Our machine had an area of 510 sq. feet in the main surfaces, and measured a little over 40 feet from tip to tip of wings. Our total weight was 745 lbs, supported by a four cylinder gasoline engine with 4 inch x 4 inch cylinders, running at 1025 revolutions per minute. On account of the coldness of the weather we were compelled to suspend further trials till next year.

Wishing you continued success in your experiments, I remain,

Respectfully yours,

Orville Wright

WRIGHT CYCLE COMPANY

1127 WEST THIRD STREET

DAYTON, OHIO

November 4th, 1905.

Captain Ferber,
Chalais, Meudon, France.

Dear Sir:

We have received your letter of October 21st, and hasten to extend congratulations to you on the great success you have achieved. Perhaps no one in the world can appreciate the greatness of your performance so fully as ourselves. It is indeed a great step to have passed from the gliding machine, with its easy control, to the discovery of methods sufficiently powerful and efficient to give mastery of the unruly motor machines. After the experiences of men of such great ability as Langley, Maxim, and Ader, who spent years of time and millions of money without any result, we had not believed it possible that we should be in danger of being overtaken within five or ten years at least. France is indeed fortunate in finding a Ferber. We extend felicitations the more heartily because we do not believe that your success will decrease the value of our own discoveries. For when it becomes known that France is in possession of a practical flying machine other countries must at once avail themselves of our scientific discoveries and practical experience. With Russia and Austria-Hungary in their present troubled condition and the German Emperor in a truculent mood, a spark may produce an explosion at any minute. No government dare take the risk of waiting to develope practical flying machines independently. To be even one year behind other governments might result in losses compared with which the modest amount we shall ask for our invention would be insignificant.

But even though France already has reached a high degree of success, it may wish to avail itself of our discoveries, partly to supplement its own work; or, perhaps, partly to accurately inform itself of the state of the art as it will exist in those countries which buy the secrets of our motor machine.

Under the present circumstances we would consent to reduce our price to the French government to one million francs, the money to be paid only after the genuine value of our discoveries had been demonstrated by a flight of one of our machines in the presence of official representatives of the government a distance of not less than fifty kilometers in not more than one hour of time. The price would include a complete machine, instruction in our discoveries relating to the scientific principles of the art, formulas for the designing of machines of other sizes, speeds, etc; and personal instruction of operators in the use of the machine. Inasmuch as the work of teaching would require our personal attention, we would necessarily be compelled to give precedence in time to those who secured the first engagements.

Very respectfully yours,

Wilbur & Orville Wright

A letter written by Orville Wright to "Major" Ferber (then Captain) eleven days after the first flight on 17 December 1903. The ink additions are explanations or translations into French measurements, in Orville Wright's hand. Those in pencil are by Captain Ferber.

1905: A "business letter" from the Wright brothers to Captain Ferber congratulating him on his experiments of May 1905, on his power-driven glider, at Chalais-Meudon, and seeking his assistance in their negotiations with the French Government

The power-driven Levavasseur aeroplane tested at Villotran in 1903.

General view and detail of one of the propellers and of the wing structure.

M.P. Roux's mechanical steam bird, at the moment of take-off and on its launching track (1904).

POWERED FLYING MACHINES

In 1903, the efforts of Ferber and Archdeacon in France to promote interest in heavier-than-air flight began to be rewarded.

The first French aeroplane with an internal combustion engine was built by the the mechanical engineer Levavasseur at the expense of M. Gastambide. Equipped with the first "Antoinette" engine, also the work of Levavasseur, it was tested without success at Villorran, near Chantilly.

A glider built in 1904 by Private Peyret (left) and Sergeant Paulhan (right).

In 1904 M. Roux experimented several times with a curious bird-like machine, fitted out with a traction propeller and a steam engine. Taking off from an inclined track that turned upwards again at its extremity, the machine was launched into the air, but was unable to stay airborne.

In the same year, Colonel Charles Renard drew up an admirable programme for the testing of aeroplanes and proposed the organisation of a competition for aircraft motors; while continuing to pursue his tests on helicopter models.

He died suddenly on 13 April 1905, thus depriving aeronautical science of its leading figure.

Colonel Renard's helicopter (1904).

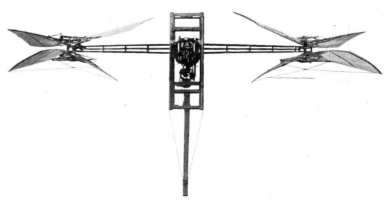

The Dufaux brothers' helicopter, which left the ground at Saint-Cloud in 1905.

Professor Montgomery's glider *Santa-Clara* (1905)

The *Santa-Clara*'s hot-air balloon being inflated.

Esnault-Pelterie landing (1904).

Gabriel Voisin in the *Archdeacon* aeroplane at Berck (1904).

The Aeronautic Club glider (1906).

GLIDERS 1902–1906

The *Archdeacon No. 2* at Issy (March 1905).

The Wright brothers and Chanute were not the only researchers working on flight in America. Among others was Professor Montgomery of Santa Clara in California, who began his experiments with aviation in 1884. As a result of his early experiences, the Professor adopted a design combining wings in tandem with a variable curvature mechanism. His experimental method was to fix the glider under a vast hot-air balloon, which raised the machine and its pilot several hundred feet; the aviator then separated his machine from the balloon and started a glide which was often very long and accompanied by manoeuvres, turns etc. Unfortunately in 1905 the machine of one of the testers, Maloney, a cable having broken on take-off, became unstable and folded up in the air, causing his death. Several years later, in 1911, Professor Montgomery was himself the victim of his experiments, dying, so it is said, of a heart attack during a glide on one of his machines.

At the same time in France, Ernest Archdeacon, a pioneer of automobiles, the tele-phone and sporting ballooning, inspired by Ferber's attempts, led a vigorous campaign from 1902 to have the experiment of the Wrights and Chanute repeated in France. Encouraged by a conference given there by the latter, Archdeacon had a glider made, copied from that of the Wright brothers. Trials took place in 1904 on the Berck sand dunes; the aviator was a young Lyonnais, Gabriel Voisin. The flights, though short, were very satisfactory, confirming Voisin's early interest in the aeroplane. Captain Ferber also participated.

The example of Archdeacon was soon followed: Robert Esnault-Pelterie also built a similar glider which he tried out in 1904, but the longitudinal equilibrium was defective and the results were poor. Nevertheless, as with Gabriel Voisin, a new vocation was born in him.

In 1905, Archdeacon built a new machine which he was going to equip with an engine. Fortunately a preliminary test flight was made,

The *Archdeacon-Voisin* aeroplane on the Seine (1905).

Gabriel Voisin in 1908.

The *Blériot-Voisin* aeroplane on the Seine (1905).

The *Demouveaux* glider (1901).

The *Berger-Gardey* glider.

One of Albert Bazin's gliders.

the craft being towed by a car on the parade ground at Issy; the aircraft broke up in the air and came down in pieces.

Also in 1905 Gabriel Voisin was commissioned to build, at the Surcouf workshops, two large gliders for Ernest Archdeacon and Louis Blériot; they contained most of the characteristics of the future Voisin aeroplanes. Both of them, mounted on twin floats, were tried out on the Seine

mouveaux's large glider which broke at the first attempt.

All over the country, numerous researchers revealed themselves from 1904 to 1907: Bazin, at Marseilles, built gliders imitating sea birds, using flapping paddles for propulsion; Solirène, at Palavas, threw himself from a tower and crashed violently, but harmlessly, into the sea; Gardey, at Lyons broke a leg with the Berger glider, im-

The Solirène glider (1904).

Robart's glider at Amiens (1904).

Solirène's glide at Palavas.

between Sèvres and Billancourt, being towed by a fast launch – a method which allowed the power needed for take-off to be measured.

Gabriel Voisin was the test pilot. On 8 June 1905, the *Archdeacon* machine took off, travelled 150 yards and landed without incident. On the next test, however, the floats punctured and the aeroplane sank into the river.

Once repaired, the machine was tested again on 18 July and towed in flight for 300 yards by launch. The Blériot machine tried out shortly after took off as well but, yawing violently, touched the surface and turned on its side, temporarily imprisoning Voisin under water.

Gabriel Voisin, in association with Bleriot and

later with his brother, became aviation's first industrialist. Working for inventors or selling his own aeroplanes, his machines, well built and safe, helped many pioneers to learn without undue risk.

The idea of the practicability of aviation grew rapidly in France. As early as 1901, a competition had been organised at the Parc des Princes but had primarily attracted kites, apart from M. De-

prudently launched from a great height by means of an inclined track; Lavezzari, at Berck, made several attempts in 1904, as did Robart at Amiens; Joseph Weiss tested some remarkable gliders in England.

A heavier-than-air section of the Aéro-Club of France was created in 1903. This organisation, which arranged many worthwhile competitions, instituted an aviator's licence in 1909.

In 1906, the Aeronautic Club of France created the world's first real gliding school, near Palaiseau, where aircraft of the Chanute type were used; there were many pupils, some of whom later made names for themselves in aviation.

Experiments with Lavezzari's glider at Berck in 1904.

Charles Voisin making a flight of 65 yards at Bagatelle on board Delagrange's Voisin biplane (30 March 1907).

A bad landing by the Blériot *Canard* (21 March 1907).

The Blériot *Libellule* flying 184 metres at Issy (17 September 1907).

PROGRESS IN FRANCE DURING 1907

By the end of 1907, eight aviators had flown heavier-than-air craft in France: they were Santos-Dumont, Vuia, Charles Voisin, Blériot, Henry Farman, Esnault-Pelterie, Delagrange and de Pischof.

Vuia made quite a number of small hops at Bagatelle.

Léon Delagrange had bought their first biplane for Gabriel Voisin and his brother Charles. Laborious tests followed one another at Vincennes, then at Bagatelle. For the first flights it was decided that Charles Voisin would be the pilot. On 16 March, the aircraft took off for about a hundred yards and on the 30th it managed 65 yards in 6 seconds, clearing the ground by between 6 and 13 ft. On 2 and 5 November, Delagrange himself achieved several flights, the last of which ended in the destruction of the machine. In the meantime, Louis Blériot was making his first flights: his "duck" monoplane had wings of varnished parchment and an Antoinette 24 h.p. motor. On 5 April, he made a flight of 5 to 6 yards at Bagatelle. He made further short flights on 8 and 15 April but the machine was basically too fragile and on 19 April was destroyed. Blériot then tried a tandem monoplane. There was no elevator; the pilot reestablished the balance by moving on a sliding seat! Tested at Issy, the *Libellule* cleared 25 yards on 11 July, 160 on the 25th, and 150 on 6 August. Finally, on 17 September, Blériot flew 201 yards, reaching an altitude of 60 ft. and ending by crashing his machine into the ground, but with no harm to himself.

Henry Farman, an English artist and sportsman, piloted a Voisin biplane; his flights started on 30 September and, demonstrating an innate skill as a pilot, he achieved 843 yards at Issy as early as 26 October.

In October and November, Esnault-Pelterie made a series of flights at Buc in his monoplane, the motor for which he had also designed, and Alfred de Pischof left the ground at Issy on 5 and 6 December 1907 in a biplane of his own construction.

The Blériot-Voisin biplane on lake Enghien (1906).

Pischof's first biplane at Issy (1907).

Henry Farman coming up to the finishing line at the end of his 1 kilometre circuit on the airfield at Issy-les-Moulineaux, 13 January 1908.

THE FIRST RECORDED ONE KILOMETRE CIRCUIT: THE DEUTSCH-ARCHDEACON GRAND PRIX OF AVIATION

Henry Farman in 1907.

Henry Farman, Henri Deutsch de la Meurthe, Charles Voisin.

The first kilometre circuit described by an aeroplane in the presence of official sporting authorities was achieved by Henry Farman, who by this action also won the Deutsch-Archdeacon Grand Prix of 50,000 francs.

It took just one minute 28 seconds at Issy-les-Moulineaux on 13 January 1908, for the well-known aviator to achieve a round trip of 500 metres, turning around a post, in his Voisin biplane with an Antoinette 50 h.p. motor.

Henry Farman in his Voisin biplane finishing the first official circuit of 1 kilometre at Issy, 13 January 1908.

The departure of the first passenger flight: Léon Delagrange carrying Henry Farman in his Voisin biplane, at Issy, 28 March 1908.

THE FIRST PASSENGERS

The first passenger in a powered aircraft was Henry Farman, who was taken in the air by Léon Delagrange on 28 March 1908 on board his Voisin biplane, on the airfield at Issy-les-Moulineaux. This flight was a simple straight line of several hundred metres.

The first woman to leave the ground in an aeroplane was a Frenchwoman, Madame Thérèse Peltier, who was the passenger of Delagrange on 8 July 1908 at Milan. After several flights as a

Léon Delagrange (1873–1910)

passenger, Madame Peltier began her apprenticeship as a pilot and accomplished, before anyone else, several short solo flights in Voisin's biplane, but she did not continue with it.

Madly enthusiastic, Ernest Archdeacon had the pleasure of flying with Henry Farman over a distance of more than 1 kilometre, as early as 30 May 1908. This flight, the longest one at that date with two people on board, was achieved at Gand, where an airfield had been prepared to receive

Henri Farman and his aircraft. Shortly after, at Issy, Henry Farman took up other people, notably his father. During the following months, a great number of passengers were "baptised" by Wilbur Wright when he visited France. It should be noted that all these early passenger flights were accomplished without an accident.

The year 1908 saw numerous flying time records beaten by Léon Delagrange alone, who flew for 16 min. 30 sec. at Turin, then in September for 29 min. 53 sec. at Issy in a Voisin equipped with vertical partitions forming cells between the wings to increase the stability.

Henry Farman and Ernest Archdeacon (1908).

Henry Farman and Ernest Archdeacon take off at Gand.

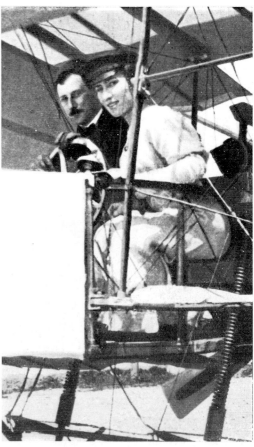

Madame Peltier: first woman passenger and pilot.

The first cross-country aeroplane journey in Europe: Henry Farman in his Voisin biplane making the trip by air from Bouy to Rheims.

THE FIRST CROSS-COUNTRY

Henry Farman was also the first man in Europe to make a cross-country flight.

Having established himself at the Chalons camp with his Voisin biplane that he could modify at his leisure, he set off on 30 October 1908 from Bouy in the direction of Rheims. He has left the following account of this historic flight.

"At first I was a bit emotional . . . The departure for this first journey had rather alarmed me.

What, I asked myself, am I going to do when I arrive above those large poplars that I can see way over there, in the direction of Mourmelon-le-Petit? For the moment, all is well. The ground is flat and the countryside is very agreeable.

But, during these reflections, the poplars are growing in an astonishing fashion. The crows, who were holding a squawking gathering, are flying off horrified at my approach. Ah! those 100 ft. poplars! Should I pass them on the right? on the left? My indecision does not last long, for I am scarcely 50 yards from the vast high grove. Oh well, here goes! A touch on the elevator and the aircraft rises up rapidly; it goes over, while with

an anxious eye I look to see whether I am clearing the tree-tops.

My tranquillity is, however, short-lived. Here is the Mourmelon windmill and now Mourmelon itself. Bah!, I though, one only dies once! The windmill, the village, the railway – I go over them all. A critical moment in an emotional journey.

And then, I'm not sure about the height. I am told I was flying at 150 ft. Maybe I was, because I went up as high as possible so as not to be caught by the poplars.

I was giving my full attention to steering the machine, to the noise of the motor which 'misfired' from time to time and worried me, to the roaring of the propeller. But I nevertheless enjoyed, at that instant, the greatest joy of my life: the charm of gliding above my fellow men while the scenery flew by in strips and where, from all sides, people were running towards me who seemed tiny, tiny. At that moment I found myself in pure air, caressed by a gentle breeze, and the sun lit up the way, limpid and serene. It is my most cherished memory."

The landing went off perfectly on the cavalry ground at Rheims. The 1/ miles had been covered in 20 minutes.

Farman clearing 82 ft. at Chalons, 31 October 1908.

Henry Farman landing at Rheims after the first cross-country flight.

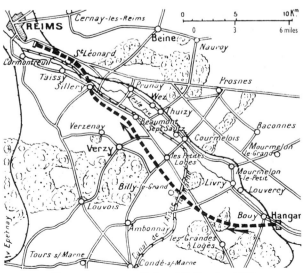

The cross-country flight of 30 October 1908.

The first scrutinised flight in America: the *Red Wing*, piloted by F.W. Baldwin.

Glenn Curtiss winning the Scientific American prize (4 July 1908) in *June-Bug*.

McCurdy in the *Silver Dart* in March 1909.

Glenn Curtiss (1878–1931).

McCurdy and Curtiss' *White Wing* (18 May 1908).

PUBLIC FLIGHTS IN AMERICA

After the great initial flights of the Wright brothers' which were witnessed by a limited number of spectators, all, with the exception of Chanute, laymen, it was not until 1908 that aeroplanes were flown publicly in America.

The *Aerial Experiment Association* created by Alexander Graham Bell, the famous inventor of the telephone, having taken on Glenn Curtiss to assist in building the motors, constructed an interesting series of machines.

The *Red Wing*, equipped with skates, made a first flight of about a hundred yards on 12 March 1908 over the ice-covered Lake Keuka (New York), piloted by F.W. Baldwin. The *White Wing* flew, piloted by McCurdy and later by Curtiss, several times from 18 May 1908 at Hammond-sport. Finally the *June Bug* won the Scientific American cup on 4 July by covering more than 1 kilometre, piloted by Curtiss.

Continually improving its machines, the Association created the *Silver Dart* on which McCurdy flew over the frozen lake at Baddeck (Nova Scotia), covering 4½ miles, the first flight made in Canada.

Following flights reached a maximum flying time of 38 minutes and distance of 15 miles.

The *Cygnet 2*, formed of 5,500 tetrahedral units, constructed by Graham Bell and McCurdy, tested without success at Baddeck on 22 February 1909.

Stages in the launching of a Wright biplane, photographed from a balloon in Italy in 1909. The aeroplane in its launching position; the take off; the machine in the air.

WILBUR WRIGHT IN FRANCE

The arrival of Wilbur Wright in France was an event which had important consequences. He arrived in July 1908, and installed himself at the Etablissements Bollée, at Le Mans, bringing a machine of his 1907 type with which to give his flying demonstrations. He was lent the airfield at Hunaudières, and later the camp at Auvours.

Scepticism still reigned as to the value and accuracy of the accounts of the Wrights' experiments. As soon as he had made his first safe, magnificent flight on 8 August 1908, however, all doubts gave way to a well justified admiration. The ease of the flight, due partly to the excellent

performances of the machine achieved by the use of wing-flexing as a means of control and partly to the brilliance of the pilot, conquered the public and made all the aviators aware of the incontestable superiority of the American machine.

The personality of Wilbur Wright, his noble face, his extreme reserve, the mystery which seemed to surround him, his ascetic life, all made a striking impression. Some of his expressions, concise and excellent, have remained classics. When he was asked how he flew his aeroplane, he replied: "like a bird".

Success rapidly followed success: on 3 September, a flight of more than 10 min., on the 16th one of 29 min. 18 sec., then a flight with a passenger, Ernest Zens; on the 22nd, a trip of 41⅓ miles in 1 hour 32 min. Numerous long flights followed: on 3 October, Wright carried a passenger for more than fifty-five minutes and on the 6th he flew 1 hour 4 min. with M. Fordyce, the first passenger to have stayed more than one hour in an aeroplane. By 15 October, thirty passengers had already been taken up, whereas all the French pilots together had flown only a handful of people. Paul Doumer, then a Senator but later President of the French Republic, and assassinated in 1932, made a ten-minute flight with him on 31 October. Shortly after, the lessons started: the first three pupils of Wilbur Wright were the Comte de Lambert, Paul Tissandier and Captain Lucas-Girardville.

The great pilot finished the year with three exploits: on 18 December, a flight officially of 61 miles, but in fact of 75 miles accomplished in 1 hr.

Wilbur Wright's pupils at Pau: left to right, Paul Tissandier, Sallenave, Comte de Castillon de Saint-Victor, Captain Lucas-Girardville, Louis Blériot.

Wilbur Wright (1867–1912). Photographed at Auvours in 1908.

54 min.; then an ascent to 375 ft.; finally on 31 December, 76½ miles (in fact 93 miles) in 139 min.

He then went to Pau where he continued to teach his pupils, of whom the two best were the Comte de Lambert and Paul Tissandier. His brother Orville joined him there.

Orville Wright, during the course of the summer of 1908, had presented the American government with a machine similar to Wilbur's. The flights took place at Fort Myers, near Washington. It was there that, on 9 September 1908, Orville made the first human flight of more than an hour, a performance he renewed on the three following days with 1 hr. 5 min., 1 hr. 10 min. and 1 hr. 15 min. These remarkable demonstrations were interrupted by the catastrophe of 18 September.

In 1909, Wilbur Wright went to Rome to make a series of flights and trained Lieutenant Calderara. Shortly after, Orville made similar displays in Berlin, carrying Messrs. Hildebrandt, Hergesell and a pupil, Captain Engelhardt.

Wilbur Wright's duration record (1 hour 31' 25"), at Auvours, 22 September 1908.

Wilbur Wright beating the altitude record at 305 ft. (Auvours 18 December 1908).

Eugène Lefebvre, the first pilot to be a casualty of aviation, in his Wright biplane.

THE FIRST CASUALTIES

The first years of power-driven aeroplanes were as free from serious accident as were the beginnings of ballooning. The first catastrophe came at the moment where aeroplanes started to give practical displays; it happened on 18 September 1908, at Fort Myers, near Washington, where Orville Wright was making official tests before a military commission. The aeroplane was flying at a low height when a shroud caught in a propeller blade and tore it off. The aircraft crashed, seriously injuring Orville and his passenger Lt. Thomas Selfridge, who died the same night.

The first pilot to be killed in an aeroplane was Eugéne Lefebvre, who died at Juvisy, in a Wright, on 7 September 1909; on 22 September 1909, Captain Ferber was killed at Boulogne-sur-Mer when he overturned in his Voisin biplane.

Thomas Selfridge (†*F*1908) and Graham Bell.

Eugène Lefebvre (1898–†*F*1909)

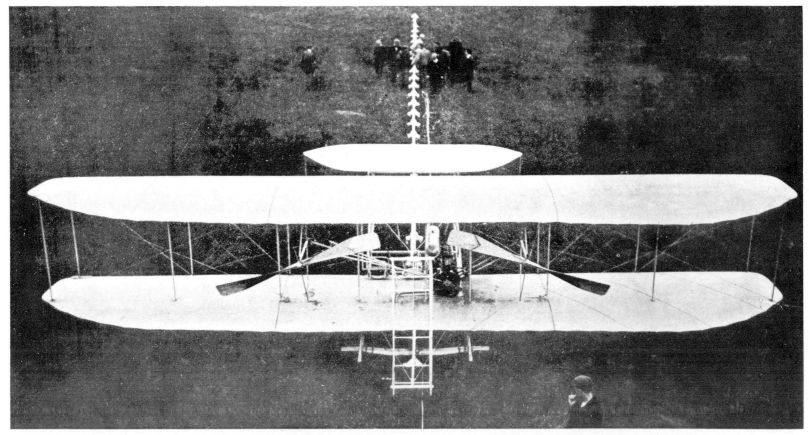

The first Wright biplane built in France by the Société Ariel (1909) on its launching track.

Paul Cornu's helicopter, the first to have left the ground in free flight with its pilot (13 November 1907).

The gyroplane *Breguet-Richet No. 1*, the first helicopter to have lifted off the ground with a pilot.

THE FIRST HELICOPTER FLIGHTS

In 1907, at Douai, Louis and Jacques Breguet and Professor Richet experimented with a helicopter with four vertical propellers, driven by an Antoinette 45 h.p. motor. With no control instruments, this machine was only designed to establish its capacity to lift its own weight and that of a pilot, the engineer Volumard. The experiment was successful and, in September, the Breguet-Richet "gyroplane", weighing 1270 lb., rose to 2 ft. On 29 September, it reached 5 ft. but no free flight took place, the machine always being guided or held down by four helpers.

The first free flight of a helicopter was accomplished on 13 November 1907, near Lisieux. The aircraft, with two propellers driven by a 24 h.p. Antoinette and equipped with two control surfaces, had been entirely constructed by its inventor, an ordinary mechanic, Paul Cornu. On the first flight, the aircraft, manned by Cornu, reached 1 ft. On the following flight, the machine took off so sharply that it swept up to 5 ft., not only the inventor, but also his brother, who was hanging on to the chassis, increasing its weight from 570 lb. to 720 lb. Although brief, these flights are very important historically. Several other flights followed, but Paul Cornu, a remarkable pioneer, had to abandon everything, for lack of resources.

The following year, on 22 July, the Breguet-Richet gyroplane, *No. II bis*, an enormous machine derived from both the aeroplane and the helicopter, rose to a height of 13 ft., but damaged itself on landing.

In 1912 in Denmark Ellehammer got a helicopter with two concentric blades to fly with a pilot on board. The lower blade could be used as a parachute. The whole load was lifted to 2 ft. from the ground.

The gyroplane *Breguet-Richet No. II bis* (1908).

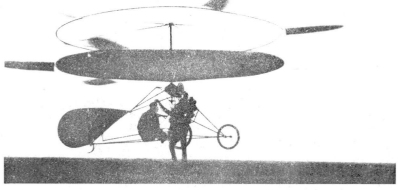

The *Ellehammer* helicopter in flight with its pilot (1912).

Tsar Nicholas II and his retinue visiting the French aeroplanes at the first meeting at Saint Petersburg. On the left, Léon Morane's Blériot.

The *Grade* monoplane of 1909,

piloted by its inventor.

HEAVIER-THAN-AIR FLIGHT IN THE REST OF EUROPE

France had acquired the lead in heavier-than-air flight and it was often French pilots who were the first to fly abroad.

As early as the spring of 1908, Delagrange was invited to Italy where he flew at Rome on 23 May, then at Milan and Turin. The earliest Italian aviator was Lieutenant Calderara, a pupil of Orville Wright, in Rome in 1909. At the Brescia meeting in September 1909, Curtiss took Gabriele d'Annunzio for his first flight.

Above: the first flight of a German aeroplane, the triplane Grade. Below: the first flight in Germany by Ellehammer at Kiel.

Denmark had made surprising strides in the field of aviation: the pioneer Ellehammer made public flights there in his triplane in February 1908, then in September 1909 Delegrange made his, followed in 1910 by those of the Dane, Folmer Hansen.

The first flight in Germany was also made by Ellehammer who, in his biplane, flew at Kiel on 28 June 1908, in the presence of 30,000 spectators. The first German aeroplane piloted by the first German pilot was Grade's triplane which flew a few yards at Magdebourg on 12 January 1909. The first long flight by a German was also made by Grade in his monoplane at Bork on 10 September 1909.

The *Ellehammer* triplane flying in Denmark (February 1908).

The Etrich and Wells machine, gliding without an engine, in Austria (1908).

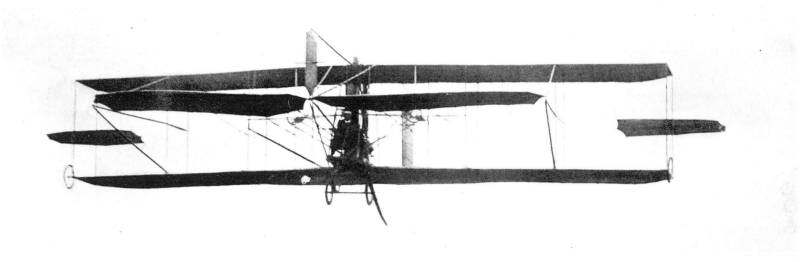

One of the first English aeroplanes: Cody's biplane *Cathedral*, in flight (1909).

England came slowly to aviation. Apart from Henry Farman, the first Englishman to have flown was Griffith Brewer, a passenger of Wilbur Wright at Auvours on 8 October 1908. The first English pilot was Moore Brabazon who flew in France on a Voisin from December 1908 and who also accomplished the first flights in Great Britain at Eastchurch on 30 April and 2 May 1909. He was followed closely by A.V. Roe who in 1908 and 1909 tested a triplane with which he seems to have made his first flights at Lea Marshes on 13 July 1909. Roe was a pioneer of British aviation along with C.F. Cody, of American origin, who built a large biplane and tested it in 1908. After many failures, Cody made long flights from August and September 1909. He was killed in a flying accident in 1913.

Legagneux, in a Voisin, was the first to fly in Austria, at Vienna on 23 April 1909. The first Austrian pilot and constructor was Igo Etrich, who flew in his monoplane *Taube* at Wiener Neustadt from 29 November 1906 and was followed by Illner and Warchalovski.

In Holland, aviation started with several flights in a Wright by the Comte de Lambert, then on 18 July 1909 by Lefebvre, near The Hague. The first Dutch pilots were Wijnmalen and de Riemsdyck.

Sweden saw its first flight with Legagneux in a Voisin on 29 July 1909 at Stockholm, then with the Dane Folmer Hansen. Its first pilot was the Baron de Cederstrom. The Sund was crossed for the first time, from Copenhagen to Malmo, by Svendsen in a Voisin on 17 July 1910.

Blériot was the first to fly in Rumania, at Bucharest on 30 October 1909, while Kaspar was the earliest aviator and constructor of what is now Czechoslovakia, flying at Prague in 1909.

Russia was introduced to aviation in 1909 by the flights accomplished at Odessa by Van den Schkrouff in a Voisin on 25 July, and by Cattaneo

F. Cody (1861–†*F*1913)

on 24 August, followed by those of Legagneux at Moscow on 17 September and finally by those of Guyot at Saint Petersburg and Moscow in November. Guyot was the first to fly in what is now Poland, at Warsaw on 7 April 1910.

Aviation started in 1909 in Turkey by the

flights of De Caters at Constantinople in November and of Blériot on 12 December. In December 1909 the Frenchmen Zipfel, and, on 21 and 27 April 1910, Mamet, were the first to fly in Portugal at Belem.

In Spain, the earliest aviators were, simultaneously in March and April 1910, Gaudart and Poillot at Barcelona, Le Blon at San Sebastian, Mamet at Madrid and Olieslaegers at Seville.

On 13 March 1910, Switzerland saw a Wright aeroplane for the first time flying over the ice on a lake at Saint Moritz, piloted by the German Captain Engelhardt. The first Swiss aviators were Rupp and Dufaux, who in 1910 flew in a biplane which became successively an aeroplane and a seaplane.

It is interesting to note that in South America it was not American aeroplanes or pilots that showed the new means of air locomotion; all the first machines and most of the pilots came from France. Henri Brégi was the first to go up in an aeroplane in South America at Buenos Aires in January and February 1910 in a Voisin biplane. He was followed in Argentina by the Italians Ponzelli and Cattaneo, and the Frenchmen Aubrun and Valleton. A little later, Brégi introduced aviation to the West Indies, flying at Havana.

Ruggerone, an Italian pilot, was the first to fly in Brazil, also in 1910.

In Central America, aviation started in 1909 with flights made in Mexico in a Voisin by Braniff, an amateur sportsman, who had been trained in France.

The first Swiss aeroplane: the Dufaux biplane (1910).

A.V. Roe in his triplane in 1909.

Santos-Dumont's first "Demoiselle" (1907–1908).

Esnault-Pelterie's first red monoplane at Buc (1907).

Captain Ferber at Issy in his biplane *No. 9* (1908).

Henry Farman's first biplane at Châlons (1909).

Léon Delagrange's endurance record at Issy (1908).

The Goupy biplane, piloted by Jules Védrines (1909).

FRENCH AIRCRAFT OF 1908

1908 saw a major expansion of activity in aircraft production in France; several constructors established themselves, a number of whom were still in business at the start of the Second World War. Blériot abandoned all his other activities; Henry Farman set himself up as a manufacturer and was joined at Buc by his brother Maurice. Voisin enlarged his workshops, as did the Antoinette company, and Esnault-Pelterie moved from experimentation to construction. Several less important firms were created: Goupy, who brought out an excellent little biplane with a traction propeller and a fuselage, was a pioneer of this configuration; de Pischof and Koechlin produced interesting monoplanes, as did Raoul Vendôme.

The 1908 Paris Automobile Show included a large aeronautics section and assembled sixteen aeroplanes as well as an Astra dirigible and a machine by Ader. At this time, aviation was easily accessible to amateurs and several members of the Aéro-Club built successful aeroplanes themselves: René Gasnier flew in the Angers area and Paul Zens at Gonesse.

Santos-Dumont produced a tiny machine, the *Demoiselle*, with a body of bamboo which was terrifyingly fragile. Nevertheless, this machine, weighing around 220 lb., was built and sold for flying schools and displays without giving rise to any fatal accident.

Encouraged by his first flights in 1907, Louis Blériot abandoned his automobile headlight business and undertook a whole series of machines during the year. Blériot invariably built machines with traction propellers and a single wing. To save weight, and also for the sake of economy, the aeroplanes in which Blériot made his flights in 1908 were covered, not with fabric, but with rice paper, a stronger material than one would think. Nevertheless, one can easily imagine the emotion of the great pilot of these early flights, with doubtfully tuned motors, undercarriages without shock absorbers, a structure which was far too light and finally this paper covering! In contrast Blériot, like Santos-Dumont and the Voisin brothers, used only metal propellers; Blériot's generally had four blades.

The *Blériot No. VI* was the first aeroplane to have a completely covered fuselage to decrease drag, and had solid wings set low on the fuselage which gave it a very modern aspect. Unfortunately, an accident interrupted the tests.

The *Blériot-VIII bis*, with an Antoinette 50 h.p. motor, powerful controls and ailerons, gave, from the beginning, excellent results. On this aeroplane Louis Blériot accomplished the first cross-country from town to town and back on 31 October 1908, the very day after Farman's exploit. Blériot was the first to use rigid hinged ailerons at the ends of the wings, appearing first on his 1907 tandem, rather than Wright's wing-flexing system.

In 1909 Blériot built a more powerful high-wing monoplane. The earliest flight with three people was made at Issy on this machine, on 12 June 1909, by Louis Blériot with Santos-Dumont and André Fournier as passengers.

The *Blériot No. VI* tested in 1908.

The monoplane *Blériot-VIII* at Toury, 31 October 1908.

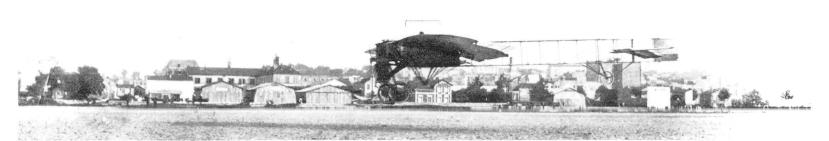

The *Blériot VIII-bis* during an 800-yard flight at Issy-les-Moulineaux (1908).

The Antionette 100 h.p. V-16 engine on Latham's aeroplane for the Gordon-Bennett Cup (1910).

Antoinette 50 h.p. V.8 engine on an Antoinette monoplane (1908).

Panhard 100 h.p. engine with 4 cylinders in line for de Bolotoff's biplane (1908).

The first Gnome engine, photographed in rotation (1908).

Externally mounted 50 h.p. Gnome rotary engine on a Henry Farman biplane (1909).

Clerget-Clement 50 h.p. engine with 7 cylinders in star (1908).

Gnome engine with reduction-gear on a Breguet (1910).

ENGINES

The earliest internal combustion engines were designed for specific aircraft like those of Langley, Manly and the Wrights. They were followed by Levavasseur's 24 h.p. V.8 Antoinette, which was produced industrially and adapted to various aeroplanes. From this Levavasseur developed his famous 50 h.p. Antoinette, also a V.8., and later a 100 h.p. V.16.

The early days of aviation can be divided into two periods as far as engines are concerned: that of the Antoinette and that of the Gnome. The first of these equipped all the major aeroplanes between 1906 and 1908, using the principle of the multiple cylinder engine with rapid rotation. From 1909, the rotary Gnome, designed by the Seguin brothers, took over. Although the princi-

ple of rotary engines – that is, engines that turn round a fixed shaft – was known and had already been applied, the externally mounted Gnome engine was a very audacious conception, and created a real revolution in the aviation industry.

Immediate interest in research into light engines for the aviation industry had been shown as soon as Santos-Dumont made his first flights. Widely varying solutions were proposed and certain of these were only developed much later: Levavasseur and the Seguin brothers were widely copied, but inventive genius knew no bounds.

Fixed engines were divided by the method of cooling – either by water or by air. The arrangement of the cylinders, however, varied tremendously: from Wright's simple 4 cylinders in a vertical line (1907), to Grégoire's inverted cylinders (1909) and Labor's 6 cylinders in line (1910), a system much used in Germany. Anzani

designed 3-cylinder fan and Y-shaped motors. The fan-mounted cylinders increased to 6 in the Lemasson engine of 1910. In 1907 Esnault-Pelterie invented his R.E.P. with groups of 3 and 2 cylinders in fan. This was the first motor to be cooled directly by air. However, Darracq, Dutheil and Chalmers, Nieuport, Clément and, later, Gnome, made engines with opposed cylinders as this tended to produce a shorter machine. Gobron made an X-shaped engine that was used for a flight in 1909. Star-shaped engines, mounted horizontally, were produced by Farcot and Clérget in 1908. Anzani and Canton-Unne used the same layout in a vertical position, with cooling by air and water.

Many attempts were made to modify the rotary motors developed by Verdet (the Rhone) and Clérget, among them the Ligez, which had double rotation.

Esnault-Pelterie R.E.P. 60 h.p. engine (7 cylinders in fan on an R.E.P. monoplane: (1908).

25 h.p. Darracq engine with two horizontally-opposed cylinders on the Santos-Dumont *Demoiselle* (1908).

Gobron 50 h.p. engine with 8 cylinders arranged in the form of an X on a Voisin belonging to de Caters (1909).

Renault 50 h.p. V.8 engine on the first Breguet biplane (1909).

THE PROGRESS OF THE DIRIGIBLE

There was a major increase of interest in the dirigible balloon between 1904 and 1912. This expansion began in France following the *Lebaudy* experiments. In 1906 the Voisin establishment delivered a new dirigible to the army, inspired by the *Lebaudy*, but more powerful – the *Patrie*. After a year of use, during which it served to train a number of officer pilots and mechanics and counted Clemenceau amongst its passengers, this handsome airship accomplished the journey from Meudon to Verdun without a stopover, but on its next flight on 2 December 1907 had to make a forced landing away from its base, and, crewless, was blown away in the night by a storm; it touched land in Ireland where it lost a propeller, then disappeared out to sea.

At the same time, Surcouf was building the dirigible *Ville-de-Paris* for Henry Deutsch de la Meurthe, on which the rear stabilising planes were replaced by flexible tubes inflated with hydrogen; this device was to be found on many subsequent dirigibles. The *Ville-de-Paris* was offered to the country by Deutsch to replace the *Patrie*.

Mallet also brought out a small single-seater dirigible, destined for the Comte de la Vaulx. A horizontal boom between the balloon and the basket carried the propeller, which was driven by means of a long telescopic transmission.

Malécot, an independent inventor, made an interesting machine, a little heavier than air which, being tilted by the moving of a basket which acted as a counter-weight, combined the natures of dirigible and aeroplane owing to the

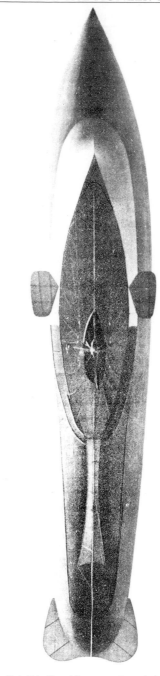

The dirigible *Republique* seen from below (1909).

large lifting surfaces placed under the belly of the balloon. This aircraft made a number of successful outings at Meaux and Issy in 1907 and 1908.

In Germany the same period was marked by the appearance of the first of the *Parseval* and *Gross* series of dirigibles. Those created by Major von Parseval were completely flexible; all the

elements, except the rudders and the basket could be rolled up. Even the propeller was composed of blades in soft fabric that were made taut by centrifugal force during rotation. A whole series of these dirigibles was tested or put into service between 1906 and 1914, mostly for German military ballooning. Major Gross, a ballooning officer, specialised in the construction of semi-rigid dirigibles. These two types and the rigid zeppelins were all used by the German army from 1909.

In England, a dirigible named *Nulli-Secundus* appeared in October 1907, which made a flight of some 50 miles from Farnborough round St Paul's Cathedral and back as far as the Crystal Palace in 3 hrs. 35 mins. It was, however, not of very advanced design and was far from justifying its ambitious title.

Later E.T. Willows built, entirely at his own expense, a suite of small dirigibles, and in 1910 succeeded in making a journey, with stopovers, from Cardiff to London, Douai and Paris.

In Italy, Captains Crocco and Ricaldoni and Major Morris created the type of semi-rigid dirigibles which were finally adopted in that country. These all had a frame which was flexible vertically but rigid transversely fixed to the lower part of the envelope along its centre-line. This system gave excellent results. At the same time the Comte de Schio, Usuelli, Piccoli, and especially Forlanini, produced several dirigibles. The Forlaninis were semi-rigid and performed well.

As soon as aviation became well established, controversy arose between its partisans and those of the dirigible. Rare were those who could conceive that these two means of locomotion, far from opposing each other, ought to complement one another. The campaigns in the press were based not so much on technical arguments as on

The *Ville-de-Paris* leaving Valmy for Verdun (1908).

Zodiac demountable dirigible (1909).

The combination dirigible *Malecot* at Issy-les-Moulineaux (1908).

A dirigible race at Saint Louis (Missouri) in September 1907.

prejudice: the zeppelin was reproached for being "kolossal", and incarnating the German character, the flexible dirigible was described as a "gas bubble" or an "aerial mastodon", while advocates of the dirigible threw scorn on aeroplanes, laying stress on the risks run in the case of engine failure.

In fact, although there were many incidents, seldom serious in spite of the furore they caused, there were few dirigible catastrophes. The most famous of these was that of the *République* in 1909: a propeller blade tore off and punctured the envelope, Captain Marchal, Lieutenant Chauré and Warrant Officers Reau and Vincenot were killed on the spot.

During this period two major French ballooning workshops became public companies: the Surcouf establishment became the Astra company, and the Maurice Mallet workshop became the Zodiac company. The Zodiac company concentrated on small dirigibles which could be dismantled; it created, with the *Zodiac III* and its by-products, a large number of models which were well designed and constructed and which equipped the French, Dutch, Russian and Belgian military ballooning centres.

The test pilots for the Zodiac dirigibles were the Comte de La Vaulx and André Schelcher. The Astra dirigibles were piloted by Henry Kapferer; they were larger and were bought for military use by France, Belgium, Spain, Russia and Great Britain. An Astra was used for many tourist ascents at Nancy, Lucerne and Pau; the company, using patents held by Sr. Torres Quevedo, also developed a dirigible with a trilobate envelope with an extremely ingenious internal suspension.

The Lebaudy and Clément workshops also made military dirigibles. Austria and Russia

Ascent of Berson and Suring in the *Preussen* (1901).

The *Patrie* over the Paris Opera House (1907).

bought Lebaudys; England and Russia bought Clement-Bayards. Louis Godard built Wellman's *America* and two dirigibles for Belgium.

For a long time, the United States lagged behind; the little "dirigibles" presented at trade fairs between 1905 and 1910 were poorly designed, dangerous machines. Only the old aeronaut Baldwin produced a competent military training dirigible in 1908. In 1912, Vaniman, Wellman's engineer, made a new transatlantic attempt with a dirigible which had an envelope reinforced with a metal frame. At the first test this balloon ruptured, caught fire and crashed into the sea with its crew. The dirigible *Suchard-Brucker* was also built in Germany with a view to crossing the Atlantic, but no attempt was actually made.

THE SPORT OF FREE BALLOONING

Free ballooning also attracted many exponents during the period 1900 to 1914; the French Aéro-Club in particular was responsible for developing the sport by instituting a pilot's licence, making sporting rules and organising competitions and races, from the longest distance in a straight line, to landing the closest to a given point. The Aéro-Club Park, in a charming setting at Saint Cloud, helped bring thousands of enthusiasts round to the idea of ballooning; in 1913, 479 ascents took place in this park alone. The Grand Prix of the French Aéro-Club from 1905, and the Gordon-Bennett cup from 1906 were the two great annual events: they produced some remarkable performances, like the great endurance records of the Swiss Colonel Schaeck (73 hr. 47 min. in 1908, of which more than 48 hours were above the North Sea), and the long distance records of Bienaimé and Leblanc in 1912 (1360 and 1243 miles from Stuttgart to Russia).

Professors Berson and Suring, specialists in high altitude expeditions, reached the height of 35,400 ft. in Berlin on 31 July 1901, a record that was only beaten by Professor Piccard thirty years later. On 28 May 1913 in France, Maurice Bienaimé, Jacques Schneider and Senouque went up to 33,150 ft.

The Comte de La Vaulx's long distance record was beaten in January 1912 by Dubonnet, with 1231 miles, then by Leblanc and Bienaimé and finally by Rumpelmayer, accompanied by Mme Goldschmidt, who covered 1500 miles from France to Russia between 19 and 21 March 1913. Germany, however, won and kept this record and also the endurance one. From 13 to 17 December 1913, Kaulen, Schmitz and Kwefft stayed in the air for 87 hours, covering 1756 miles as the crow flies, and about 2250 in actual distance, from Bitterfeld in Saxony to Perm in the Urals. Then Berliner and two passengers left Bitterfeld on 8 February 1914 and came down between Perm and Ekaterinburg, having covered 1895 miles in 47 hours. Remarkable balloon journeys were also made in America by Hawley and Post, Harmon and Honeywell, and by Spelterini and de Beauclair above the Alps.

Ballooning clubs were formed throughout Europe, through which many people were introduced to air navigation; many of the early aviators acquired precious information during free ascents. On the technical side the use of the rip-panel to prevent being dragged on landing became standard practice. Finally, for the pure love of the sport, for the wonderful sensation that only the free balloon – silent, floating along at random – can give, innumerable people spent hours they will never forget, in the air, in the wicker basket.

Bienaimé (left) and Schneider (right) photographed by Senouque at 33,000 ft. during the ascent of 28 May 1913.

A stop-over near Milan by Schelcher on 9 September 1906.

Léon Levavasseur (1863–1922)

Sideview of the beautiful lines of the Antoinette monoplane (Mourmelon, 1910).

Dual controls on the 1910 Antoinette.

Latham's Antoinette-29, 2nd for distance at Rheims in 1909: lateral stability controlled by wing-flexing.

Latham's Antoinette-13, 5th for distance at Rheims in 1909: lateral stability controlled by ailerons.

LEVAVASSEUR, LATHAM, AND THE CHANNEL ATTEMPT

Léon Levavasseur invented the Antoinette engine and thereby had a decisive influence on early aviation; all important performances between 1906 and 1908, except for the Wrights', were obtained with Antoinette engines, the first in the world to have been manufactured commercially for aviation.

An engineer who had also attended the Beaux Arts, Levavasseur retained much of the artist in him; no other aeroplane could match the beauty of the lines of the 1909 Antoinette.

Around 1902 he began to concentrate on the problem of a light power unit for boats and aeroplanes and designed a V-8 engine containing a mass of new elements and mechanical devices: the engine functioned at a high temperature, with the water evaporating and steam condensing in a long radiator. It was high revving and it had direct fuel injection. From this first 24 h.p. engine 50, 60 and 100 h.p. models followed, the last having 16 cylinders with brass liners.

After the failure of his 1903 aeroplane, Levavasseur only starting building aeroplanes again in 1908 with the *Gastambide-Mengin* and then the Antoinette series, named after the daughter of Jules Gastambide, Levavasseur's partner.

In his aeroplanes, as in his engines, Levavasseur was original and inventive: the wing of the Antoinette was the first to have a progressively reducing thickness, the first too to have a profile with clearly defined dorsal and ventral curvatures. The structure was equally interesting; the longerons consisted of triangulated lattice girders which Levavasseur used again in his monoplane for the 1911 military competition. This latter machine had lines that would not have appeared out of place twenty-five years later. It was the first monoplane with fully cantilevered wings, with a streamlined undercarriage, with the engine completely enclosed by the fuselage and with an adjustable tailplane. But it had been hastily built, the engine was not powerful enough and several technical faults rendered the machine unusable. The Antoinette company, in a bad financial position, closed.

After building yet another interesting monoplane with a variable wing surface in 1921, Léon Levavasseur died, in poverty, on 24 February 1922.

Hubert Latham, a Frenchman of British extraction, started flying in 1908 and valiantly risked his life many times, although lacking the skill of most of his fellow pilots. A great fan of the Antoinette monoplane, he broke many altitude and speed records with it. After the Antoinette company closed down, he went to America; in 1912, during the course of a hunt near Fort Lamy, Latham, who had escaped injury in so many aeroplane crashes, was killed by a wounded buffalo.

Latham's popularity reached its peak during his attempt to fly from France to England. In the summer of 1909 three aviators were gathered on the cliffs of the Pas-de-Calais, determined to make the attempt: Latham at Sangatte, Blériot at Baraques, and the Comte de Lambert at Wissant.

On 19 July, under perfect weather conditions, Latham took off from Blanc-Nez at 0645. Rising to some 1000 ft., an altitude then unheard of for aeroplanes, he headed for England, flying easily over the calm water. He had passed over the torpedo boat *Harpon*, which was escorting him, when his engine gave out. Within a minute his aeroplane had settled gently in the water in the middle of the Channel, 10 miles from the coast. Calmly, with what became a celebrated gesture, Latham lit a cigarette, and awaited the *Harpon*.

Six days later, he had the disappointment of seeing Blériot succeed. On 29 July he took off again; just short of the English coast another breakdown brought him down unharmed in the sea again.

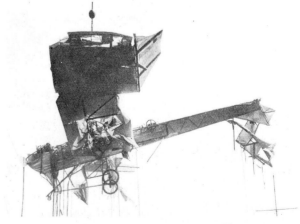

The *Antoinette-IV* in the sea awaiting rescue (19 July 1909).

Hubert Latham aboard the *Harpon*.

The *Antoinette-IV* being hoisted aboard the tugboat *Calaisien*.

The "channel crossing type" monoplane *Blériot-XI*.

Blériot setting off over the Channel.

On board the *Escopette*: Blériot flying over the sea.

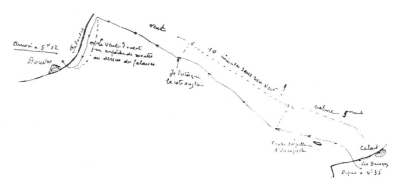

Sketch of the crossing from France to England drawn by Louis Blériot.

BLERIOT CROSSES THE CHANNEL

On 25 July 1909 Louis Blériot showed what could be expected in the new-born field of aviation by flying from Calais to Dover.

This great exploit, the value of which became established with time, was accomplished very simply and with none of the frightening experiences he had known on most of his previous flights. But the aeroplane he used, a type XI which he had built himself, was of very irregular construction, very flimsy in some places, very robust in others; it was equipped with an 25 h.p. engine, whose reliability was still doubtful. A sort of sausage of material blown up with air was carried for flotation in case of accident.

He set out from Baraques, to the south-west of Calais, at 0435 in the morning after a short trial flight. The great question was whether the engine was powerful enough: it was. The average altitude was 250–300 ft, with a maximum of 500 ft., which represented the "ceiling" for this machine. Blériot soon flew over the destroyer *Escopette*, in charge of supervising the crossing, and disappeared into the mist.

Louis Blériot in 1909.

"For about ten minutes I was on my own, isolated, lost in the middle of the foaming sea, seeing no point on the horizon, perceiving no boat. Also my eyes were fixed on the oil distributor and on the level of fuel consumption.

These ten minutes seemed long and, truly, I was happy to glimpse . . . a grey line which broke away from the sea . . . It was the English coast . . . I headed for this white mountain, but was caught in the wind and the mist . . . My machine responded obediently to my thoughts . . . I could no longer see Dover . . . I could see three boats . . . They seemed to be heading towards a port. I followed them calmly . . . I followed the cliff from north to south but the wind, against which I was fighting, got even stronger. A break in the coast appeared to my right, just before Dover Castle. I was madly happy. I headed for it, I rushed for it. I was above ground!"

The landing at 0512 was a rough one on a small sloping meadow at North Fall. The propeller and both wheels were broken. The full distance travelled was about 24 miles.

There were great receptions but they seem modest when you consider the greatness of the exploit, which marked a new era in the history of aviation, an era of practical results.

After the landing: Louis Blériot with the *Daily Mail* and Charles Fontaine.

The *Bleriot XI* (with wings folded) crossing the Place de l'Opera in Paris.

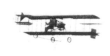

At the Juvisy aviation fortnight: a Witzig-Liore-Dutilleul and a Voisin (1909).

Curtiss passing Ferber (under the pseudonym of de Rue) at Rheims (1909).

Chavez in a Farman at Nice (1910).

Comte Charles de Lambert in his Wright.

President Fallières at Rheims (1909).

Roger Sommer in a Farman at Rheims (1909).

AVIATION MEETINGS

Aviation meetings, where a paying public was given the opportunity to see several aeroplanes flying at once, started in 1909. The first important meeting took place at the Port-Aviation airfield, between Juvisy and Savigny, on 23 May 1909. Several meetings followed at Vichy, Douai and Biarritz alongside numerous displays of individual aeroplanes, already common in 1908.

The great Rheims (Bétheny) aviation week, coming just after Blériot's performance, was a veritable triumph: the good organisation, the number and length of the flights, the records which were beaten by Henry Farman, Paulhan, Latham and Lefebvre, the Gordon-Bennett Cup which was won by Curtiss, the absence of accidents, all contributed to its success. The public was deeply affected by it and the authorities were keen to sanction the importance given to this developing sport by their presence.

In October 1909 a great fortnight at Juvisy revealed aviation to crowds of Parisians; it was marked by the first flight over Paris, by the Comte de Lambert in his Wright biplane. For the first few days the public came in such numbers that there were not enough trains to take them back to Paris, which gave rise to serious incidents.

In 1910 there was another week at Rheims after meetings at Cannes, Nice, Lyon, Tours and Rouen. Other countries imitated France and large reunions were held at Blackpool and Doncaster, Spa, Brescia, Berlin, Cologne and Frankfurt from 1909; at Heliopolis, Los Angeles, Brussels and Saint Petersburg from 1910. Gabriele d'Annunzio went up in the air for the first time, piloted by Curtiss, at the Brescia meeting.

In 1912, the demand for these large meetings slackened; instead there were, on the one hand, displays by two or three machines in small towns, with joy-rides for the public and, on the other, reunions of a sporting nature generally including a long race, such as the Anjou circuit won by Garros in 1912.

The Blériot being pushed by the cavalry at the Rheims meeting in 1909.

Guffroy's R.E.P. being drawn by a horse at Rheims. 1910.

The Lyons meeting: in flight, Paulhan in a Farman, Métrot in a Voisin and Legagneux in a Sommer (8 May 1910).

The *Zeppelin-II* caught in the pear tree at Jebenhausen.

The preparation of the temporary prow.

THE AIRSHIP AND THE PEAR TREE

The admirable German pioneer, Count Zeppelin, an opinionated but pertinacious inventor, had built four large dirigibles. The last one, just when it was about to become successful, was burned in a storm during a forced stop at Echterdingen on 5 August 1908. A fund headed by the Kaiser was set up to replace it, to which the public subscribed enthusiastically.

The result was a new dirigible, christened the *Zeppelin-II* (although in fact the fifth), which came out in May 1909. It was 446 ft. long and had a capacity of 536,400 cu. ft.

On its third ascent it beat all endurance records with an exceptional performance. Leaving Friedrichshafen on 29 May at 2150 in the direction of Berlin, it was obliged to turn at Bitterfeld (Sax-

ony) at 1900 the next day. It ran out of petrol and was forced to land at Jebenhausen near Gopping-en on 31 May at 1120, having covered 602 miles in 37½ hrs., an extraordinary feat for the two Daimler 110 h.p. engines. Unfortunately on landing the front of the dirigible impaled itself on a large pear tree and was completely demolished. Then one of the most extraordinary things in the history of aeronautics happened: the crew amputated all the front end of the dirigible, that is, three units out of seventeen. The airship was lightened by removing the forward engine and a number of accessories, while at the same time a temporary prow was prepared; on 1 June at 1520 the Zeppelin took off again and, after another stop, came down on the landing stage at Friedrichshafen. It had been out of its hangar for 80 hrs 10 min., of which 47 hrs. 30 min. had been spent in the air.

The *Zeppelin-II* ready to set off again after being repaired.

The *Zeppelin-II* sets off, abandoning its old prow on the ground.

Profile of the *Zeppelin-II* in its entirety . . . and after the repair, where the full extent of the amputation can be seen.

Henri Fabre and the engine of the world's first seaplane

The *Canard* seen from behind with the floats emerging from the water.

THE FIRST SEAPLANE

The world's first successful seaplane was French. On the Etang de Berre near Marseilles on 28 March 1910 a power-driven aeroplane successfully for the first time left the water and came back to land on it, piloted by its inventor, Henri Fabre.

An engineer and navigator, Henri Fabre had experimented earlier with a three-engined seaplane, which was not successful, before constructing in 1910 his highly original *Canard*.

The wings, which could be furled up like sails, were each supported by a single exterior spar of

Paulhan on his arrival in Manchester. Right, Henry Farman, who built the aircraft (28 April 1910).

cellular construction. Two beams, one above the other, united the wings and the control surfaces at the front end. The pilot was seated on the middle of the upper beam. The 50 h.p. Gnome engine was right at the back. The whole machine rested on three floats invented by Fabre. With a surface of 258 sq. ft. and a span of 49 ft the machine weighed 1045 lb. in the air.

On 28 March 1910, Fabre made four flights – the first time he himself had flown. The first flights, which were formally certified, took place in front of the port at La Mède, then that of Châteauneuf-les-Martigues.

After a run of 300 yards over the water, the Canard took off, was perfectly stable for about 550 yards and came down without any difficulty. On the second flight, it covered nearly 900 yards and rose to more than 15 ft. Two other equally successful flights followed. The following day the seaplane flew from La Mède to the Ferrières bridge at Martigues, covering 3½ miles and proving itself remarkably stable.

On 18 May, during a new flight of equal distance, the aircraft rose to 65 ft. but it landed too quickly and broke up, throwing its inventor into the water. It was reconstructed and may be seen in the Musée de L'Aéronautique.

COMPETITIONS IN 1910

1910 saw a number of great performances: Dubonnet crossed Paris from one side to the other on 24 April and Louis Paulhan won the Daily Mail Prize by completing the 185 miles between

London and Manchester in a flying time of 4 hr. 12 min. on 27 and 28 April, beating the English contender Graham White into second place.

The Paris-Brussels-Paris competition, for a journey to be accomplished in less than 36 hours, with no fixed date, was won by a Dutchman, Wijnmalen, nine other attempts having failed.

The Michelin Cup, for the pilot making the longest journey without a stop, aroused great competiton, particularly between Tabuteau, in a Maurice-Farman, and Legagneux, in a Blériot. Tabuteau won on 30 December, with just under 362 miles. The endurance record was taken to 8hrs. 12 min. by Henry Farman.

Henry Farman refueling his biplane before the Michelin Cup (Etampes, 18 December 1910).

One of the first biplanes of the Caudron brothers (1910).

Emile Dubonnet landing his Tellier monoplane at Bagatelle after crossing Paris.

The workshops of the Voisin brothers at Billancourt in 1908, showing parts of Voisin biplanes, Goupy triplanes, and the fuselage of Henry Farman's *Flying Fish*.

THE AVIATION INDUSTRY

The first factory for the commercial production of aircraft was that of the Voisin brothers which operated from 1906.

In 1908 other factories were opened by the Antoinette company at Puteaux and by Henry Farman at Mourmelon; then, in 1909, by Louis Breguet at Douai and Louis Blériot in Paris. Most of these were still producing in the 1930s. Outside France the first aviation industrialist to appear was Glenn Curtiss in the United States – apart from the Wright brothers of course.

A static test on an R.E.P. monoplane in 1911.

Construction standards varied at first, but the work was carried out scientifically from the start by a certain number of aeroplane manufacturers; Robert Esnault-Pelterie was the first to apply static tests, loading the wings with measured quantities of sand.

The growth of aeroplane production can be gauged from the French statistics: in 1911, 1,350 aeroplanes were built; in 1912, 1,425 and in 1913, 1,428 aeroplanes and 146 seaplanes while 1,400, 2,217 and 2,240 engines and 8,000, 8,000 and 14,900 propellers were produced. The last statistic gives some idea of the treatment that these items were subject to.

The assembly shop of the Louis Breguet workshop at Douai in 1912: on the right, a Breguet with a Renault 80 h.p. engine.

A Zens biplane, with a 50 h.p. Antoinette engine, 1908.

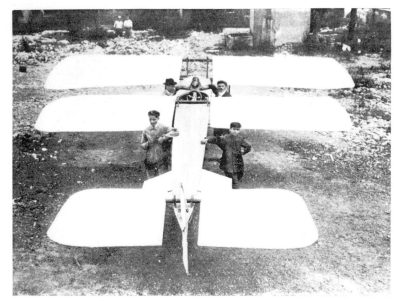

Pischof and Koechlin's tandem monoplane (1908).

An Odier-Vendôme biplane in flight at Issy-les-Moulineaux (1910).

The Saulnier high-wing monoplane, piloted by Darioli at Issy (1909).

The Liore monoplane with two propellers (1911).

The monoplane *Albatross* built by Zodiac (1910).

Paul Kaufmann's thick-winged monoplane (1911).

Undercarriage, without axle, and Anzani engine of the Vendôme monoplane (1909).

1910 Breguet biplane, front view.

1910 Breguet biplane, rear view.

1912 Breguet with large wing-span.

Breguet's propeller with articulated blades (1911).

Léon Bathiat flying at Rheims (1910).

The first Breguet aeroplane at Douai (3 July 1909).

Louis Breguet in his second biplane at Douai (end of 1909).

A squadron of Breguet military three-seaters with Canton-Unné engines in 1913.

A Breguet military biplane, with a Gnome engine fitted with reduction gear, folded to facilitate transport (1910–1911).

Chavez' first attempt at crossing the Alps (18 September 1910).

THE FIRST CROSSING OF THE ALPS

Geo Chavez was both hero and martyr of the first crossing of the Alps in an aeroplane. A likeable man and a fine pilot, he was of Peruvian nationality, although he was born and lived in Paris.

Five pilots had gathered at Brig in the autumn of 1910 for a competition to fly from Switzerland to Milan by the Simplon Pass. Several unsuccessful attempts had been made by Chavez,

Geo Chavez (1887–†F1910)

Weymann and Taddeoli when, on 23 September at 1329, Chavez left in his Blériot. Twenty minutes later, he had passed the Simplon hospice at 6,600 ft., flown over the abrupt Gorges du Gondo; and was coming in to land on the Domodossola airfield. At that moment, only 30 ft. from the ground, a structural failure occurred in his aircraft and the machine fell almost vertically. Chavez was seriously injured and taken to hospital, where he died on 27 September.

The Alps were not crossed again until the Peruvian Bielovucic succeeded in doing so in 1913.

Geo Chavez being lifted from the wreckage of his aeroplane at Domodossola.

ACCIDENTS: FATAL AND OTHERWISE

Flight was not achieved without the loss of a large number of human lives. The gloomy prognostication of Réne Quinton was almost fulfilled: "Flying will really have arrived when one pilot is killed every day."

There were a number of fairly common causes of accidents in the early days: breaking of wings in flight, particularly of the Antoinette, which killed Wachter, Laffont Pola and Blanc; the use of too powerful an engine, as in the case of Delagrange; inadequate repair of controls, which caused the fatal dive of Fernandez. Others were lost at sea, like Cecil Grace who disappeared into the North Sea fog. Also common were accidents arising from maladjustments of the controls or deformation of them or the wings in flight, such as led to the deaths of Montalent and his mechanic, thrown bodily out of their machine when it went into an unexpected dive.

The majority of accidents, however, may be put down either to ignorance or to overstretching the capabilities of an aircraft or of its components. Fire played a surprisingly small part; it was nevertheless the cause of death of Lieutenants Grailly and Princeteau, and of Landron, in 1911. Even so it was not fire in the air that killed; these were all accidents during taxiing that resulted in the rupture of fuel tanks.

The first casualty from overturning while taxiing was Captain Ferber, at Boulogne on 24 September 1909. Fatal collisions were also rare; one such, however, killed Deroye and his passenger at Buc in 1914. A certain number of people were killed by aircraft falling into crowds, perhaps the best known being M. Berteaux, the French Minister for War, at Issy in 1911, during the start of the Paris-Madrid Air Race.

But the early days of aviation were really marked by an incalculable number of "little mishaps" on the one hand, and by very few serious accidents on the other. Despite the fragility of the aircraft and especially the unreliability of their engines, two classic causes of forced landings, the risk was not so great as one might think, due to the very low landing speeds. Over-powered but with very low wing-loadings, generally having ample control surfaces and sufficient stability, these old aeroplanes came down with ease in the most unfavourable places and for the most part the crew stepped out unscathed or simply bruised. They rarely caught fire and it was easy to escape. Even when an aeroplane did overturn or hit something solid, its own lack of solidity and the fact that all the various bits broke off one by one, meant that the impact of the shock was greatly diminished.

Death of Blanc at Mourmelon (17 October 1912).

Death of Montalent and his mechanic at Rouen (25 April 1913). The two bodies can be seen leaving the aircraft.

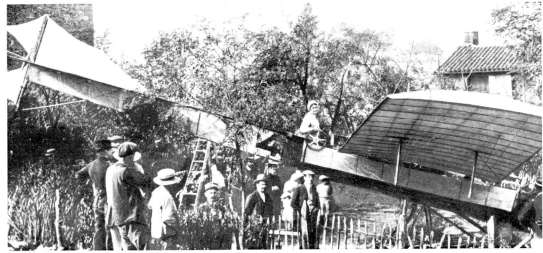

Mlle Marvingt's forced but safe landing on the Bowling Ground of the Café de la Terrasse at Saint-Etienne (1911).

Robinson overturning harmlessly at Antibes (1912).

Brindejonc flies into a crane (1911).

Frey's accident at the Cannes meeting (1910).

Robert Esnault-Pelterie in 1907.

Henri Brégi (1888–†*F*1917)

Louis Breguet in 1909.

Charles S. Rolls (1877–†*F*1910)

Maurice Farman in 1893.

THE PRE-WAR PILOTS

Among those who were at one and the same time inventors, manufacturers and pilots in those early years can be found Robert Esnault-Pelterie, engineer and scholar, who later devoted himself to research into inter-stellar navigation; Louis Breguet, who became one of the world's major manufacturers and whose 14 and 19 models were market leaders for years; Alfred de Pischof, a modest man but a brave and ambitious innovator, who was killed flying; Roger Sommer, a pupil and later a rival of Henry Farman, an amateur who became a manufacturer; Maurice Farman, who came to heavier-than-air flying much later than his brother Henry, although he had been

Hubert Latham (1883–1912)

interested in aeronautics earlier than him, having started ballooning as early as 1893.

Among the early record-holders can be seen the faces of Charles Rolls, a pupil of Wright's, one of the first aviation ehthusiasts in England and the first to have made the double crossing of the English Channel; Henri Brégi, who introduced aviation to South America and to Morocco, and who was killed in the Great War; Hubert Latham; Jan Olislaegers, the reliable Belgian champion, holder of many records and a fervent propagandist abroad; the Morane brothers, Léon who held the altitude record before becoming a manufacturer, and his brother and successor Robert, also an able pilot.

The period of the development of aviation was marked by the figures of Réne Labouchère, who

Reinhold Boehm
in 1931.

Robert and Léon Morane (1885–1918)
in 1910.

Werner Landmann
(1892–1928)

Jan Olieslaegers
in 1910.

René Labouchère
in 1909.

Emmanuel Hélen
in 1911.

Roger Sommer
in 1909.

Alfred de Pischof
(1882–†*F*1922)

Georges Legagneux
(1882–1914)

Alfred Leblanc
(1869–1921)

Marcel Hanriot
in 1911.

Jean Bielovucic
in 1911.

Charles T Weymann
in 1911.

started flying at the age of twenty-three, first with Antoinette and later with Potez where he became the chief test pilot; Emmanuel Hélen, the endurance champion who flew for Nieuport; Legagneux, holder of many altitude records; Alfred Leblanc, winner of the Eastern Circuit; C.T. Weymann, winner of the Gordon-Bennett Cup in 1911; Bielovucic, who was the first to fly from Paris to Bordeaux.

The great champions of 1912 and 1913 were Jules Védrines, Edmond Audemars, a very skilful pilot and the first to fly from Paris to Berlin (in 1912); Eugène Gilbert, a great and reliable pilot; Hamel, the best English pilot, who often confronted Garros during his brief career, terminated when he died at sea, and who piloted Miss

Jules Vedrines (1881–1919)

Quimby during the first channel crossing by a woman; Géo Fourny, the first man to fly over 1000 kilometres; Boehm, the first to fly for longer than twenty-four hours; Prévost, the first to cover 200 kilometres in less than an hour; Landmann, the great German pilot.

Women played their role in the early days too: the first women to hold a pilot's licence was the Baronne Raymonde de Laroche, who first piloted an aeroplane single-handed on 22 October 1909 and got her licence (no. 36) on 8 March 1910; Mlle Marvingt held many records and was an enthusiastic propagandist; Mlles. Dutrieu and Herveux, energetic and intrepid pilots; Madame Pallier, a thoughtful aviatrice who was the first to carry a passenger.

Baronne de Laroche
(1886–†F1919)

Mlle. Marie Marvingt
in 1910.

Mlle. Hélenè Dutrieu
in 1911.

Mlle Jeanne Herveux
in 1911.

Madame Pallier
in 1913.

Edmond Audemars
in 1911.

Gustave Hamel (1889–†F1914)
and Miss Davies.

Eugène Gilbert
(1889–1918)

Géo Fourny
in 1911.

Maurice Prévost
in 1913.

The 1910 Nieuport monoplane

Edouard Nieuport (1875–1911)

The Nieuport 28 h.p. engine.

THE LIFE AND DEATH OF EDOUARD NIEUPORT

Edouard Nieuport's career is a fine example of the work done by the great pioneers of aviation who were at the same time inventors, manufacturers and pilots. His short but eventful career had a decisive influence on the future of aviation and many of his original ideas contributed to the development of fast aeroplanes.

Edouard de Nieport (but called Nieuport), an officer's son, was born in Blida in 1875. He abandoned his formal studies in order to devote himself to mechanical sports and to pursue on his own a course of technical instruction which better satisfied his creative bent. He took to aviation in 1908, giving it all his time and, in 1911, his life. His first monoplane, tested at Issy, flew at the first attempt. Drawing on these experiences, at the beginning of 1910 Nieuport made the monoplane which became a classic and which perpetuated his name. His aviation work is characterised by his research into the reduction of drag and the consequent improvement of performance. In one of his first inventions Blériot also realised this was necessary. Breguet equally tried in his earliest

with Nieuport 28 h.p. engine.

biplanes to reduce the number of masts and to streamline the struts, but it was Nieuport who first made an aeroplane where the shrouds were limited to two on each wing, where the fuselage was covered and completely sheltered the pilot, and where the undercarriage was reduced to the smallest dimensions possible. At Rheims, using an 18 h.p. Darracq engine, Nieuport held his own with machines of 50 h.p. and more. He later equipped his monoplane with a 28 h.p. engine which he had designed with Nieuport magneto and Nieuport sparking plugs; he even designed the propeller himself; he is a rare example of an aviator who flew on a machine entirely of his design. With his "28 CV", he broke the 10 and 15 kilometre speed records and on 11 May 1910 at Mourmelon took all the records from 1 to 100 kilometres by achieving a speed of 75 mph. Nieuport then made, using the same design, machines of 50 and 100 h.p., and then military three-seaters. The French navy was equipped for a long time with Nieuport monoplanes with floats.

On 16 September 1911, during the course of a military display at Charny, Nieuport was killed, stalling a wing during a turn. In 1913 his brother Charles suffered the same fate.

The death of Edouard Nieuport at Charny (16 September 1911): the crash; taking away the fatally injured pilot.

The Antoinette-Levavasseur monoplane presented at the 1911 military competition. Although this machine never flew more than a few yards it was the forerunner of all later aeroplanes, with thick wings, no shrouds and streamlined undercarriage.

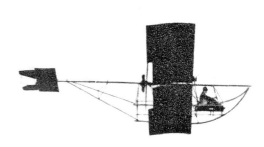

Ponche and Primard's entirely metal *Tubavion* monoplane in flight in 1912.

The Tatin-Paulhan *Torpille (Torpedo)* with pusher propeller at the rear of the fuselage (1911).

The Paumier touring biplane of 1912.

The Hanriot trainer monoplane of 1911.

The tailless Arnoux monoplane tested at Issy in 1913–1914.

The tailless Dunne monoplane which flew from London to Paris in 1914.

The first four-engined aeroplane: Sikorsky's *Il'ya Muromets*, which flew in Russia in 1913 with 16 passengers on board in a closed cabin.
This forerunner of all multi-engined aircraft was equipped with four 90 h.p. Mercedes engines.

Above: The French Moroccan Campaign of 1907–1908. The captive balloon *Dar-el-Beida* fording a river near Casablanca.

General Joffre and the Sapper Brinde-jonc des Moulinais (1914).

The pilot's seat on the first French army aeroplanes: Lt de Caumont (1882–1910) in a Sommer (1910).

Bomb launching device presented at Châlons in 1912 by Lt Bousquet

Latham, as a sapper pilot, on manoeuvres in Picardy (1910).

THE BEGINNINGS OF MILITARY AVIATION

Captive balloons were used with success in 1904 and 1905 by the Japanese in Manchuria and in Morocco by the French army from 1907 on. They were much used by the Italians in the Tripoli Campaign of 1911–1912, and by the Bulgarians in the Balkans. The Italians also used the dirigibles *P-1* and *P-3* in Libya.

Military flying with heavier-than-air machines started in France in 1909; there was considerable rivalry between the Artillery and the Engineers which for a time each had their own air force.

The first military aviation mission took place on 9 June 1910 with a flight from Châlons to Vincennes by Lieutenant Féquant and Captain Marconnet. Important military manoeuvres in Picardy in September 1910 demonstrated the resources of military aviation: fourteen aeroplanes took part and four dirigibles. Civil pilots from the reserve flew with the regulars.

In April 1910, General Roques, Commander of the Engineers, succeeded in grouping together all aeronautics in a single section, apart from a research laboratory at Vincennes. The military pilot's licence, the test for which included a 60-mile cross-country journey, was instituted at the end of that year. There were at that time thirty-nine pilots and twenty-nine military aeroplanes in the French army. A major competition for new designs for military aeroplanes was held in 1911, and a campaign was launched to find new sites for airfields, while a private fund was set up to endow France with machines and aerodromes.

Until the war aviation figured in all the French annual manoeuvres. At the end of 1910 the French navy designated its first pilots, bought an aeroplane and, a year later, a seaplane. In October 1911 it created a centre at Saint Raphael. On 24 February 1913 it instituted its central service of

On the great Western manoeuvres (September 1912): the French 5th Squadron equipped with Maurice-Farman biplanes.

Anti-aircraft machine gun on a French car (1910).

Machine gun on a Nieuport two-seater (1911).

German mobile anti-aircraft cannon on a tractor (1911).

At the South-Western manoeuvres (1913): assembling a Henry Farman at Agen.

A Nieuport military aircraft and its trailer-tent (1911).

naval flying.

France's example was soon followed by other countries. The United States were the first to have a military aeroplane, bought from the Wright brothers in 1908.

In Great Britain, tests began in 1909 and aviation was organised in 1911 to become the Royal Flying Corps the following year, divided into a military and a naval section. Military aviation started in Italy and in Germany in 1909 and was reorganised in 1912, at the same time as in Austria and Russia.

The first time an aeroplane was actually used in war was the reconnaissance flight made from Tripoli to Azizia on 22 October 1911 by Captain Piazza in a Blériot on a mission lasting about one hour. Captain Piazza later made a night sortie in 1912. The first aviator wounded in flight by a missile was Lieutenant Cannonière on 13 March 1912.

During the Italo-Turkish war aeroplanes were constantly used by the Italians in Tripoli and Cirenaica, and when the war in the Balkans started Turkey, Bulgaria, Serbia and Rumania all improvised air forces using the most diverse elements, each country raising between nine to fifteen machines. In Mexico the aviator Salinas flew during the 1912 revolution. Aeroplanes were also used for observation and the launching of missiles during the French conquest of Morocco.

Italian-Turkish war (1913): landing of a German monoplane by the Italians near Tripoli.

Lieutenant Do Hu on a Blériot reconnaissance plane in Morocco (1911)

Balkans War (1912): the Bulgarian Lt. Taraxchieflis leaving on a reconnaissance flight.

Italian-Turkish war: a group of Italian aviation officers and a Blériot at Tripoli.

Eugène Renaux's Maurice-Farman at the summit of the Puy de Dôme on 7 March 1911.

Védrines arriving at San Sebastian during the Paris-Madrid race on 23 May 1911.

Rénaux and Senouque.

Védrines welcomed in Madrid on 26 May.

Beaumont, carried in triumph at Brooklands.

Lt Bague leaving Nice on 5 March 1911.

FLYING IN 1911

The Michelin brothers, convinced early on of the potential of aviation, organised several competitions during 1911: a bomb-aiming contest at Châlons to develop the idea of aerial bombardment, the Michelin Cup for long distance, and the Grand Prix Paris-Puy de Dôme to encourage air touring.

The prize money for this last was 100,000 francs and the competition consisted in flying from Paris via Saint Cloud to the Puy de Dôme in less than six hours, and landing on a small plateau near the summit. The pilot had to be accompanied by a passenger. Stopovers were permitted. The landing point was at an altitude of 4,600 ft. and the distance to be covered was 227 miles. The winner, on 7 March, was Eugène Renaux, accompanied by Albert Senouque.

1911 was also the year of long international races, almost all of which were won by French pilots. Organised by the newspapers, these races attracted a great number of competitors and some impressive performances resulted.

On 21 May a huge crowd was gathered at Issy to watch the departure of the Paris-Madrid Air Race when the French War Minister, Berteaux, was killed by an aircraft. The rest of the competi-tion was put off until the following day. Only a Morane-Borel finished the course (on 26 May) going by Angoulême and San Sebastian. It was piloted by an ex-mechanic, Jules Védrines.

On 28 May, eleven competitors left Le Buc for Rome, 910 miles away. Beaumont (pseudonym of Lt Conneau) arrived at Rome first on 31 May, followed the next day by Garros, both in Blériots, and de Frey and Vidart on 2 and 5 June.

Shortly after, on 18 June, forty aviators left Vincennes for the European Circuit: Paris-Liège-Spa-Utrecht-Brussels-Calais-London-Paris. Three fatal accidents cast a tragic shadow over the race but nine competitors finished the 1000 mile trip. Beaumont and Garros came first once again in their Blériots, then Vidart and Védrines.

Beaumont was to also win the England and Scotland tour, from 22 to 26 July, over 1000 miles. He was closely followed by Védrines in a Morane.

In Germany Konig won the national circuit, covering 935 miles with a passenger.

One of the most moving journeys of 1911 was the sea crossing of Lieutenant Bague. A young and daring pilot, Bague left Nice for Corsica on 5 March but was thrown off course by the wind and the fog and had to crash-land his Blériot on the little Italian island of Gorgona, after 126 miles over the water. During a new attempt, on 5 June, Bague disappeared into the Mediterranean.

A curious record was also set up: that of the number of passengers. On 23 March, at Douai, Louis Bréguet flew eleven passengers for 3 miles with a 100 h.p. engine, and the following day Sommer, with 70 h.p., flew twelve passengers for half a mile.

It was at this time too that air tourism started to develop: flying was easy then, on aeroplanes which had low landing speeds and could come down in very restricted places, and this encouraged many more pilots than one would think to practise this sport. Alongside professional pilots like the Farman brothers, who went on Sunday aeroplane outings for pleasure, a lot of flying was done between 1910 and 1914 by real amateurs, flying cross-country without accident and landing in fields, independently or in groups. Air rallies too attracted a number of aircraft from Toussus or Le Buc; the pilots and passengers meeting for friendly lunches in the country.

At the end of 1911, the records were: speed, 104.2 mph. by Védrines in a Deperdussin; non-stop flying, 459.7 miles by Gobé in a Nieuport; altitude 12,825 ft. by Garros in a Blériot; endurance, 11 hours and 29 seconds by Fourny in a Maurice-Farman. 345 new pilot licences were delivered in France during the year, the total having been 360 at the end of 1910.

Bréguet in a Bréguet biplane carrying eleven passengers

Léon Morane autographing postcards (1910).

Sommer in a Sommer biplane carrying twelve passengers

The *America* over the polar sea
(2 September 1907).

Wellman and Vaniman's *America* leaving its hangar on
Danes' Island at Spitzbergen (2 September 1907).

The *America*, intact, escaping after
the crew had been rescued.

THE *AMERICA* AND OTHER AIRSHIPS

In 1906, Walter Wellman conceived a plan to fly from Spitzbergen to the North Pole in a dirigible. Leaving its hangar on Danes Island, from which the Andrée expedition had set out ten years before, on 2 September 1907, the *America* almost immediately lost itself in the fog. An emergency landing was made on a glacier, where the aeronauts had to wait two days before they could be rescued. A second attempt in August 1909 had a similar result.

The *America* was then modified with a view to crossing the Atlantic, and on 15 October 1910, left Atlantic City with Wellman, Vaniman and four mechanics on board. By the afternoon of 16 October it was off the Southern tip of Nova Scotia having travelled nearly 600 miles in a North-easterly direction. At five in the morning of 18 October the *America*'s crew, who had managed to get their life-boat, still attached to the airship, down to the water, were rescued by the steamer *Trent* 500 miles south-east of Atlantic City, on a line between it and Bermuda, having been blown nearly 600 miles off-course by a storm. During the rescue the dirigible escaped and was lost for ever. The air journey had lasted about 69 hours.

The rescue of Wellman and his companions in the Atlantic (18 October 1910).
The lifeboat and the wake from the stabilising float can be clearly seen.

The German dirigible *Suchard-Brucker* with its lifeboat gondola. (1912).
The transatlantic attempt, for which it had been built, never took place.

The *Morning Post* (a Lebaudy) at the departure for the second Channel crossing in a dirigible (Moisson-Farnborough) on 26 October 1910.
The basket is equipped with a pneumatic float and sea-anchor; at the front of the basket, the pilot Louis Capazza.

On board the *Commandant-Coutelle* (Zodiac) over Paris, 14 July 1913.

The *Clement-Bayard II* landing at Wormwood Scrubs at the end of the first crossing of the Channel in a dirigible (La Motte-Breuil-London), 16 October 1910.

On board the *Captaine-Ferber* (Zodiac) over the clouds, 15 February 1912.

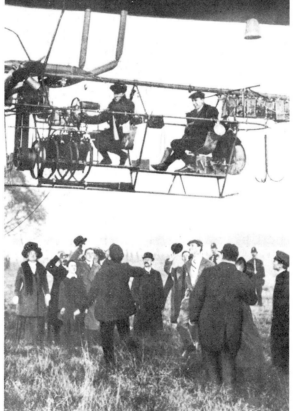

The *Adjutant-Reau* (Astra), which set a French endurance record with 21 hr. 21 min. on 19 September 1911.

The basket of Willow's *City of Cardiff* on its departure from London for France, 4 November 1910.

The *Spiess*, the only rigid French dirigible, built by the Zodiac company and tested in 1913.

The skeleton of the second rigid zeppelin (1906) outside its floating hangar.

The interior of the *Deutschland*'s keel.

The passenger cabin of the Zeppelin *Deutschland* (24 June 1910).

The Empress of Germany congratulating Count Zeppelin at the landing of the *Zeppelin III* at the Tegel aerodrome after the Lake Constance-Berlin flight, 2⁰ August 1909.

THE ZEPPELINS

The perseverance of Count Zeppelin was rewarded on 29 August 1909 when he landed at Berlin on board his sixth rigid dirigible. The Kaiser, the Empress and a whole crowd of breathless admirers were waiting for him at the end of a journey made by stages, which had begun two days previously on Lake Constance. Having acquired the support of the Emperor William II as well as that of the King of Wurtemberg, who along with the Crown Prince was a passenger on this flight, Count Zeppelin was from then on able to build and develop new types of more and more advanced large rigid dirigibles.

Although his solution met with incredulity in France, Zeppelin persevered with his research in a field which still offered one of the most promising visions of future mass air transport. Undismayed by setbacks he made more and more dirigibles, training crews and a remarkable workshop staff. Many reverses still awaited him and many zeppelins crashed or caught fire for various reasons, but the old inventor drew lessons from their demise, and it is a fact that until the two catastrophes of 1913 (a fire in the air and a loss at sea) there had been no deaths in the whole Zeppelin saga. Moreover thanks to the fund-raising programme in Germany Zeppelin had found a moral and material support that encompassed the whole nation.

In 1910, the *Deutschland* was the first tourist rigid dirigible with a passenger cabin. It was followed by the *Ersatz Deutschland*, the *Schwaben*, the *Viktoria Luise*, the *Hansa* and the *Sachsen*. The operating figures of these last three give an idea of the remarkable security acquired, as early as 1912, by zeppelins, contrary to what a prejudiced press was saying in France: between March 1912 and November 1913 the *Viktoria Luise* made 384 flights, carrying 8,134 people; the *Hansa* 297 flights with 6,217 people; the *Sachsen* 206 flights with 4,758 people – a total of 19,109 people transported without an accident.

Between July 1900 and July 1914, twenty-five civilian or military Zeppelins were built and tested.

The *L Z-8 Ersatz Deutschland*, a passenger dirigible (1911) which replaced the *Deutschland* (wrecked 28 June 1910).

Ferdinand von Zeppelin

The *Ersatz Deutschland* at Dusseldorf on 16 May 1911. The dirigible collided with the door screen of the hangar and folded up. The passengers were saved by a firemen's ladder.

161

The first Curtiss seaplane at San Diego (26 January 1911).

The first seaplane with a hull piloted by Curtiss and Post (1912).

AVIATION IN THE UNITED STATES

Powered flight was born in the United States but only developed slowly there.

Wilbur Wright was the first to fly above New York. Having equipped his aircraft with a canoe, he started his flight from Governor's Island and turned round the Statue of Liberty on 29 September 1909. Five days later, he flew the length of the city, going up the Hudson as far as Grant's tomb and returning to his starting point.

Curtiss was the pioneer of cross-country flying in America; on 28 May 1910 he left Albany, followed the Hudson, made a stop, touched down at New York and flew on as far as Governor's Island, having covered 136 miles in 2 hr. 32 min. flying time and in a total time of 5 hr. 58 min.

On 14 November 1910, Ely, in a Curtiss, left the cruiser *Birmingham* to land ashore. On 18 January 1911, Ely managed to land on the cruiser *Pennsylvania* which had been fitted out with a platform 130 ft. by 60 ft. He took off again to land near San Francisco.

On 26 January 1911, at San Diego, Curtiss

The 1910 Wright *Baby*: Hoxsey ending his 92-mile flight, Springfields – Saint Louis (10 October 1910).

made his first flights in a seaplane with floats and shortly after built the first flying boat with a hull.

On 30 January 1911, MacCurdy flew off from Key West Havana. He had travelled 90 miles over the sea when a breakdown forced him to land near an escort ship.

The crossing of the United States from the Atlantic to the Pacific was accomplished in those far-off days with such rudimentary means that this performance, too little known, is one of the most interesting ones historically.

Rodgers left New York on 17 September 1911 aboard a Wright *Baby* biplane with a 35 h.p. engine. On 3 November, forty-eight days later, he landed at Los Angeles, having flown for a total of 83 hours and covered about 3,000 miles, with sixty-eight stopovers, under extremely difficult circumstances over often deserted country in a miniscule machine which he had had to repair endless times, but as he had exceeded the stipulated time limit, the Hearst Prize was not awarded to him. Rodgers died in an accident in 1912.

Shortly before, from 15 to 25 August, Atwood had flown from Saint Louis to New York – 1450 miles in eleven days with a flying time of 28 hr. 9 min. He was also flying a basic Wright *Baby*.

Wilbur Wright flying over the Hudson in front of New York; the old skyline is dominated by the Singer Building.

Preparations for a night flight at Hendon in 1913: the aeroplane fitted with electric floodlights.

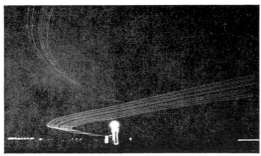

Night flying at Hendon: the camera lens was left open to record the luminous trails of the aircraft.

Quinton numeration system using reflecting silvered glass balls visible by day and night (1910).

NIGHTFLYING

The first night flight was made at Châlons by Henry Farman in one of his biplanes which was simply lit by primitive paper Chinese lanterns. Isolated attempts followed, until in 1911 displays of night flights with the aeroplane illuminated by electric floodlights were given by Grandseigne in a Caudron. He was the first to fly over Paris at night. Shortly after, Schemel, an amateur pilot, accomplished several nocturnal flights. The importance of night-time flying was soon understood and the low landing speeds at that time made it a much easier undertaking than later on. In 1913, a series of night flights accompanied by night bombing trials were made in England at Hendon.

In 1910 René Quinton, President of the National Air League, led a campaign for the identification of towns by numbers and followed this up by experiments with a day- and night-time system which consisted of numbers formed of silvered glass balls which shone in artificial light as in the sun. A very striking effort was made in Germany where a network of aeronautical beacons was installed in the early part of 1914: twenty-one aerodromes were fitted with acetylene or electric lights – revolving, fixed or flashing – for identification. The success of the great endurance flights accomplished in 1914, with nocturnal flights between towns, was largely due to this organisation of beacons and lights.

Three phases in Pégoud's parachute drop at Buc on 19 August 1913: the aviator abandoning his Blériot; the aeroplane rising vertically; parachutist and aeroplane reaching the ground at the same time.

A jump of 10 ft. by Reichelt in a "parachute-suit" (October 1910).

PARACHUTING

In 1910 Reichelt, an Austrian tailor, tried out a "parachute-suit", which was much too small, with a jump from a height of 10 ft. Encouraged by this all too small-scale experiment, Reichelt threw himself from the first floor of the Eiffel Tower on 6 February 1912 and flattened himself on the ground.

The first parachute drops from an aeroplane were accomplished on 1 and 10 March 1912 at Saint Louis (U.S.A.) by Berry, who jumped from a biplane piloted by Jannus. His belt was attached to the cords of a parachute placed in a bag under the lower wing of the aircraft.

The parachute drop of Jean Ors at Juvisy on 12 February 1914: note the hoops attached to the rigging of the parachute as it opens behind the Deperdussin.

On 19 August 1913 at Buc, Pégoud, a young, unknown aviator, left his Blériot monoplane in mid-flight. His parachute, which had been stored on top of the fuselage, opened easily and Pégoud landed on a tree while the aeroplane, left to its own devices, crashed beside him after some extraordinary somersaults. The parachute was made by Bonnet.

His example was followed by Jean Ors, an inventor, who jumped from Lemoine's monoplane on 12 February 1914 at Juvisy, then by Le Bourhis who made a descent in a Bonnet parachute. The first woman parachutist was Madame Cayat de Castella, who gave several displays of jumping from aeroplanes and was killed at Brussels in July 1914.

The Morane-Saulnier monoplane in which Garros crossed the Mediterranean (23 September 1913).

The arrival of Roland Garros at Bizerta.

THE GLORIOUS YEAR OF 1913

1912 had been a year of transition when aviation seemed to hesitate between the successes of 1911 and the triumphs of 1913.

Among the few events were journeys made from France to Touggourt, Ouargla and Senegal; the crossing of the Channel by a woman pilot, Miss Quimby, following shortly on the first woman passenger crossing, of Miss Davies with Hamel; the Paris-Berlin journey by Audemars and the victory of Garros on the Anjou circuit.

The name of Garros, one of the most famous in the history of aviation, is however chiefly remembered for the first air crossing of the Mediterranean which occured in 1913.

Partial crossings had preceded this admirable exploit: after Bague's attempts, Cagliani, the Italian aviator, flew from Livorno to Bastia in 1912, and on 18 December 1912, Garros himself had left Tunis and landed in Sicily at Marsala, having covered 142 miles over the sea, then, with stops, reached Naples and Rome on 22 December.

At last, on 23 September 1913, Garros accomplished – under the most daring conditions – the non-stop crossing from France to Africa. His machine was a modest Morane-Saulnier monoplane with a 60 h.p. Gnome engine. He had no floats.

Having left Saint Raphael at 0547 with 55 gallons of fuel he was off Calvi around 0700; he then followed the coast of Corsica from a dis-

tance, and reached Sardinia, flying over Cagliari at 1045, where he was tempted to stop. But he continued southwards heading over the sea again for more than 185 miles. As the African coast

Roland Garros (1888–†*F*1918)

came in sight the engine started misfiring for lack of fuel. By the time he landed at Bizerta there was only 1 gallon of fuel left!

The second great performance of 1913 was the

tour of the capitals of Europe by Brindejonc des Moulinais.

Fired by the idea of demonstrating the qualities of a French aeroplane to the rest of Europe, Brindejonc des Moulinais, decided on a programme of demonstration flights – flying in any kind of wind, landing on unknown and difficult ground, making long trips navigating as best he could and crossing large expanses of sea.

His first day was marked by an incredible journey: Paris-Warsaw; 845 miles, joining France to Russia (as it was then) in just a few hours.

The departure took place on 10 June, early in the morning, from the Villacoublay aerodrome. Brindejonc was piloting a Morane-Saulnier monoplane with an 80 h.p. Gnome engine and Chauvière propeller. Taking off at 0357 he landed at 0645 to refuel at Wanne, leaving there at 0855 to land at the Johannisthal aerodrome at Berlin at 1100. A violent storm provided a tail wind for the last leg and enabled him to land at Warsaw at 1715.

Hoping to fly in one day from Warsaw to Saint Petersburg, Brindejonc waited five days for the storm to stop, but the continuing north wind forced him to make stops at Vilna, Dvinsk, where he broke a wheel, and Psko where the airfield was in a dangerous condition. His departure was extremely perilous, but at 1110 on 18 June Brindejonc arrived at Saint Petersburg where he was triumphantly welcomed. He left on 23 June for Tallinn, from where he took off two days later for Stockholm. This stage of 250 miles included 185 miles over the sea. On 29 June, Brindejonc flew

The arrival of Brindejonc des Moulinais at Saint Petersburg.

Brindejonc des Moulinais leaving for his tour of the capitals of Europe (10 June 1913).

Marc Bonnier (1887–†**F**1916)

Bonnier and Barnier's difficult take-off at Jerusalem. The town is on the left; to the right the Mount of Olives.

from Stockholm to Copenhagen with a brief stop at Halmstad. The welcome became warmer in each capital while the weather got worse. On 1 July the aviator flew Copenhagen-Hamburg-The

Védrines passing over the *Bruix* in the harbour of Beirut, during his flight from Paris to Cairo.

Hague. Finally, in spite of rain which forced him to navigate by compass as far as Cambrai, Brinde-jonc landed in the middle of an enthusiastic crowd at Villacoublay, having covered more than 3000 miles, 300 of them over the sea. Apart from the

incident with the wheel at Dvinsk, no problem at all had arisen. The Gnome engine had made the whole journey without the change of a single part. Brindejonc was decorated with the Légion d'Honneur and died over Verdun in 1916.

The year 1913 ended with a series of magnificent journeys towards the East, made under very difficult conditions with ordinary equipment and rudimentary means, but the success of which exceeded all expectations.

On 20 October Daucourt, who had been the first to fly from Paris to Berlin, and his passenger, J. Roux, left from Issy on board a Borel. The goal of their journey, which had been carefully prepared, was Cairo. After an encouraging start, despite the difficulty of crossing the Balkans in that troubled time, on 26 November Daucourt, by then alone, crashed his aircraft in the Taurus Mountains, 2,500 miles from Paris.

With no preparation at all, alone, aided only by his wild energy which helped him overcome all obstacles, whether natural or man-made, Jules Védrines was the first to accomplish the Paris-Cairo journey. He left Villacoublay in October and waited a month at Nancy for favourable conditions before taking off on 20 November in a non-stop flight to Prague, crossing the whole of Germany without a stop because he had not obtained permission to fly over certain forbidden zones. He was piloting a Blériot with a 80 h.p. Gnome engine, with no special equipment. Re-fuelling his engine as best he could with what petrol he could lay his hands on, hardly using a map, not having worked out his route in advance, Védrines reached Constantinople on 5 December where he found a compatriot, Bonnier, who had

left before him. He rested for several days and then set off again via Konya (405 miles), Tortosa, near Tripoli in Syria (435 miles including crossing the Taurus Mountains at 11,500 ft.), Beirut and

Védrines visiting the Pyramids and the Sphinx after his flight from Paris to Cairo.

Jaffa, finally arriving in Cairo on 29 December, after a total of 3,500 miles.

Marc Bonnier, one of aviation's most sympathetic personalities, began his Paris-Cairo flight on 10 November 1913, in the company of his

A stopover by Marc Pourpe on his Cairo-Khartoum flight.

Marc Pourpe (1887–†**F**1914).

The arrival of Marc Pourpe at Khartoum (12 January 1914).

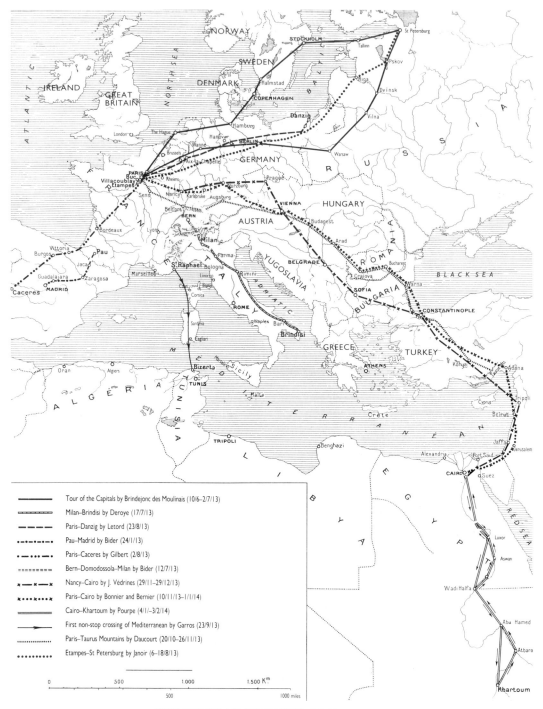

THE GREAT AIR JOURNEYS OF 1913 AND 1914

Legend:
- ——— Tour of the Capitals by Brindejonc des Moulinais (10/6–2/7/13)
- ━━━━ Milan–Brindisi by Deroye (17/7/13)
- – – – Paris–Danzig by Letord (23/8/13)
- –·–·– Pau–Madrid by Bider (24/1/13)
- ·—··—· Paris–Caceres by Gilbert (2/8/13)
- ========= Bern–Domodossola–Milan by Bider (12/7/13)
- x—x—x Nancy–Cairo by J. Védrines (29/11–29/12/13)
- x····x···· Paris–Cairo by Bonnier and Bernier (10/11/13–1/1/14)
- ═════ Cairo–Khartoum by Pourpe (4/1–3/2/14)
- ———→ First non-stop crossing of Mediterranean by Garros (23/9/13)
- ·············· Paris–Taurus Mountains by Daucourt (20/10–26/11/13)
- ·········· Etampes–St Petersburg by Janoir (6–18/8/13)

mechanic, Barnier, in a Nieuport with an 80 h.p. Gnome engine, and arrived safely in Cairo on 1 January 1914.

These two journeys added considerably to French prestige in the Near East. They remain, in the history of aviation, two magnificent pioneering performances. They were admirably complemented by Marc Pourpe's round trip from Cairo to Khartoum, and back.

Having undertaken in 1912 a long exhibition tour with a Blériot in the Indies, in Malaysia, in Cambodia and in Indochina, Marc Pourpe was familiar with all the difficulties of flying in far-off countries. On 4 January 1914, some days after the arrival of his fellow countrymen in Cairo, he decided to extend their route. In a Morane-Saulnier with a 60 h.p. Gnome engine, he flew off from Cairo, reached Luxor and Wadi Haifa, crossed the Nubian desert in torrid heat for 200 miles, arrived at Abu Hamed on 10 January and two days later landed at Khartoum, having covered more than 1250 miles where no one had flown before. He set out on the return journey on 19 January, via Atbara, Abu Hamed, Asswan and Luxor, and arrived in Cairo on 3 February. The whole trip was of some 2,800 miles which were covered with no failure by pilot or equipment.

Like Garros and Brindejonc des Moulinais, who both died in the war, these three great pilots later gave their lives for aviation: Védrines died in 1919 at Saint-Rambert-d'Albon, victim of an accident during a long-distance attempt; Marc Bonnier fell in 1916 on the Russian front, preceded by Marc Pourpe, accidentally killed on 2 December 1914 at the Somme.

These were the greatest journeys of 1913. Some other performances which caused no accidents and made this year one of the greatest in the history of aviation are shown on the accompanying map.

The Michelin Cup for 1913 required pilots to amass the greatest number of kilometres during an unlimited period in which they had to fly every day a distance equivalent to flying continuously at an average speed of at least 50 kph (31 mph) between the rising and the setting of the sun. No repairs to aeroplane or engine were allowed. In spite of these exceptionally tough conditions Fourny, in a Maurice-Farman with a Renault engine, flew 9,929 miles from 25 August to 16 September but was beaten by Hélen, in a Nieuport with a Gnome engine, who flew 9,996 miles from 22 October to 29 November, having covered in reality 12,975 miles with two hundred and one landings; but having had to deduct nearly 3000 miles owing to an accidental breach of the rules.

The Gordon-Bennet Cup, which had been won in 1912 by Jules Védrines, was held at Rheims on 29 September 1913; for the first time a man flew 200 kilometres (124 miles) in less than an hour. This great performance was put up by Maurice Prévost piloting a monocoque Deperdussin monoplane designed by Bechereau, equipped with a Gnome engine of only 160 h.p. Twelve world records were broken with this exploit. Prévost was closely followed by Emile Védrines who reached 122.6 mph. in a Ponnier monoplane and by Gilbert with 119.2 mph. in a Deperdussin similar to that of the winner. This aeroplane remained the prototype for all the speed monoplanes which followed.

At 200 kilometres an hour (124.2 mph): Prévost in flight in the Deperdussin, which won the Gordon-Bennet Cup in 1913. Note the pure lines of this racing monoplane designed by Becherean.

Pégoud about to attach his Blériot in flight to the cable installed at Buc (1913).

The Means smoke transmitter. Signalling in Morse code using the Means smoke transmitter from a Breguet aeroplane. The Blériot attaching pincers.

APPLICATIONS OF AVIATION

On 18 February 1911 a Captain Windham received permission from the authorities at Allahabad in India to start transporting mail, using an aeroplane belonging to a Frenchman, Pequet, between Allahabad and an exhibition positioned several miles away. Although brief and improvised, this first air postal service functioned with success and 6,000 maps were transported.

In August 1911, the Coronation of King George V was made the occasion to open a temporary air postal service between London and Windsor by the Graham White company, which transported 130,000 postcards. Several attempts were also made in 1911 in the United States.

In the same year, Védrines began carrying newspapers between Issy and Deauville; in 1912 and 1913 official tests were made by the French Army for the transport of mail. On 13 October 1913, Lt. Ronin

delivered the Paris mail for the West Indies to the liner *Perou* while at sea, shortening its delivery time by two weeks. Although an isolated event, this was the first real air/sea postal link.

Most major countries made similar experiments but no permanent service could be maintained. In Germany in 1912 civilian zeppelins also provided occasional air postal services.

In 1913 Blériot investigated possible alternatives to landing strips in order to allow aircraft to land on ships, and, employing Pégoud as test pilot, experimented successfully with a system of attaching aeroplanes in flight to a wire stretched between posts. The aeroplane could also release itself from the wire.

Radiotelegraphic transmissions had been executed in a free balloon by the Revd. Bacon as early as 1902 in England, but no attempt was made to repeat the experiments from an aeroplane until Morton in the United States transmitted a message on 28 August 1910 from a plane flying at 500 ft. to the aerodrome of Sheep's Head Bay. Tests of wireless telegraphy were also made in France by Maurice Farman and Senouque, between October and December 1910, with machines made by Ancel.

An alternative method of sending messages from an aeroplane in flight to the ground was the Means system of signalling by Morse code using smoke signals, which was tried out by Louis Breguet. This had limited success but the experience gained led later to the art of sky-writing.

For a long time Blériot had wanted to prove that the manoeuvrability of his machines was as important to their safety as the stability which was being advocated by another school of thought; his idea was to demonstrate that a pilot in a difficult position could still execute many manoeuvres which would save him. Impressed by Pégoud's performance when he abandoned his aeroplane in order to make his first parachute drop, Blériot invited him to make a demonstration on an ordinary Blériot monoplane, equipped with a 50 h.p. Gnome engine.

On 1 September 1913 at Juvisy, and two days later at Buc, Pégoud executed his first inverted flights. On the 21st he tried, without entirely

succeeding, a "flick turn" – turning the aircraft while maintaining a horizontal posture – made tail slips, a vertical figure S, a spin, and finally a loop. (He was not in fact the first to execute this manoeuvre; the Russian Lt. Nesterov was the first to loop the loop, whether meaning to or not, several days earlier in a 70 h.p. Nieuport.)

Pégoud repeated his demonstration at Hendon and at Buc where he flew inverted for 59 seconds, then looped the loop eight times running. He later gave other displays at Buc, Vienna and Berlin. At Buc on 10 December he looped the loop accompanied successively by three journalists – André Guymon, Mathieu and Max Bruyère.

On 21 November Chanteloup copied Pégoud in a Caudron, then it was the turn of Chevilliard, Hanouille and Hucks. By the spring of 1914 there were around fifty pilots who had looped the loop – which had become the classical attraction at meetings. Only military aviation, which was soon to use virtuoso performances in combat, remained very reticent about this kind of exercise.

Adolphe Pégoud (1887–1915) equipped with harness for inverted flights.

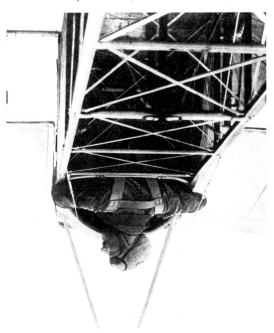

Pégoud giving a demonstration of aerobatics at Buc (1913).

Boehm's Albatross, the first to fly for more than twenty-four hours.

Parmelin equipped with a breathing mask for his crossing of the Alps.

FLYING IN 1914

The period from January to August 1914 was rich in records even if it could not compare with 1913.

German fliers came to the fore in a remarkable way, with a series of feats which were extraordinary when you consider that their engines were under-powered in relation to their weight and consumption, although already very sturdy. These engines, from 75 to 100 h.p., all had 6 cylinders in line and were cooled by water.

A great many records with passengers were made or beaten by Garaix on the Paul-Schmitt aeroplane: but these records, where the regulations were far too easy, lacked interest: on 22 April in France, Garaix managed to bestow 27 records on himself in one hour!

On 11 February the Swiss aviator Parmelin, flew from Geneva to Aosta over the Mont Blanc in a Deperdussin. The Monaco rally was won by Garros and the Schneider cup by the Englishman, Pixton, at 87 mph. Gilbert, on 8 and 9 June, won the Michelin Cup by a tour round France in sixteen stages of 2,000 miles in 39 hr. 35 min 42 sec.

Endurance performances characterised the year. On 3 February Langer flew for 14 hr. 7 min. in a Roland biplane. On 7 February Inhold left Mulhouse on an Aviatik biplane, with a Mercedes 100 h.p. engine, and landed at Munich after having been in the air for 16 hr. 20 min. and having covered a circuit of over 1000 miles. On 11 February, Langer flew from Berlin and landed sixteen hours later near Posen. The record was restored to France on 4 May by Poulet on a Caudron with a 60 h.p. Rhone engine which flew for 16 hr. 28 min. at Etampes. On 23 June Basser in a Rumpler stayed in the air for 18 hr. 12 min. while Landmann, who had taken off at the same time, stopped at the end of 17 hr. 17 min. Landmann took his revenge on 27 and 28 June

Porte's hydroplane *America*, built by Curtiss at Wanamaker's expense for the Atlantic crossing (1914).

with a flight of 21 hr. 50 min. in his Albatross. Finally, on 10 July Boehm left Johannistahl in an Albatros biplane with a 75 h.p. Mercedes engine, carrying 132 gallons of fuel, and was the first to break the "barrier" of twenty-four hours in an aeroplane, landing the next day after a flight of 24 hr. 12 min. The excellent night signalling in Germany greatly helped these records.

The most notable altitude performances were: with a passenger – 18,040 ft. by Linnekogel in Germany and 20,240 ft. by Bier in Austria; solo flights: Newbery at Buenos Aires, 20,400 ft. Linnekogel, 21,650 ft.; and on 14 July Celrich, 26,730 ft. on a DFW, again witha 100 h.p.

Mercedes engine. On 1 August 1914, the Norwegian commander Frygve Gran accomplished the England-Norway air crossing with stops. This exploit went unnoticed beside the other events of that day.

The possibility of an air crossing of the Atlantic had already been much studied by Curtiss, who in June 1914 had built and tested a transatlantic flying boat which had a remarkably modern aspect and which the English Lieutenant Porte was to pilot from Newfoundland to the Azores, and on to Vigo and Plymouth. Unfortunately the attempt had to be postponed and was overtaken by the outbreak of war.

Rumpler limousine with cabin (1914).

The *Taube* (pigeon), a monoplane by Etrich (1914).

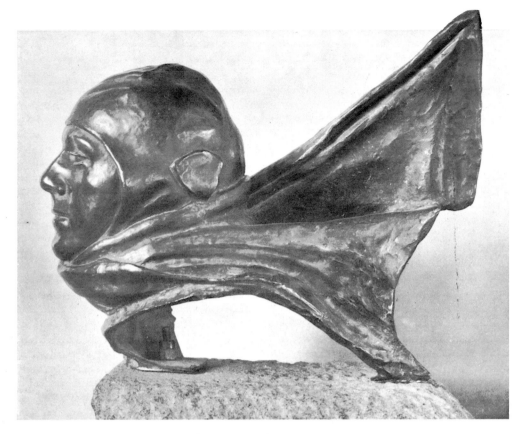

CHAPTER IV

AIRCRAFT AT WAR

1914–1918

And so it was that in the few short years between 1900 and 1914 man's attempts to conquer the skies had finally placed in his hands not one but two possible means of aerial navigation: the airship and the aeroplane.

No sooner were these flying machines born, hardly had their shape and structure been defined, than they were to play their part in the great storm which from 1914 to 1918 stands out as a self-contained interlude in the history of the modern world. In the story of manned flight these years were also a completely separate episode. Faced by a limitless demand, the fledgling aircraft industry, despite almost incredible industrial developments, was ever unequal to the needs and appetite of an all-devouring monster. Ten or twenty years earlier men such as Ader or the Wright brothers had met with mixed success when they requested even the most modest financial support from public bodies; now, suddenly, untold millions became available to engineers and businessmen. For three years they were criticised for their sluggishness. Aeronautics, and aeroplanes especially, became an indispensable part of the war effort. The Central Powers, strangled by the blockade, forced themselves to meet enormous production targets, from which the German aircraft industry learned both method and discipline. In the Allied camp, better supplied

with raw materials and manpower and limited only by the appetites of other armaments, a still greater effort tried in vain to fulfil programmes which called for the presence of thousands of aircraft at the Front, but failed to recognise that this would require tens of thousands of airframes, engines and new parts for the navigation and combat equipment to be manufactured in the rear. The rate of attrition was terrible; it was more a case of constant destruction. Rare were the planes and the men that were suited in all respects to the demands of war in the air. Both the efforts and the thinking of those responsible for aircraft manufacture tended towards an illusory goal: mastery of the skies. Almost as soon as they had been conceived, the French single-wing fighter and the German two-seater reconnaissance plane had already been outclassed, first on the enemy's drawing board and soon afterwards in the skies above the battlefield. Against this uneven background of constant jostling for the upper hand, the air supremacy noted by the opposing camps in their communiqués was, if ever true, only the expression of brief local or technical superiority. For most of the time such affirmations indicated a dream that the aircraft industry was called upon to make reality.

But just as victory on the ground belongs to the "big battalions", so too victory in the air de-

pended on numerical superiority; when numbers were equal, victory was determined by superiority alone, a superiority gained by the best performance; when airframes were identical, the most powerful engine decided the outcome; when power was the same, it was the lighter aircraft that triumphed. The war therefore stimulated technology, but the verdict remains open as to whether this stimulus encouraged or hindered the practical development of flying in general.

In the pages that follow a necessarily chronological arrangement might give the impression that we have tried to write a history of aviation in the Great War in two or three thousand lines. This has certainly not been our intention. What we want to suggest and what one should try to see in the succession of pictures, many of which are still too poignant to permit a fully objective survey, is the rapid, forced and brutal development of aeronautical technology between 1914 and 1918. This evolutionary process escaped abruptly from the control of the pioneers who had given birth to the art of flying and came to be totally dictated by external factors, namely the purposes of war and destruction. These ends, it may justifiably be argued, prevented airships, and even more so aeroplanes, from developing in their own way, and undoubtedly altered the course of a technology that was still in its infancy.

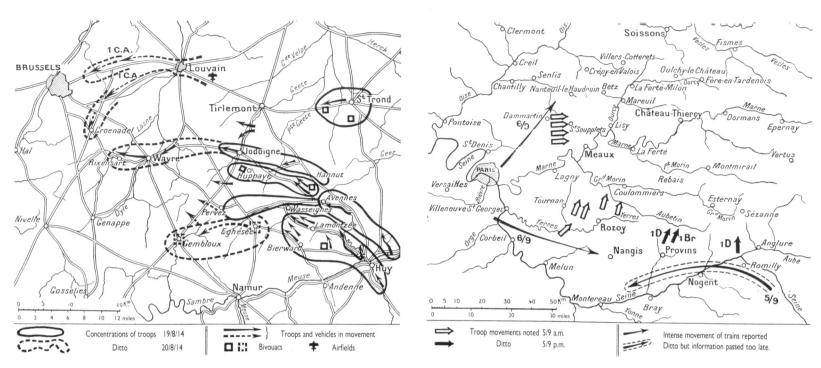

Allied aerial reconnaissance at the time of the German rush across Belgium.

German aerial observations on the eve of the First Battle of the Marne.

The observations made by Allied aircraft on 19 and 20 August 1914 were remarkably accurate. The air crews realised at a very early stage the huge numbers of enemy troops involved in the advance, and reported the overall change in direction towards the south-west as soon as it occurred. However, they did not manage to convince the High Command of the importance of their findings until it was too late. German reconnaissance crews ran into exactly the same problem when on 5 September 1914 they observed intense movements of trains that should have revealed the intentions of General Joffre.

THE WAR OF MOVEMENT

The great freedom of movement of the aeroplane, the sheer extent of its reconnaissance capability and the speed with which it could relay its observations assured it a major role in the gathering of intelligence. It might have been supposed that for the same reasons it would have brought new assurance and flexibility to warfare, for it was capable of replacing intuition and hypothesis with observed data. But it would have had to have been a weapon of super-human power for its reconnaissance to have been given the full credit it deserved, especially at time when information from the skies upset the strategists at military headquarters by unveiling a different kind of war from the one that they had planned to fight.

Be that as it may, from the first days of August the principal activity of the Allied air force, in liaison with the armies on the ground, was to undertake strategic reconnaissance and to reveal the enemy's intentions. The conditions were

relatively favourable for this type of work: there were not yet any aerial battles, groundfire directed at low-flying aircraft was ineffective, the season was propitious and the days were long. In the morning and evening several crews from each squadron would penetrate up to 30 miles behind the enemy lines; in the morning they noted the direction of the enemy advance, and in the evening they reported the enemy's new position. The sheer size of units on the march and the need to advance continuously made it impossible to hide the direction that the armies were taking from aerial observation. Thus it was that as early as 20 August the importance of the mighty onrush through Belgium was recognised, and the subsequent change of direction towards the south-west was observed. Similarly it was aerial intelligence that contributed in large measure to the French Second Army's victorious counter-attack on the Mortagne. From 1 to 4 September air crews tracked the progress of the German columns as they headed directly towards Paris, then turned south-east and finally bore down on Ferté-sous-Jouarre and Château-Thierry, leaving the capital to the west; thus informed by aerial intelligence, Joffre took the decision on 5 September which was to result in victory on the Marne.

The Germans, of course, knew how to obtain similar information and strategic aerial reconnaissance is said to have contributed to victory at Tannenberg on the Russian front. On 5 September German aerial observers also noted the frantic movement of trains along the Seine valley from east to west, which, on the eve of the battle of the Marne, should have disclosed or at least revealed in broad outline, General Joffre's intentions. Unfortunately for the Germans these crucial observations were rendered useless through not being relayed in time to the High Command and thence

to the army on the German right wing.

During August 1914, however, the German airforce was less exclusively dedicated than the French to strategic observation. It seems that the task assigned to the enemy squadrons was threefold: long-distance reconnaissance, permanent observation on a level with the army's line of advance, and finally liaison and transmission of orders between the staff-officers of the armies and corps marching south-east and then south. Thus divided between various missions, and taking into account their extremely feeble resources, it is

Roland Garros called up.

Pégoud's two-seater Blériot (Verdun, 20 October 1914).

Shot down by an English fighter near Bixschoote in the spring of 1915, a German pilot who has just died of his wounds lies on the fuselage of his aircraft like an effigy on a tomb.

Gilbert's third victory (10 January 1915). The German observer Lt. von Falkenstein lies in the foreground, killed by one of four bullets fired by Lt. de Puechredon from Gilbert's Morane-Saulnier.

hardly surprising that the German air-crews had great difficulty in satisfying all the demands placed upon them.

Once battle had been joined in Lorraine and on the Marne, aeroplanes became available for other uses. These tasks were immediately apparent, but the way in which they were carried out was defined more slowly. It should be remarked, however, that as early as the 10 September a note from G.H.Q. recommended that aeroplanes be attached to the artillery corps "as soon as the strategic role of aeroplanes becomes less important", and on 9 November 1914, with the fronts barely stabilised, G.H.Q. stipulated that "no major offensive is to be undertaken unless weather conditions permit the use of aeroplanes."

All this activity in the air did not pass by

without combat or loss of life. Around eighty enemy planes were brought down on all fronts in 1914. Allied losses were not much below this figure. Amongst these first casualties, was Senator Roymond, who, forced to land on 21 October between the opposing front lines, was mortally wounded during an infantry skirmish in which his aeroplane was the prize; on 2 December Marc Pourpe died in his crashed aeroplane; in Russia, the famous Captain Nesterov was killed when he collided with his adversary.

Skirmishes were ever more numerous. After Frantz and Quénault's victory, Stribick and David triumphed on 28 October; Gaubert and Captain Blaise fought an aerial duel which ended in their prey dropping from the sky. On 2 November, Captain Vergnette and Gilbert, the

famous civilian pilot, brought down a German plane with the third shot from Vergnette's rifle; with Bayle, Gilbert scored another victory in December, and then a third with Lt. de Puechredon on 10 January 1915. Gilbert, a pioneer and a pilot of astonishing virtuosity, seemed about to embark on a distinguished career but this was shortly interrupted when he had to land in Switzerland after an air-raid on the hangars at Friedrichshafen. After two escapes, Gilbert was once more in France on active service, but was killed on 17 May 1918 while test-flying a new aeroplane. On 1 April 1915 Lt. Robert, the observer in a plane flown by the then unknown pilot Jean Navarre, also shot down his adversary with a rifle. The ascendancy of the sharp-shooters, however, was almost over.

The French expedition of 27 May 1915 against Ludwigshafen: the planes and the crews. Bottom right: a makeshift bomb-rack aboard a Voisin biplane.

Airfields become more permanent. Left: an aerodrome on the Argonne front in early 1915; Morane-Saulnier monoplanes and Farman biplanes with skis in front of tents alternating with the first Bessonneau hangars. Right: a Caudron G-3 takes off on a reconnaissance mission to the north of Verdun.

THE AIR FORCES "DIG IN"

By the end of 1914 the position of the Western Front had stabilised. From the North Sea to the Vosges, the two sides faced each other across distances determined by the thickness of a wall of sandbags or by a glacis of several hundred metres swept by the crossfire of machine-guns. Henceforth there was no need for strategic reconnaissance; tactical use of aeroplanes, triggered alternately by the plans or fears of the commanders, became an increasingly less random experiment following on from the improvisations of 1914. The squadrons settled down. For some time airfields were still equipped with individual shelters, then the huge Bessonneau hangars appeared, symbolising the immobility of a front which the air-crews could be sure of finding in exactly the same place every morning.

Liaisons were also stabilised; whether preparing a "breakthrough" or anticipating an attempted enemy incursion, it became necessary to study enemy defences, and in particular the artillery batteries which had to be matched or outgunned. The essential mission was therefore observation of enemy firepower, and the airforce worked side by side with the artillery.

We have already come a long way from the first aerial range-findings, either by conventional circling, which the Germans were doing as early as August 1914, or by dropping coloured flares on batteries or large concentrations of troops, as Lt. Roeckel began to do the following month. In December 1914 range-finding by wireless was already in operation among French squadrons around Saint-Mihiel and in Flanders. In February 1915 this method had become generally established; the aeroplane – successfully complemented by the kite balloon which assured permanent surveillance and telephone communication – triumphed over all resistance and all other routines. However, the simultaneous presence of numerous aeroplanes transmitting wireless signals in the same sector gave rise to problems of interference and new techniques of wireless telegraphy had to be invented and adapted to cope with this.

Another technique which was proving its value was that of aerial photography; we shall see later the role it was to play in the study of the enemy's defences and intentions, and then in the battle itself. On the airfields, where the military stalemate and the dreary weather gave rise to lengthy periods of inactivity, everybody busied themselves making technical enhancements to their planes. The aircraft construction industry, which was organising itself slowly and painfully in the rear, was still largely ineffective, and so the air-crews had to fall back on their own resources;

above all, planes needed to be increasingly better armed. In May, at the time of the Artois offensive, reconnaissance sorties deep into enemy territory had rarely encountered stiff opposition; by September 1915 the skies over Champagne, where the airforce was preparing for the next "breakthrough", were to become a far more hostile place. This was because firing through the propeller blades had become a reality.

As early as April, Garros, alone in his plane, had shot down in flames an enemy two-seater, thanks to an armour-plated propeller which he had contrived; he had been allowed to install a forward-firing fixed machine-gun to his plane. But in July the Germans began to equip the Fokker with a machine-gun synchronised with the engine; soon their two-seaters were being fitted with the same weapon in addition to the observer's gun turret. Nevertheless with this new weapon the single-seater became pre-eminent as the "specialised" fighter aeroplane. In this type of aircraft Pégoud reigned supreme. On 3 April he scored his third victory; on 31 August he was killed after his sixth. In Alsace, over Petit-Croix, he was hit by the machine-gunner of a German two-seater who, warned of his adversary's tactics, fired at Pégoud from below and brought him down. On 19 July, an unknown aviator, still almost a boy, scored a victory: this pilot's name was Guynemer.

Life and death of Pégoud. Left: the aviator in cheerful mood next to a sign proclaiming "Long live Pégoud", made to mark his most recent victory. Right: on 31 August 1915, his comrades at the Belfort squadron escort his remains; the canvas from his shattered plane has become his shroud.

OTHER THEATRES OF WAR: THE EASTERN MEDITERRANEAN

While the allied airforces were adapting to "seige warfare" on the Western Front, other teams of aviators in quite different conditions were confronted with less well defined tasks.

Such was initially the case with the first regular formation of the French naval airforce, the "Nieuport Squadron". Caught unawares by mobilisation with a complement of only three machines, the squadron rallied at Nice where, during the month of August 1914, it was brought up to a strength of eight seaplanes. In September it was moved to Bizerta, from where it helped to safeguard naval transport in the Mediterranean. When it was later sent to Malta, a section was despatched to Antivari and then to Lake Scutari in order to maintain surveillance over Cattaro.

On 1 December the "Nieuport Squadron" arrived at Port Said, which was to be its base for the next year and a half, having been placed under the command of the British Army in Egypt that was defending the Suez Canal. From the Dardanelles to Soloum, from Smyrna to Jeddah, these teams of little seaplanes with French pilots and British observers continuously followed the movements of the Turks. Under the orders of Lt. Cdr. de L'Escaille, they bombarded railway junctions, encampments and columns of troops, and pushed their reconnaissance more than 50 miles inland, all too often having to put down their floats on rough ground without the makeshift landings ever involving loss of life. However, the specialised nature of the working conditions led to heavy sacrifices. Lt. Grall made a miraculous journey back through the Turkish line in December 1914; a year later the pilot Lt. Saizieu and his observer, the British Flying Officer Ledger, were killed attempting to prevent the capture of their aeroplane after a heroic fight.

Meanwhile the English air effort was being organised more effectively; in the spring of 1916 it was ready to relieve the French squadron; on 18 April the eight Nieuports – several of which had been in service for eighteen months – reached Argostoli where from that time on they were used against the submarine menace.

In the meantime the drama of the Dardanelles had begun and there too the Allied airforces found themselves involved in the fighting. It was from the relative quiet of islands such as Tenedos, 20 miles away from the battle, that the British teams led by Samson and French pilots under the command of Césari set off to "work" over the hell of the peninsula. Their adversaries in the sky were the German-Turkish squadrons of which the 24 German machines destined for the Dardanelles had flown non-stop to Constantinople from Herkulesbad in Hungary in the autumn of 1915.

1915 also saw the arrival in Serbia of a French squadron led by Commander Vitrat. After many tribulations and some bold missions, particularly against Austrian ironclads, the squadron took part in the agonising Serbian retreat of October 1915; at the end of December it was redeployed at St. Jean-de-Médua.

A French Nieuport with floats is winched aboard the British cruiser *Doris*.

Lt. Cdr. Delange's seaplane is hoisted aboard on returning from a reconnaissance mission.

The Dardanelles campaign. A British biplane, heavily loaded with bombs, about to leave the island of Thasos.

A British attack on a Zeppelin base: an Avro is wheeled into a hangar by French soldiers at Belfort after bombing Friedrichshafen.

German medal struck to commemorate the Zeppelin raid on London on 17–18 August 1915.

A Farman from the home defence force of fortified Paris in the beam of the searchlights at Le Bourget airfield.

BOMBING RAIDS

From the end of 1914 Commander Barès, the French airforce chief at General Headquarters, advocated launching powerful and regular attacks against large-scale targets, instead of the sporadic expeditions that had characterised the first few months of the war. During October and November 1914 a few raids in Flanders involving eight to ten planes had pointed the way forward. These were the origins of the bomber units of which the first, called G.B.1, comprising three flights of Voisins, was formed in May 1915, under Squadron-Leader de Goÿs.

On 27 May the eighteen crews of aviators set off from Malzéville airfield to bombard the important Badische-Anilin factories at Ludwigshafen and Oppau. Less than six hours later, their mission accomplished, the squadron was back; the only plane to be lost was that of de Goÿs himself, who with his pilot, Bunau-Varilla, had been taken prisoner. In spite of this loss, the unit's first expedition had more than justified the value of the equipment and resources that had been committed to bombing raids. Bomber unit G.B.1 was increased in size to four flights.

Eighteen days later, while the repercussions of the first raid were still being felt, twenty-three aircraft bombed Karlsruhe; only two did not return. Then, with the addition of three other bombing groups to the original one, as many as sixty-two aeroplanes attacked the blast furnaces at Dillingen on 25 August 1915. But these expeditions became increasingly hazardous: a raid on Saarbrücken cost nine aircraft, and among the dead was the pioneering airman Captain Albert Féquant.

It soon became necessary to face facts: the development of enemy fighter aircraft made daylight bombing raids by slow, heavily laden Voisins impossible. Bombers such as these,

which penetrated over 125 miles into enemy territory, were incapable of defending themselves on the return journey. And so the force of 100 aeroplanes was redeployed to other tasks. The brief offensive superiority, which had been boldly exploited, melted away when faced with the technical progress of the enemy defence.

The experience of the French with bomber units was repeated by the Germans with their airships. At the beginning of the war the enemy command had twelve airships at its disposal, ten of which had rigid frames. However, this new weapon was employed without adequate preparation, and initially in conditions that seemed to fly in the face of all common sense. The fact that the available airships were shared between the army and navy contributed further to this muddled planning.

The first tasks assigned were daylight reconnaissance missions: in August alone three airships were shot down or incapacitated by infantry fire over Belgium and Alsace. This costly experience soon led to Zeppelins being used only at night. From bases in Belgium they bombed Antwerp and Ostend during September and October, and carried out several useful reconnaissance flights. The British wasted no time in attacking the Zeppelin bases: hence the air raids on Friedrichshafen and Dusseldorf where, on 8 October, the Z-IX was destroyed. In the spring of 1915 London and Paris were designated as targets for the Zeppelin commanders. Fog during the night of 17–18 March frustrated an attack on London and three tons of bombs were dropped on Calais instead. Three nights later the Z-X and the LZ-35 reached Paris and remained over the city for

nearly an hour despite a violent cannonade from the anti-aircraft guns. Nor were the defending fighters able to take advantage of those fleeting moments when the airships were caught in the beams of searchlights. However, the Z-X, which had been hit by shell-splinters, had to make an emergency landing near Saint-Quentin and be dismantled where it lay.

A few days after this attack the Zeppelin commanders were forbidden to make further raids on London, and from 14 April to 26 May the only attacks that took place were on Norfolk, Suffolk, Essex and Kent. But when the ban on bombing the English capital was lifted on 28 May, the new rigid-framed LZ-38, containing 1,129,000 cu. ft. of gas, attacked London on 31 May; seven people were killed, thirty-five were wounded, and a good deal of incendiary damage was done.

On 7 June the LZ-37 returned to bomb Calais but was shot down over Ghent by Pilot-Officer Warneford; the whole crew, with the exception of one man, was killed. A few minutes later another British airman destroyed a second large Zeppelin in its hangar at Brussels-Evere. During the night of 8–9 August 1915 the naval airship L-12 was hit by the guns at Dover and was obliged to put down on the sea, where it broke up, although the Germans managed to tow it to Ostend, despite repeated attacks by seaplanes.

By the end of 1915 Great Britain had been bombed twenty times by airships and 197 people had lost their lives in the raids. At a time when the war dead were being counted in hundreds of thousands, these casualties ought not to have excited much attention. The civilian population, however, felt that it was not being properly defended and this impression was strong enough to cause considerable unease in government circles, especially following a raid on Hull on 6 June. Equally, the German authorities were able to use these expeditions against hitherto unmolested territory as fodder for their propaganda machine and as encouragement for German national pride.

The German airship L-12 floating off Ostend after being damaged by cannon at Dover on 9 August 1915.

The airship *Fleurus* with a gas capacity of 230,000 cu. ft. at Verdun in August 1914.

The *Commandant-Coutelle* brought down by a shell near Verdun (June 1915).

The *Adjudant-Vincenot* with a gas capacity of 350,000 cu. ft. at Crère-coeur on the Somme in 1916.

FRENCH AIRSHIPS AND BALLOONS

The role played by airships in the French army was a minor one. Once war had been declared there was a rush to arm the few airships available but for the most part these dirigibles were slow and possessed neither a wide radius of action nor a particularly high "ceiling". The only ones of any practical use were the *Fleurus*, the *Montgolfier*, the *Adjutant-Vincenot* and the *Dupuy-de-Lôme*. The crew of the *Fleurus* had the distinction of being the first allied military personnel to enter Germany itself once hostilities had begun; they left Verdun during the night of 9–10 August 1914, reconnoitred the railway lines in the Saar basin and pushed on as far as Trier, where they bombed a railway station.

The *Dupuy-de-Lôme* was unfortunately brought down near Rheims by some French soldiers who mistook it for a Zeppelin; airships were forever being fired on by their own side when returning to base – the Germans experienced several similar receptions. The *Adjutant-Vincenot* carried out the greatest number of reconnaissance and bombing missions; it was brought down after it had been in continuous service for two years, and even then it was not badly damaged. More powerful airships were reconditioned or constructed, notably the *Coutelle*, the *d'Arlandes* and the *Champagne*, which were built by the manufacturers Zodiac, and the *Alsace* and the *Pilâtre-de-Rozier*, which were built at the Astra workshops.

No French airship was ever attacked by an enemy aeroplane, but all were hit by projectiles of some kind: the *Alsace* was shot down over the German lines, the *Coutelle*, the *Adjutant-Vincenot* and the *Champagne* over the French. Remarkably there were only two fatalities until the *Pilâtre-de-Rozier* was shot down in flames with its whole crew on 23 February 1917. This catastrophe and

A French captive balloon in flames, photographed by the observer while descending by parachute.

the increasing difficulties experienced during airship sorties put a stop to the use of dirigibles over land, and they were handed over to the navy.

The development of aeroplanes had induced the French War Ministry to take the unfortunate decision to disband all field ballooning units in 1911, and the fleet of captive balloons in 1913. Only units for servicing airships had been retained. But from August 1914 the Germans used captive kite-balloons to observe French movements. The various ballooning sections and their equipment were therefore hastily reassembled and by the middle of September eight units were operating; by the end of the war there were seventy-six companies of field balloonists scattered along the Front. The theatre of operations covered by French field balloons was extensive; French balloonists and their equipment were sent to the British, Italian, American and Eastern Fronts.

However, from the end of 1914, serious flaws inherent in the French spherical type of captive balloon led to the adoption of the German Drachen [kite] balloon, nicknamed the "sausage". In May 1916 a new sort of captive balloon that was elongated in shape, the 'M' type, was brought out, and the old Renard steam-driven winches were replaced with new devices powered by automobile engines. Parachutes were issued to all observers, saving the lives of many.

The observer's job in a captive balloon was at once difficult and dangerous. A watch generally lasted a dozen hours, sometimes fifteen and even eighteen; but continuous observation was invaluable in revealing the movements of the enemy and directing artillery fire.

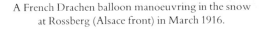

A French Drachen balloon manoeuvring in the snow at Rossberg (Alsace front) in March 1916.

An observer attaching himself to the exterior parachute. Note cover on left.

An M type balloon (30,000 cu. ft.) on the Meuse front at Saint-Symphorien in September 1916.

The crews of the M.F.-25 unit at Laheycourt (Meuse) in the autumn of 1915.

Captain Vuillemin, commander of the C-11 unit, at Verdun in September 1915.

THE AIRMEN OF 1915

On 2 August 1914 the French army had less than one hundred and fifty suitable aeroplanes for its fighting units. By the end of 1915 the squadrons at the Front had some eight hundred machines at their disposal. From this growing military airforce manned by volunteers an appeal went out.

Pilots were needed: many non-commissioned officers and young cavalry or Army Service Corps officers, depressed by the military stalemate, obtained permission to train for flying. Observers had to be physically fit in order to cope with demanding work, and sufficiently intelligent to be able to assimilate rapidly a great deal of technical information. Many young artillerymen who had helped in the first range-finding exercises found their true vocation and were welcomed into the air service. Many wounded footsoldiers who for various reasons could no longer serve in the infantry and were sometimes due to be invalided out of military service altogether asked to be transferred to the airforce. After a hasty induction course at the briskly run flying school at Le Bourget, each man would join a squadron about which, in most cases, he knew nothing.

One or two, however, requested a transfer to "Happe's unit", attracted by the already legendary figure of a commander who led from the front in raids that seemed to throw all caution to the winds; such men dreamed of military glory and the chance of seeing their names mentioned in citations.

Another recruit might have a friend who was an observer in "Vuillemin's unit", the C-11, and would pull all the strings he could to get himself posted to the "quiet sector" around Verdun and to a squadron which was later to become famous. Then there were those for whom flying meant the exciting prospect of seeing the ground from the

sky. Recruits such as these would learn to decode from aerial photographs the conventional signs that revealed the enemy's defence and movements, taking into account the nature of the terrain below them.

All the new recruits quickly settled into this small, disparate group of pilots and observers who were usually paired off in "teams" and expected to be ready for any eventuality.

(Middle) Captain Happe (1882–1930) in 1915 at the time of the raids on Rottweil and Habsheim.

Navarre's first victory: while General Franchet d'Espèrey makes Lt. Robert, Navarre's observer, a Knight of the Legion of Honour, Navarre (wearing an airforce arm-band) waits to receive the Military Cross (8 April 1915).

Types of two-seater aircraft in use during the winter of 1915–1916, while the Germans were already using reconnaissance planes with a rigid fuselage which were well protected from the rear, French reconnaissance teams were still experimenting with various ad hoc modifications to their Farmans, for example the "Coupet ring" which allowed the observer to fire backwards (more or less) across the upper wing.

Infantry positions on the Belgian front. The particular desolation of the war on this front comes across in this picture, where the quality of the photography combined with the effects of light and wind on the surface of the water have produced almost the effect of an engraving. The dug-in positions confront each other on either side of the Yser, clinging precariously to both banks of the river and protected more effectively against soil erosion than against the enemy by means of timber supports, scaffolding and concrete reinforcement. The most heavily protected positions appear as little white rectangles. Towards the rear the communication trenches run across the waterlogged soil in which every shell crater reflects the sunlight; at night the paths on either side of these trenches were easier to use.

THE BELGIAN AIRFORCE

It was probably the Belgian airforce that brought to its highest standard the technique of aerial photography during the war: the picture above gives some idea of the quality achieved by such flyers as Capt. Jammotte and Lts. d'Hendecourt and Wouters. However, from the very beginning of the conflict, when Belgians supplied much valuable strategic information, the airmen who sported a black, yellow and red roundel by no means limited themselves to photographic reconnaissance.

In liaison with ground units, and frequently at a disadvantage technically (which did not, however, prevent Commander Jacquet from scoring five victories in his observation biplane), the Belgian airforce stood its ground steadfastly and suffered cruel losses.

In both offensive and defensive missions, the Belgian fighter squadrons also demonstrated their worth, amply attested by the eleven victories of André de Meulemeester, the ten scored by Thieffry, who later died opening up the great trails of Africa, the six by Olieslagers, and lastly the rapid and thrilling tally of victories notched up by the great Belgian ace Willy Coppens. The wartime aviator known later as Chevalier Willy Coppens de Houthulst scored a total of thirty-six victories in the cockpit of his single-seater Hanriot HD-1, the little plane whose merits were amply demonstrated by the Belgians and the Italians.

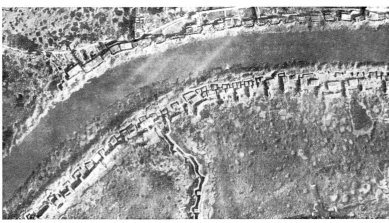

The details of the trench system are even clearer here. The pressure exerted by the mud and water is contained by wooden palisades.

A two-seater observation plane of Engish design on a formerly fashionable Belgian beach in the spring of 1915.

Photographic reconnaissance in 1915–1916. Left: an aircraft of the M.F.-25 unit about to take off. The 50 cm. focus camera juts out from the floor of the cockpit; note also the machine-gun on a raised mounting to allow the observer to fire backwards. Centre: a new 120 cm. focus camera in an aircraft of the M.F.-2 unit in March 1916. Right: the cockpit of a Farman from the M.F.-32 unit riddled with bullets after a skirmish.

AN ARMED VIGIL: THE EVE OF VERDUN

By the end of 1915 there was still no decisive outcome in sight. The great hopes of the Artois and Champagne offensives had come to nothing. Now that winter had set in a certain uneasiness was developing. The resources which the enemy was known to possess, the length of time it would take to prepare a new Allied offensive and the mystery of this vast, silent front where aerial observation was now hampered by rain and fog all combined to create an atmosphere of armed vigilance.

The Germans were going to attack, but where? The Allies looked to their aeroplanes to give, if not the exact location of the threatened zone, then at least some confirmation of the many rumours that were circulating.

One of these rumours proved to be well founded. From the beginning of January 1916 the zone between the Argonne and the Meuse was thought

to be the sector in which the enemy would attack. Therefore the number of reconnaissance flights over the woods and gullies of Gruerie, Haute-Chevauchée and Fille-Morte, all of which offered

Take-off of a two-seater Nieuport of the type used for army reconnaissance on the Verdun front.

extremely good cover, were stepped up. Aeroplanes flew as low as possible over the salient around the Malancourt wood where all too often enemy sappers could be seen driving their

advance-trenches like tentacles beyond the front line. On 20 February communications around Bar-le-Duc and Revigny were bombed by a considerable number of enemy planes which were attacked by French fighter squadrons on their return to base. That night the sky was filled with the roar of engines as two Zeppelins crossed the lines. One of the giant airships was caught in the searchlights and came under concentrated anti-aircraft fire. It was hit and burst into flames over Revigny, its intended target, rolled over in the sky and crashed close to the railway station. Its hastily discharged bombs made huge craters around the railway junctions which the Germans had meant to destroy.

While the French bustled around this blazing mass of wreckage, the silence that followed the Zeppelin attack was suddenly broken by the roar of the German guns which, like a gong, announced the start of the offensive on the ring of trenches to the north and east of the old fortress town of Verdun; by dawn the airforce was already engaged in the battle.

Birth of the airfield at Brocourt. Left: in the tent which is the only shelter on an airfield as yet without hangars on the eve of the Battle of Verdun (February 1916), the observer of the army squadron is telephoning aerial H.Q. with the findings of a low-level reconnaissance mission over the suspicious front of Malancourt-Avocourt. Right: the airfield at Brocourt and the installations of the M.F.-33 unit three months later in May at the height of the battle.

Opposite: the Revigny Zeppelin. This photograph, taken at dawn from an aeroplane flying at 10,000 ft., indicates the violence of the airship's vertical fall on the snowy fields of Argonne. The debris was not dispersed but remained in a circle of approximately the same diameter as that of the airship itself

Navarre's "Baby" Nieuport, a lightweight single-seater biplane with a total surface area of 140 sq. ft. and an 80, later 110 h.p. rotary engine. It was fitted with a fixed Lewis machine-gun with a 47 cartridge magazine which can be seen above the upper wing . The gun was aimed by pointing the aircraft at the target.

Commandant de Rose (1876–†F1916), organiser and leader of the French fighter effort at Verdun, killed on 11 May 1916.

Navarre's "Baby" Nieuport climbing. This aircraft was extremely manoeuvrable and a good climber, and out-performed the enemy fighters at normal altitudes. The German planes, on the other hand, were better armed and the pilot did not have to tip the gun up vertically in mid-combat in order to fit a new magazine.

Sergeant Guynemer at Verdun in February 1916.

Sergeant-Major Maxime Lenoir.

The Navarre brothers at Verdun, Jean in the foreground.

FIGHTERS AT VERDUN

During the whole of 1915 fighter planes had unquestionably been neglected, as much from the technical as from the industrial point of view. If any progress was made at all it was due to the efforts of individuals such as de Rose, Garros and Morane.

In France Peyret and Saulnier had been researching, developing and testing a forward-firing machine-gun synchronised to the propeller since June 1914, but they had been using a type of machine-gun that complicated the process and made it unworkable in practice. It was then that

Garros, a pilot in the Morane-Saulnier Company, had his idea of replacing the faulty synchronising mechanism with a bullet-proof steel plate fixed to the propeller blades directly in front of the gun. Unfortunately this solution, though effective, reduced the speed of the aircraft considerably. More unfortunately still, when Garros was forced to land among the German lines with his armoured propeller blades, the German airforce realised at once the urgency of the problem. The Germans had copied the Morane, which to them was the Fokker; they did not, however, adopt the Garros system of armour plating.

Fokker also had the idea of synchronising gun and propeller, and certain features of the German

Maxim gun made it easier for him to put the concept into practice.

Nevertheless, his system is said to have aroused so much suspicion in the German air command that Fokker was personally made to demonstrate his equipment at the Front as a prerequisite of its being put into service. The story even goes that on this occasion Fokker flew close to an Allied two-seater which, having nothing to fear from a frontal attack, remained totally indifferent to his approach. This trusting assumption is said to have dissuaded him from making a kill; he declared that the first use of his invention should be made by a genuine combatant.

Similar systems were, as we have seen, being

Firing through the propeller: from the Garros system to the Fokker system. Left: a Morane-Saulnier with protected propeller blades. Right: a Fokker with a fixed machine-gun synchronised with the propeller, the first to be captured by the Allies at Courmelois in 1916.

After an aerial battle west of the Meuse. Sergeant Barney, a pilot from the N-37 unit, has just touched down in his little fighter biplane, behind the crippled German two-seater which he has forced to land near La Noue. A column of infantrymen is marching along the road nearby, largely indifferent to this scene.

researched on the Allied side, and not only by Peyret and Saulnier, but they were not brought into service until the summer of 1916. The Germans were already using the new weapon eight months earlier than this, and when the battle of Verdun began their numerous Fokkers, spitting out several hundred bullets a minute, swept the skies and gave them command of the air

This dominance did not actually prevent the French aerial photographers and range-finding observers from carrying out their work. But despite the heroism of the Allied fighter pilots, who were too few in number and badly armed, losses were very heavy. However, the scales were soon tipped the other way. On the orders of Commander de Rose, all available fighter planes (eight squadrons out of fifteen) were quickly mustered around Bar-le-Duc and Verdun. Among the aviators were Navarre, Guynemer, Quillien, Nungesser, de Beauchamp, Deuillin, Chaput, Lenoir and Boillot; the aeroplane they used was the Nieuport "Baby", a sturdy two-

seater transformed into a fast single-seater, less well armed but more manoeuvrable than a Fokker. Despite all this, inferior weaponry was a decisive factor: Quillien and Boillot were killed, and Guynemer was shot down – he emerged unscathed, but seventeen bullet holes were found in his aeroplane and soon afterward he was indeed wounded by two bullets. Although Navarre and Nungesser still won victory after victory in one-to-one encounters which were witnessed by both armies, it was nevertheless only by fighting in groups which gave them a numerical advantage in any particular skirmish that the French could win back air superiority, morally at first, by giving back the pilots who carried the battle into the enemy's skies a sense of their own strength and cohesion, then practically, by allowing the air-force to increase the frequency of its attacks on the enemy's fighters. Such were the tactics employed and imposed by de Rose and then Le Révérend. The plan meant that bombers and two-seaters engaged in observation or range-finding work

were often left unprotected, but these tactics did prepare the way for the Allied air supremacy on the Somme which was to become apparent four months later. Commander de Rose was killed on 11 May when he stalled close to the ground; though he never saw the results, he had been the originator of a great design.

On several occasions the intervention of fighters in the battle was more direct: they strafed troops on the ground, made reconnaissance flights and escorted bombers to their targets during daylight raids. Their most effective role, however, was undoubtedly the destruction of enemy Drachen ' balloons: the rockets devised by Lt. Cdr. Le Prieur, which were positioned obliquely in groups of four on each of the Nieuport's pair of wing-struts, could be launched at a short distance from the target balloon by means of an electrical device. On 22 May, as a French offensive was getting under way, six out of the seven enemy balloons with a view of the right bank of the Meuse were set ablaze simultaneously.

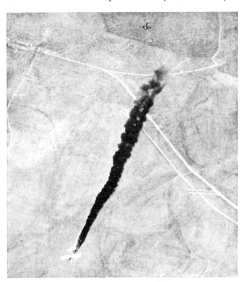

Left: a victory for Boelcke and his Fokker at Verdun. While the French biplane dives in flames towards the ground, the little black monoplane with black crosses on a white background follows it and watches it fall. Right: the first great German fighter pilots: Immelmann and (inset) Boelcke. Lt. Immelmann, who was killed on 16 June after 18 victories, is photographed here on 28 March in front of his Fokker monoplane, the German copy of the single-seater Morane-Saulnier.

Two two-seater Farman F-40 reconnaissance planes at Brocourt airfield in May 1916.

A line of craters photographed from 6,000 ft. That on the left, from a huge mine that has just exploded, judging from its undisturbed rim, is over 130 ft. across.

THE ROLE OF OBSERVATION AIRCRAFT

The need to repel at whatever cost the brutal German offensive at Verdun left no room for the former habits of the 'quiet sector'. The airforce was directly in the firing line; it was being driven from its airfields by guns and bombs; but despite daily losses, it continued to serve the combatants on the ground. Imagine an aircraft, flying at an altitude of some 5000 ft. above the area where a village once stood; the village, which has been repeatedly pounded by shells, is from this height nothing more than a chalky skeleton that traces the lay-out of former streets and roads. Elsewhere, vaguer and finer lines punctuated by the heavier earthworks of dug-outs and bunkers indicate the positions of attackers and defenders. Amidst the bleak fury of this sleeping destruction, the earth preserves one human feature, the face of cultivation which the ploughman has stamped on it over so many centuries – lines of fields that follow the slope of the land, rising towards a distant hill.

For the team at work, the artillery fire is the only thing that brings the landscape to life. First of all there is the anti-aircraft fire directed at the plane itself; yellowish tufts of smoke crack furiously about the plane, very close at times, a moment or two after they have bloomed on the ground. Towards the south can be seen the flicker of the "departing" friendly shells – this is the battery for which the aeroplane is range-finding. Seemingly almost beneath the aircraft, the friendly projectiles "arrive", sudden tree-like growths that are slowly deformed and carried away in the wind.

The pilot does his best to manoeuvre his co-aviator into a position from which he can observe without undue strain, and to reduce to a minimum the time during which the objective is out of sight; he must also try to make these idle periods coincide with the gaps between the artillery salvos. At the same time he is closely watching the vast emptiness of the sky where, at any moment, the enemy can be expected to appear. "How much space there is up there!" Brocard used to say, but this immensity can shrink to the size of a small paddock if the slow two-seater, engrossed in its task, suddenly registers the approach of black dots which all too quickly grow into Fokkers, Albatrosses or the first redoubtable German two-seater fighters. The range-finding is interrupted. But should the crew do everything it can to escape from an unequal fight which has nothing to do with the mission?

How many teams in this situation, whether forced to remain or not, confronted the oncoming enemy! And how many of them were lost after an agonising struggle, the duration of which would depend on the experience and strength of the observer! Perched in his cramped cockpit, the observer had to swing the cumbersome twin-barrelled machine-gun from one side of the fuselage to the other in his efforts to obtain a clear field of fire, while the pilot tried to tilt the aircraft to reveal the enemy posted beneath his tail. And what is to be done if the mission is too important to be interrupted? The aeroplane could be on a photographic mission, constrained to follow a particular flight path by the tract of ground that has to be recorded on film, limited in its movements by the type of lens in its camera and the scale desired.

Eight to ten minutes of concentrated action by the observer are required, including giving directions to the pilot, sighting, releasing the shutter, changing the plate or the slide every fifteen or twenty seconds, ordering a sharp turn every time a new magazine has to be inserted and then restarting the sequence of photographs further back in order to eliminate gaps in the series. The cracking of the anti-aircraft shells is getting closer, but the same altitude must be maintained.

The funeral at Noyon of a French observation crew shot down over enemy lines. Left: the funeral cortège proceeds through the occupied town. Right: at the cemetery, the leading citizens of the town and senior German officers listen to prayers at the graveside.

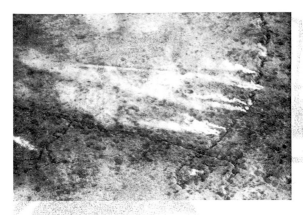

The aircraft in its infantry liaison rôle. Left: foot-soldiers mark the extent of their advance with smoke signals. Right: the attack on William Trench on 10 October 1916 during the Battle of the Somme.

OBSERVER AIRCRAFT ON THE SOMME

When the battle of the Somme began on 1 July 1916, the Allied airforce set to work in an atmosphere of summery optimism. As a reward for the painstaking work that had gone into the preparations, the first days of the offensive brought a sense of exultant success. The aeroplanes followed the infantrymen as they advanced, and their company gave the soldiers the confidence to show their presence by means of smoke signals or indicator boards.

The three months of operations on the Somme mark a high point of Allied (and especially French) aerial superiority in terms of observation. Infantry liaison, classic range-findings, rapid artillery engagements concentrating momentarily on

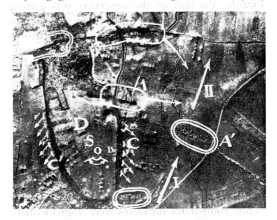

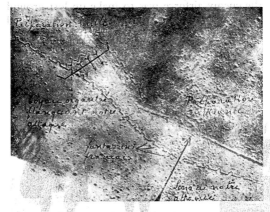

Photo reconnaissance by aircraft. Above: an analysis of enemy defences to an attack showing flanking fire (F) and positions of second line and reserve troops. Below: warning during an attack of a counter-thrust from the left.

battlefield targets, checking damage inflicted, intervening in the battle on the ground – all these activities were executed successfully and profited moreover from undeniable enemy inferiority: the Germans had fewer planes, less well defined tactics, and fewer squadrons specialising in particular tasks. The German fighter pilots in their Fokkers were for a long time pinned down at Verdun where the battle seemed to be moving towards a stalemate.

Aerial photography had by the middle of 1916 reached a remarkable stage of development. The makeshift equipment of the beginning of the war – converted balloonists' cameras and unstandardised lenses – had little by little been replaced with three standard models, the 36, 50 and 120 cm. lens cameras which, used at altitudes of around 800 ft. gave good pictures of the ground at approximate scales of 1/10,000, 1/5000 and 1/2000 respectively. But French superiority was not a result only of improved equipment; the Germans possessed a well established optical industry too and could avail themselves of excellent cameras for observation purposes. It was in the study of the photographs, in their transposition on to maps and above all in the tactical interpretation of aerial pictures that decisive progress was made. But it was still necessary to get headquarters to recognise the value of this information and to place its confidence in the occasionally bold interpretations put forward by these enterprising young men: in this field Captain Blissy was pre-eminent; a staff-officer himself, he collaborated in the observers' work and knew how to present it convincingly, in a language the generals could understand.

Once battle had been joined at Verdun and then on the Somme, the need for neat lay-outs of sectors that could be studied at length was soon replaced by a demand for the most recent pictures. Priority had to be given to looking at rapidly developed photographs to find confirmation of eyewitness observations, proof of insufficient destruction, and evidence of hasty enemy activity pointing to an imminent counter-attack on an Allied push that had not yet managed to break through. Then, while the prints were still damp, despite soaking in alcohol, this living testimony had to be carried to the highest military echelons and sometimes to the combatants themselves. These documents and their interpretation, ultimately the whole apparatus of "aerial reports" for which sector commanders took responsibility, represented the highest achievement of aerial

observation from 1916 on. The "air sectors" of the Somme, which for the most part were established in the vast open plateaux of the Picardy countryside, grouped together squadrons that were attached to a particular Corps, each ten or fifteen planes strong and reinforced by a so-called "base-squadron", one or two companies of heavy artillery and sometimes one or two other divisional units. The aerial photography sections and field balloon companies came under the same command. On average there would be about forty aeroplanes, three or four balloons, over a hundred officers and more than a thousand men in each sector. The commanding officer of the sector had a delicate role to play; not only was he responsible for the operations of a considerable force, he also needed to be a persuasive liaison officer vis-à-vis the general commanding the Army Corps and his staff.

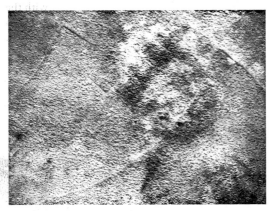

Effectiveness of bombardment assessed by aerial photography: the village of Guillemont in the British sector during the Battle of the Somme photographed to same scale on (above) 9 July and (below) 1 September 1916.

Fighter armament in 1916: Left, Brindejonc de Moulinais (1893–†F1916) whose career ended on 16 August 1916 at Verdun, and, centre, Sgt. Major Dorme with synchronised machine guns on Morane-Saulnier and Nieuport respectively. Right, Sgt. Ortoli with normal Nieuport armament.

THE ALLIED FIGHTERS VICTORIOUS

At the start of the battle of the Somme the Allies benefited, even more than the Germans had done at Verdun, from command of the air. Strangely, while the Germans managed almost immediately to re-establish parity in ground forces, for a long time they allowed their airforce to suffer through evident inferiority. It is true that most of the German airforce, and in particular the few fighter squadrons, were pinned down at Verdun; but there was also a deep rift between the German airforce and the troops struggling on the ground; the airmen, it was claimed, were never there when they were needed. The German infantry and even the artillery took little interest in their airforce and were reluctant to work alongside it. For as long as the German High Command kept its most qualified fighter pilots away from the Somme Front, the Allied fighters had control of the sky. Moreover, they retained this control by using the "offensive group" tactics that had been successful at Verdun. The central task was not in fact to "bring down the Boche", as was often said, but rather to guarantee clear skies for the observers so that their work would be of maximum use to the ground forces. And to these generally intimidatory tactics the actions of the pilots most suited to individual combat added the spectacle of mid-air duels and victories.

The adoption of these tactics coincided with the rise of Guynemer, an apprentice mechanic in January 1915, then a trainee pilot in February,

who gained his wings in April. The shy young corporal who came to the N-3 squadron in June became the frail yet stubborn combatant who seized his first triumph on 19 July 1915. A year later he had become simply "Guynemer". The 17 July 1916 saw his tenth victory, 4 September his fifteenth, and before the year was out he had scored his twenty-fifth. These victories were not quick kills of the type notched up by later aviators but fierce combats that Guynemer described thus: "I cling to my prey as if I am in a rage."

What a contrast he made with "old Dorme", the stocky Lorraine peasant startlingly identified with his single-seater fighter. Taciturn and slow on the ground, smiling and not without a touch of mockery, he would reconcile his grim task with unceasing Christian observance, writing to his family: "This evening I came across a pretty little two-seater going quietly back to base having just done its reconnaissance. I took it by surprise and shot it down in cold blood, pumping ten bullets into its undercarriage from less than ten metres away. The devil take their souls!"

By the time the battle of the Somme had stabilised, Guynemer, the champion of the N-3 unit, had scored 19 victories; Nungesser from the N-65 had won 14, Navarre 12, Dorme 11, Lenoir 10, Chaput and Chainat 9 each, Hertaux and Deuillin 7 each. These victories owed much to undeniable progress in technology: firstly, the Nieuport "Baby" had been fitted with a 110 h.p. engine, and a magazine containing 100 cartridges; then the Spad with its 140 horsepower Hispano-Suiza engine had been brought into service; its speed and synchronised machine-gun were to

make it the king of the skies. But the delicate period of transition in which mechanics and pilots familiarised themselves with the new aircraft and cured it of its inevitable teething troubles coincided with a resurgence of the enemy airforce, which had also been supplied with new planes. Halberstadt biplanes and single-seater Albatrosses with engines of almost 200 h.p., better armed than any Allied aircraft and far better climbers, were to bring added relentlessness to aerial combat. Immelmann had fallen, but his successor Boelcke scored victory after victory in his turn. German official despatches credit him with 10 victories by 3 March and 40 by 26 October, when he was killed as a result of a collision with one of his own squadron. Most of all, as the battle got bogged down in the autumn fog, rain and mud of Picardy, the task of the observers was getting harder each day. It was a time of heavy losses, and weary duties for that section of the fighter airforce dedicated to protecting the humbler two-seaters.

There were also problems of organisation. The airforces of both sides had grown so rapidly that they were barely understood except by those who had created them. It was now necessary to integrate military aviation into the fighting forces as a whole, and especially into the economy, technology and industry that fed the war effort. On the German side General von Hoeppner was chosen to execute this task from the end of 1916. Thanks to his progress (in France it was more than a year before comparable measures were implemented), the enemy airforce was to make up lost ground and turn 1917 into a hard year for the Allied aviators.

Charles Nungesser in his Nieuport in October 1916.

(Below) aeroplanes of the first "Stork Squadron", the N-3 at the Cachy airfield (Somme) 10 September 1916: Guynemer's Spad, and, behind, four Nieuport "Babies".

2/Lt. Guynemer and Capt. Brocard before the battle of the Somme.

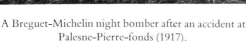

A Breguet-Michelin night bomber after an accident at Palesne-Pierre-fonds (1917).

A Moineau three-seater observation plane with one engine and two propellers.

THE ORDEAL OF 1917

The last weeks of 1916 had been harsh. The simple fact of the matter was that the Allied airforces were burdened by a technical handicap for which not even the best methods of deployment and the bravest airmen could compensate. Of the 1,418 French aircraft at the Front on 1 November 1916, 328 were single-seater fighters, but of these only 25 were Spads. Out of 837 reconnaissance planes, 802 were incapable of defending themselves effectively in combat and were classified as "sitting ducks". This state of affairs had probably not gone unnoticed at the rear, but mistakes had been made which would take more than a year to rectify, and among the new types of observer planes the most sought after model was being produced in nowhere near sufficient quantities. Lastly, the efforts to equip large military units with an airforce suited to their needs had led to the creation of many new squadrons out of nothing, the leadership of which was entrusted to personnel who had never been in a position of command before. It was this watered

down airforce, assembled before Chemin des Dames, that had the task of preparing the spring offensive. The dreadful weather hampered damage checking missions, and the air crews had to fly very close to the ground to gather the information on which the timing of zero hour and the big day itself would ultimately depend. In fact if information gained from aerial reconnaissance had been allowed to prevail, the offensive would not have been launched at dawn on 16 April. Be that as it may, the French airforce experienced significant reverses during this major setback.

Ranged against it was a larger and better equipped enemy airforce, especially the fighter units in which Boelcke and von Richthofen had inculcated new tactics and inspired renewed zeal. The dedication displayed by the French air units was total, but they suffered grave losses. Captain Doumer – a great wartime figure – was killed on 26 April during a protection mission. Despite their sacrifices the observer planes, which found an additional enemy in the weather, came to know the bitter taste of defeat.

As 1917 went on, however, the most unsuitable equipment was eliminated. The new units trained

hard and operations with a limited objective helped them to regain their best form of 1916. Despite many losses French observer teams were ready to take advantage of a range of new equipment available to them by the beginning of 1918.

The same technical inadequacy paralysed French bomber units in 1917 too. Since 1916, with the exception of raids on Karlsruhe, bombers had drawn attention to themselves mainly by audacious long-distance expeditions carried out by isolated pilots; these raids, however, had little or no military value. Even the elite bomber units such as the VB-101 or the F-25, had such imperfect equipment that they could only attack the enemy rear or the Rhineland towns with very light bomb loads. The days of the Happe unit's expeditions against Rottweil and Habsheim were long past: very heavy losses had put a stop to these bold raids. The "bomber groups" of 1915 had lost numerous units to enemy fighters and the Breguet-Michelin was to disappoint the hopes that had been placed in it. Once again the solution could only be supplied by technology, that is to say by pointing industrial production in the right direction: and that took time.

Sopwith observation and reconnaissance biplanes at an airfield on the Somme.

An advanced flying school behind the lines in 1918. Inset, left, the French pilot's insignia.

The observers' training centre at Sommesous. Inset, right, the French observer's insignia.

RECRUITMENT AND TRAINING

From 1916 onwards the place occupied by aviation in the war effort and also the losses sustained by the airforce raised an urgent recruitment problem: flying schools and training centres mushroomed as a result.

Some idea of the role they played can be gained by examining figures relating merely to French pilot training schools dependent on the army: 134 flying certificates were issued in 1914, 1,484 in 1915, 2,698 in 1916, 5,609 in 1917, and 6,909 between 1 January and 1 December 1918. Projected plans for 1919 envisioned a monthly "output" of 1,000 pilots who had not simply gained

A bizarre accident at the flying school at Plessis-Belleville.

their wings but had also been "finished" at special schools where they learned the art of aerial gunnery and how to perform aerobatics in single-

seater planes if earmarked for a fighter unit.

It was also necessary to train up mechanics and various other specialists in their thousands. The technical and tactical training of observers posed particular problems, namely the difficulty of matching quantity with quality for a job that could no longer be described as an attractive and glamorous alternative to the trenches. This training of tens of thousands of airmen and aeronautical specialists on both sides was one aspect of wartime aviation that was to have far-reaching consequences: the result was a vast aerial propaganda exercise, the effects of which were multiplied tenfold by the experiences of all those who at one level or another had been "in the airforce" or had somehow been associated with it.

A mechanic photographs a friend in front of a Nieuport of the N-3 unit at Vadelaincourt airfield. This picture illustrates the deep yearning of many ground staff, not content with the dirty and difficult job of mechanic, to share in the prestige and danger experienced by the air crews. Many great pilots, Fonck included, were mechanics first of all.

Side by side with the pilots and observer officers, especially in three-seater crews, were many non-commissioned officers and troops who served as machine-gunners, bomb-aimers, photographers and on-board mechanics. Inset: insignia of non-commissioned specialist flying personnel (machine-gunners, observers etc.)

The airship *L-49* forced to land near Borbonne-les-Bains on 20 October 1917.

The German airship *L Z-81* leaving its base to go on a bombing raid.

GERMAN AIRSHIPS FROM 1916 TO 1918

It was mainly against England that the Germans unleashed their airships in 1916. The losses incurred on these expeditions became proportionately heavier as British air defences were better organised, particularly around London. That the Germans persisted in these raids was doubtless an indication of the fact that they found them a useful way of acting upon British public opinion, which in turn caused the English authorities to retain a substantial part of their airforce at home. It also seems likely that repeated air-raid alarms slowed down British industrial production. Moreover, from the historical point of view we have adopted in this survey, it is interesting to note that the progress in aviation and in anti-aircraft defence prompted the German engineers to even greater efforts, the principal result of which was an increase in the gas capacity of rigid airships from 700,000 cu. ft. in 1914 to 2,300,000 cu. ft. in 1917; at the end of the war there were plans for a Zeppelin with a capacity of 3,700,000 cu. ft. Added to this, in an attempt to avoid their deadly enemies, cannons, missiles and, especially over England, aeroplanes firing incendiary bullets, the airship crews, led by men such as Strasser, Mathy and other great captains constantly made use of evasive manoeuvres, taking maximum advantage of the terrain over which they flew and acquiring unequalled skills in aerial navigation over long distances. Airship experiments cost the Germans dear. Of the nine dirigi-

bles that attempted to attack the industrial centres of the Midlands on the night of 31 January 1916, only two were still in service at the end of the year. One sank in the North Sea on its return journey the day after the raid, three were brought down over England, two made forced landings and a seventh had to land in Norway.

On 2 September 1916 sixteen airships – thirteen from the navy and three from the army – crossed the English coast. Only two reached metropolitan London and one of these was immediately shot down in flames by Lt. Robinson.

The forward gondola of the airship *L-59* leaving Jamboli (Bulgaria) for East Africa in the autumn of 1917.

The expedition of 23 September, launched by the navy alone with eleven airships, of which only one reached London, cost the Germans two of their newest Zeppelins, including the *L-33* which put down at Wigborough and was scuttled by its crew. And then, during the attack on 1 October, Mathy's Zeppelin, the *L-31*, was caught in the beam of the searchlights on its approach to London. "Perched atop the shafts of light as if upon the point of a pyramid" in the words of one witness, the airship was attacked and machine-gunned by Lt. Tempest. It ignited and crashed in flames at Potters Bar. From this time on London was to all intents and purposes denied to German airships. As a whole the skies over England were very dangerous: during the night of 27–28 November 1916 another two Zeppelins were brought down by British airmen. It was then that the German army gave up using its airships on the Western Front. The navy persisted in its bombing raids and in 1917 launched six attacks in which two airships were lost, and then it suffered the major disaster of 19 October. The eleven dirigibles that set out to attack England that night encountered dense fog and were blown off course by unexpected winds. Six returned to base. Of the five others, one crashed in Germany, another

was brought down by a cannon near Lunéville, the *L-49* had to put down at Bourbonne-les-Bains and the *L-45* at Sisteron, while the *L-50*, having touched ground in France when sixteen of its crew jumped from the gondola, then disappeared over the Mediterranean.

In 1918 Zeppelin missions were few and far between. The last, on the night of 5 August, cost the life of Commander Strasser, the commanding officer of the naval airship unit. He was on board the *L-70*, which was shot down in flames by the airmen Cadbury and Leckie.

In France there were only two raids on Paris in 1916, and the attack on Revigny on the eve of Verdun when the *LZ-77* was brought down on 20 March 1916. In 1917 Boulogne was bombed on 16 February.

On the Russian and Eastern Fronts, where anti-aircraft defences were sparser, airships were used for a long time with a great deal of success. From their base at Temesvar, they bombed Salonika on several occasions. From the base at Jamboli, they frequently reached Bucharest and once even got as far as Sebastopol.

But the most startling technical performance of all remains that of the *L-59*, a rigid airship 740 ft. long with a gas capacity of 2,400,000 cu. ft. This Zeppelin left Jamboli in the autumn of 1917 to go to the aid of the German forces in East Africa. It had reached the confluence of the two Niles south of Khartoum when it received a wireless message to turn back, having covered 4,350 miles in 96 hours. By the time it returned to base it had stayed airborne for six whole days and covered over 6,200 miles.

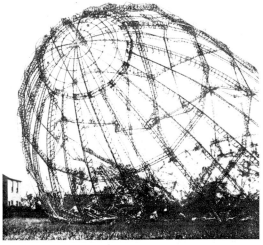

The Zeppelin *L-33* after being set ablaze by its crew on 24 September 1916 at Little Wigborough (Essex).

(Top) the airships *L-35* and *L-44* return to base on 25 September 1917 after an attack on England.

The Canadian Captain W.A. Bishop V.C., D.S.O., M.C., photographed on 6 August 1917.

FIGHTER PILOTS IN 1917

We have recently already seen that from 1916 the French airforce was the most specialised in its organisation and tactical deployment. In consequence the French fighter squadrons, far from being left to their own sporting instincts, were obliged to play a far more disciplined role in the aerial war as a whole. We have also seen that during the course of the conflict the Germans had had Boelcke and then Richthofen to instruct their fighter squadrons and train them to fly in formation in accordance with strict rules.

In the British airforce, on the other hand, even outside the fighter units, a sporting mentality seemed to be given free rein. Favoured by circumstance and technical advantage, all their pilots were fighters at the time of the Somme offensive.

But when at the end of autumn the new types of enemy aircraft began to appear in the skies, the British airmen carried on in the same frame of mind. While pilots such as Ball and MacCudden continued to notch up triumphs, many air crews aboard badly armed biplanes set out to do battle over the German lines and were lost in a one-sided fight. We should not forget that once these aerial battles started, they took on the inevitably fatal character of a duel to the death.

On 23 November 1916 Major Lance Hawker V.C., at the head of 24 Squadron of the Royal Flying Corps, joined battle with Captain Manfred von Richthofen over Bapaume. The two adversaries could only fire at each other from the front owing to their fixed machine-guns, Hawker aboard his little DH-2 with the engine at the back and therefore with clear forward views, and Richthofen in his more powerful Albatross. To

get the enemy in his sights the pilot had to position himself behind his opponent or, by gaining altitude, dive down on him from above. As they pursued each other in huge cartwheels the two planes climbed higher and higher, but soon, despite his deft handling of the agile DH-2, the inferior power of Hawker's engine became apparent and he was doomed. He tried to get back across the British lines using a zig-zag manoeuvre, but Richthofen followed him, took aim and despatched him with a bullet to the head. Such was the relentless and dogged character of a struggle between equals served by roughly comparable technology. One can only imagine how lesser fighters must have fared!

When the battle of Arras began in April 1917, the indomitable attacking spirit of the British airmen, who all too often ventured out in obsolete aircraft, was still apparent and led them to

German reconnaissance crews after a mission.

French fighter pilots at Manoncourt airfield.

Captain Guynemer setting out on a patrol shortly before his death in action on 11 September 1917.

German medal commemorating von Richthofen's victories.

Cavalry Captain Manfred von Richthofen (1892–†F1918) on 11 September 1917 after his 60th victory.

undertake almost suicidal missions: 44 aircraft were lost in one day alone on 4 April, and by British estimates 31 victories in the same month were attributable to Richthofen. Over Douai on 5 April, an aerial dog-fight took place between ten new Bristol fighter biplanes and five Albatrosses led by Richthofen. Three British planes were soon shot down. Every day the struggle grew more bitter, though Bishop, Ball and MacCudden also scored numerous victories. On 7 May, after a general free-for-all in which for the first time 56 Squadron pitted its new SE-5s equipped with Hispano engines against the enemy, the aeroplane piloted by Lothar von Richthofen, the group leader's brother, paired off in single combat with Ball's SE-5; the Englishman was killed, the German shot down at the same time, wounded by his adversary in the last seconds of a short life marked by 43 victories.

Then a bold step forward in German organisation made the British airmen's task even more difficult. Dealing with British air offensives occupied most of the German fighter pilots' time, and so at the beginning of July 1917 von Richthofen took command of a newly created German fighter wing that brought together four squadrons of

eighteen aircraft each. The squadron remained the basic tactical unit, but the wing made it easier to concentrate the fighters more quickly in one place.

As they became even more numerous in the skies, stacked above each other and often invisible, fighter pilots on both sides shared the same objective: to frustrate the enemy's missions and to protect and further their own. So many bullets were fired point-blank at vulnerable aircraft that the aviator's chances of a lengthy military career became increasingly slim.

Every day airmen set off to do battle from quiet airfields where the distant gunfire was scarcely audible. Passing from total safety to total danger they stalked each other and jockeyed for position in the sky, often high above the clouds and out of sight of the combatants on the ground, sometimes in sunlight that they alone could see. And every day the air operations bulletin announced laconically that "so and so has not returned to base".

On 5 May, Hertaux was severely wounded. On 25 May Guynemer won five victories. On the same day Dorme vanished over Flanders, shot down in battle after scoring 23 official victories. Commander du Peuty said of him that "he was a man who ordinarily would risk nothing, but when the right moment came he gambled all he had." Guynemer wrote: "The loss of Dorme is without doubt the greatest blow that the French airforce has ever suffered." However, it was to

bear an even greater loss: that of Guynemer himself on 11 September 1917.

After 31 victories Georges Guynemer had been promoted to the rank of Captain on 18 February 1917 at the age of 22. His score stood at 45 when, on the 11 June, he was made an Officer of the Legion of Honour. He was to score nine more kills and have exactly three months longer to live. Soon, as Commander Brocard feared, "the great spirit that animated this frail body would ultimately prove too much for the flesh." And as the 22-year-old himself said: "my most remarkable achievement is to have been wounded twice and shot down seven times." Yet he persisted in his foolhardy tactics. On 11 September, five days after his 54th victory, he set out on patrol with Lt. Bonzon-Verduraz over Flanders. Around 0935 he noticed an enemy plane in the distance and dived; his companion followed but was engaged by some other aircraft that appeared out of the mist. Left alone in the sky, Bonzon-Verduraz waited and then decided to return to base. No one at the airfield had seen Guynemer. He was later known to have been shot down by Lt. Wiseman, who was shot down in turn by Fonck three weeks later.

British two-seaters at the Cachy airfield in January 1917. On the wing strut of the aircraft on the right is the cloth pennant indicating the unit leader.

An Albatross shot down over the French lines in 1917; the distinctive black cross has been damaged by soldiers anxious for "souvenirs".

Breguet 14 A-2 two-seaters from an army reconnaissance squadron in February 1918.

AVIATION AND THE BATTLES OF 1918

The winter of 1917–1918 was a long, slow armed vigil, more sluggish even than the one before Verdun. There was a feeling that the outcome of the war was about to be decided, and there was also anxiety about the accumulation of enemy manpower and equipment all along the Western Front, especially the huge numbers of German reserves liberated by the Russian collapse, which were gathering in the central salient formed by the front line. From this region the enemy could transport their divisions by night to any new attack zone with equal speed. Hampered by the wintry conditions, the airforce had not been able to find out where this zone would be, and it seemed possible that the offensive might be launched on a number of possible fronts.

The German offensive began on 21 March. The attack was overpowering and opened a breach between the British and French armies opposite Montdidier; at the same time mysterious projectiles thought at first to have been dropped by enemy aircraft fell on Paris. The battlefield was enveloped in fog; the extent of the German advance was unknown. From 23 March the air-force re-established lost contact, constantly flew over the breach, strafed the ground with machine-gun fire and passed reconnaissance information on to the Allied units caught up in the battle as soon as they arrived by train and lorry. The 1918 campaign had begun: offensives, surprise attacks and counter-offensives followed one another in quick succession. The airforce, driven from its bases or hastily told to change sector, had to adapt to this new style of warfare. The problem was particularly difficult for observer planes trying to work with units on the ground, although this time the observers had at least been given decent equipment. Nearly the whole

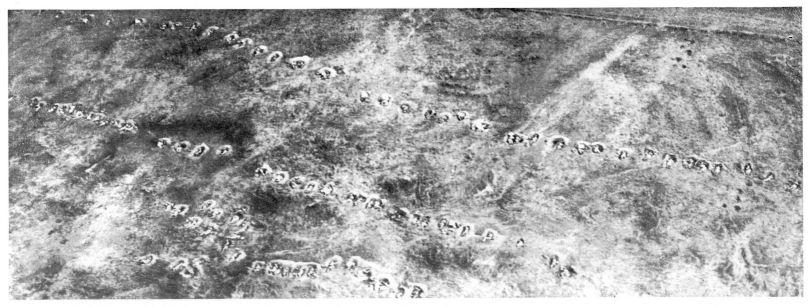

Aerial liaison with the infantry. Entrenched in hastily dug individual shelters, the foot-soldiers watch the aeroplane which is reporting their advance.

The daily transition from war to peace. Nungesser, second from left, returning with his comrades
to the officers' mess at Mont-l'Evêque (Oise) on 30 August 1918.

Mosloy farm airfield caught in the combat zone
(August 1918).

observation force had been supplied with excellent new two-seater Breguet-14 or Salmson aeroplanes, topped up by valuable and manoeuvrable two-seater Spads and Sopwiths. A serviceable and heavily armed three-seater, the Caudron R-11, had also replaced the Letort.

Once battle had commenced there was little time for specialisation. Aircraft belonging to division, army corps and heavy ordnance plunged headlong into the struggle and suffered such steady losses that they were often forced to take over each others' roles. Their permanent object was to maintain contact with the units in the ground battle, to provide low-level reconnaissance, and to direct artillery fire on to new enemy targets as these appeared on the battlefield. In this chaos there was total cooperation between all these aeroplanes that were flying at altitudes between 300 and 600 ft., supporting and protecting each other, and of which all the aircrews shared a common aim: to supply information.

Whenever there was a lull in the fighting for a matter of days or weeks, squadrons drained of pilots, observers and equipment had to be reassembled. But the fear of what tomorrow might bring haunted everyone; for this reason pilots flew continuously, countless photographs were taken, the enemy's advance and rear positions were scrutinised daily for clues as to their intentions. The tasks of army observation squadrons, and later of the "aerial reconnaissance group" led by Captain Weiller which carried out long distance missions, were of crucial importance.

This group studied the build-up of military hardware anywhere between 75 and 100 miles behind the German lines. It brought back photographs taken from a height of 20,000 to 23,000 ft., the work of isolated teams and sometimes of single pilots. Of particular strategic interest were the enemy marshalling yards and unloading points, areas containing large concentrations of depots and bivouacs.

The aircraft working for the army corps penetrated up to 20 or 25 miles behind enemy lines. In this narrower but still extremely large band of territory they also kept a daily watch on the slightest movements of men and equipment, and reported back any hint of suspicious activity. On 15 July, when the German "Friedensturm" offensive was unleashed in Champagne, Allied headquarters had already been made aware of the minutest details of its preparation by the air unit attached to the French 4th Army.

The French air offensive in the 1918 campaign had been planned for a long time. Two new factors helped to transform the situation. First, the appearance of a new daylight bomber, the Breguet 14 B-2, which had a 300 h.p. engine, petrol for five hours' flying and a ceiling of 20,000 ft.; and second, the implementation of the so-called "4,000 aeroplanes" programme, which was already sufficiently advanced to ensure genuine numerical superiority on the main front.

Fonck checking the accuracy of his shooting in May 1918 by firing from 20 yards at a ten centime coin.

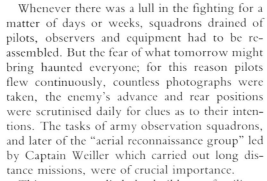

Checking the ammunition belt for the synchronised machine-gun on a Spad.

Jean Chaput (1893–†F1918) after a dog-fight in which he scored his seventeenth and eighteenth victories.

German L.V.G. aeroplane and crew shot down on 28 May east of Nesle.

A 1918 Albatross fighter in flight.

Reconnaissance of enemy communications on the eve of the German offensive in Champagne.

In fact, on 1 April 1918, the French airforce had 2,750 aeroplanes at its disposal: 1,400 for observation purposes and 1,350 intended for offensive missions. Unlike the observer aircraft, not all of the offensive group were immediately integrated into the various military units on the ground. Once the combat units whose job was to protect observer planes had been assigned and despatched, there remained a reserve force which from the beginning of 1918 numbered 600 aircraft, mainly fighter planes and day bombers. This force was organised into squadrons which were grouped together under Commander Le Révérend, and then on 14 May became the First Air Division under General Duval. This formation should have been the most important factor in the success of the French aerial offensive during the last eight months of the war. But in practice it did very little to modify the outcome of an aerial campaign in which victory and defeat were really determined by the relative

strengths of the opposing sides and by the exacting demands of the war on the ground.

How could the Division stand aloof when on 21 March 1918 the British front collapsed above Montdidier? From then on there could only be one order: keep in touch with the infantry and hold back the enemy for as long as possible. The offensive airforce was thrown into the breach, machine-gunning columns on the ground and noting the progress of the advance: it defended as well as observed. How could it stand aloof when the enemy streamed down from the heights of Chemin des Dames towards Château-Thierry? The Air Division took over the role of the artillery. Only a huge surplus of men and machines could have permitted the luxury of a force whose sole aim was to "wipe out the enemy airforce" independently of the struggle on the ground.

The creation of the First Air Division gave

daylight bombers a unity and cohesion which allowed them to carry out formidable raids. However, it was unable to mount joint bomber and fighter expeditions, partly because single-seaters could not fly deep into enemy airspace without placing themselves in jeopardy, and partly because once battle was joined on the ground they could not be spared from the task of dealing with enemy planes intent on attacking Allied observation and range-finding aircraft. In 1918, as in the previous year, the French fighter squadrons though differently organised on the whole fought the same kind of engagements as before. Once again the public thrilled to their triumphs and mourned their losses.

With Guynemer gone, it was the small, resolute Fonck, a cool-headed and deadly marksman, who topped the list of French aces. At the end of March he had claimed 33 victories while Nungesser had 31 and Madon 25. On 9 May Fonck shot

The customary opponents of the "Richthofen Circus": Major E. Mannock, D.S.O., his officers and the squadron mascots at the Saint-Omer aerodrome on 21 June 1918. The aeroplanes are SE 5-A single-seater fighters with 220 h.p. Hispano-Suiza engines.

lost; he had shot down 20 Drachen balloons and 15 aircraft. On 5 October Garros, a truly great and heroic pioneer, finally lost his life in aerial combat. On 27 October Coiffard, with 34 victories under his belt, of which 14 had been scored in the space of 22 days, was mortally wounded during a protection mission. Strangely enough the British, who up to 1917 had sacrificed so much to their hunting instincts, were admirably self-controlled for a change. In particular, confrontations between fighter units were subordinated to the protection either by close escort or by offensive patrolling of observer and range-finding planes.

For the fighter pilots themselves the struggle became even more bitter. The Germans used the astonishing climbing capability of their Fokker triplanes to good advantage, and it proved necessary to fit the SE-5 with a more powerful engine, until the appearance of the Sopwith "Camel" finally re-established equality. It was at this stage – during the spring of 1918 – that two momentous events took place. On 23 March there was an aerial battle over Le Catelet involving more than 70 British and German planes. It lasted nearly half an hour. Eighteen planes went down, nosediving in flames, exploding in mid-air or spinning slowly as they plunged to earth. Fourteen of them were British.

But 21 April was an even blacker day for the Germans. At dawn, the 20-year-old English Captain Roy Brown of 209 Squadron dragged himself to his aeroplane in order to go out on patrol. He was exhausted and had not eaten but he set out from the airfield accompanied by six comrades. Over the confused area where the great battle was taking place on the ground, the seven Sopwith Camels ran into about twenty enemy fighters. Caught up in the free-for-all, Lt. May, a young newcomer to the squadron, shot down a Fokker in flames. Then, obeying strict orders not to engage in combat and to avoid "dog-fighting", he dived earthwards and flew west at a height of 200 ft. A red triplane broke away from the battle and

Von Richthofen, under the wing of his aeroplane, being prepared for take-off.

down six planes on two patrols one hour apart. His first three victims, killed ten and then five seconds after each other, all came down within 800 yards of each other. Fonck had fired only twenty-two bullets. By 11 November Fonck had 75 official victories to his credit. Nungesser had 43, Madon 41, Bourjade 28, Pinsard 27, Haeglen and Marinovitch 22 each, Hertaux 21 and Deuillin 20. French losses had also been heavy. On 6 May Lt. Chaput perished; on 19 May the great American fighter pilot Lufbery, with 17 kills to his credit, went down after a long association with the French airforce in the La Fayette squadron. On 1 August Guérin was killed on take-off after 23 victories in 14 months. On 16 September Boyau, as great an airman as Chaput, was also

Major W.G. Barker, V.C., D.S.O., M.C., and his Sopwith Camel.

swooped down towards May's biplane. Seeing this, Roy Brown dived in pursuit of the pursuer, fixed him in his sights and fired. Manfred von Richthofen, the pilot of the Fokker, fell to earth, his heart pierced by a single bullet. His enemies, in accordance with a tradition which the British airforce followed throughout the war, buried him with full military honours.

Shortly before his death Richthofen had advocated the replacement of the Fokker triplane as a matter of the utmost urgency, since by then it had been matched and surpassed by the enemy. Perhaps this appeal hastened the development of that truly great fighter aircraft, the Fokker D-7 biplane, which the Germans used to fend off Allied fighters right up to the Armistice.

Richthofen's coffin being carried into Bertangles cemetery by six British officers.

An enemy's funeral: Richthofen buried at Bertangles on 22 April 1918. Airmen from No. 3 Squadron of the Australian Flying Corps fire a military salute.

ROUNDELS AGAINST BLACK CROSSES

The four photographs we have reproduced on the following pages represent the most extraordinarily striking images that we know of relating to the war in the air. In our mind there is no doubting the authenticity of these photographs taken in mid-combat by a Royal Air Force fighter pilot. This airman installed a camera in the fuselage of his aeroplane, set the shutter before take-off to make one exposure per flight, and took a single photograph in mid-combat. Most of the pictures obtained in this way were taken in the same line as the machine-gun sights so the pilot tried position-ing the camera obliquely, or even pointing it backwards or upwards. These experiments re-duced the already slim chance he had of obtaining centrally positioned images, but when this bold technique succeeded he was rewarded with some of the most striking shots of all.

In total probably a hundred negatives – of which fifty-seven depict aerial combats – were obtained by this extraordinary amateur photo-grapher on the lookout not only for enemy fighter aircraft but also for intensely personal souvenirs of the war. He too, however, was eventually shot down and killed.

Because his photography was a secret between himself and a few friends (he was in fact flagrantly violating the regulations relating to the use of personal cameras at the Front), we know very little about the actual techniques that he em-ployed. It seems likely, however, that his camera made use of a very wide aperture and an extreme-ly brief exposure. In fact, despite occasionally having been taken at almost point blank range from a fast-moving aircraft, the images are re-markably sharp. Above all, however, they are exceptionally poignant. The only words that could possibly be adequate to describe them are those of the lost pilot himself, extracts from the diary that he kept throughout his life at the Front. The commentary provided by this methodical man describes precisely and truthfully, and with directness and unselfconscious humour, the con-ditions in which each image was obtained.

Aeroplanes: British S E 5, German Albatross. From the Cockburn-Lange collection.

THE EAGLE'S PREY

"Caught rather unusual picture to-day. Here is shining example of what not to do when having a bit of a do with the Huns – *let him get on your tail*! Let us hope that the fledglings from C.F.S. will study this picture long and carefully in the next war and that their instructions will point out the lesson it contains. Wish I could send them a print now! Here is little T. . . A. . ., getting pipped for the first time and the last time. Poor little beggar. I had placed the camera to snap backwards and trust to luck if I got anything. I did, and wish to God I hadn't. It makes me boil to see them sending us pilots now who've only had five or six hours in a fighter: its just chicken-feed for these Huns we've been up against . . . . ."

". . . Don't know what their Squadron is but they are a crack lot of pilots and we are having a bloody time with them. Had begun to think I was fairly good pilot, but after Tuesday and to-day when I came home full of Krupp steel my ego is somewhat deflated. Ones in particular which give us the most trouble are a crowd of vari-coloured parrots, but they can fly like eagles. Met up with them to-day and they got that kid A. . . God knows how many more of us they will collect before we see the last of them."

Aeroplanes: British S E 5s, German Fokker D-7s From the Cockburn – Lange collection.

THE ACES RISE AND FALL

"*Thursday*. Bloody day for our squadron with a vengeance. . . . Met our Fokker friends again and had glorious (?) fight all by ourselves. Got four of them, one of which is credited to me, so I feel wonderful, oh wonderful. Yes, by God, wonderful that's the word. Two of my men gone and one of Mac's, and all we can do is to sit here impotent against those powers that mow down men like those three . . . As we got four and probably lost three we are one up on the Hun anyway. Our flights were stepping along God's highway in the bright sunshine above the feathery clouds (Shakespeare probably) in the hope of not seeing any Huns to spoil a pleasant patrol, and then we did just that very little thing. Had no choice in the matter so watched them. They were below us so we slipped into the sun and went down on them. Just as I was about to shoot a nice one he slipped away from me, and I flopped around like a clumsy hen, trying to find an inexperienced Hun! But apparently they were all au fait to-day with the gentle art of fighting, so I made up my mind I had to fly or be flopped. Got a Hun in my ring sight several times, but never for long enough to shoot. Managed after a while to attract the attention of a fellow with the letter P on his wing. We climbed around each other in the most approved style. I tried a little trick H —— had pounded into my thick nut, the beer boy made the expected move, and I pipped him. The photo shows the Hun just before he dropped down in a spin and then burst into flames. I was stupidly watching him go down when I heard an all too familiar sound, I had just enough time for a quick turn to avoid going the same way as my prize. No chance of resting on your laurels in this game. I had my hands full trying to avoid this newcomer when someone – I think it was McE . . . got him off my back and I found myself in a cloud."

Aeroplane: British Nieuport N 17. From the Cockburn – Lange collection.

"HEARD SOMEBODY'S WING GO AND FOR A SECOND THOUGHT IT WAS MINE"

"*Thursday*. Got stunning snap to-day, although pretty awful. Up this afternoon and after had been over lines about half hour saw scrap between Nieups. from — Sq. and two-seaters. Turned into it and as we got near saw Hun burning up, Nieup circling it. Hun scouts appeared just then and scrap became general. Noticed the Nieup. which was circling Hun in flames suddenly pull loop and just then one of the scouts dashed across my sights and I popped at him. Heard somebody's wing go and for second thought it was mine – what a feeling! Second later saw Nieup. going down in pieces. Suppose scout which I pipped had hit him first when he was on top of loop, or he may have been badly hit and strain of loop broke plane up. Didn't see my Hun go down so don't know if I hit him or not. Jock developed plate this evening and result sort of hit us amidships. Pretty ghastly. Must have broken up at instant I pressed the trigger when popping the Hun. We got through to — Sq. and inquired about their losses to-day. Only lost one, new man. . . . Only thing can imagine is that if he was new man probably so excited at bagging Hun that forgot he was in France with war on and looped, fatal thing to do, never know where hit, in scrap."

Aeroplanes: British Bristol, German Fokker D-7 From the Cockburn – Lange collection.

"SAW THE TWO PLANES LOCKED IN A DEATH GRIP"

"Sunday. God! What a sight! Can still hear crash of impact. Scrap started over Bristol which was doing shoot over near ——. We were above Bristol when Fokkers hove in sight, and without waiting to see what was what dived on Bristol. All got there together, and for second air was tight jumble of wings and tails. Impossible to try to hit anything, to get out for air and flying room was first thing. When I finally did get on a Hun's tail and press the triggers I saw the Bristol out of the corner of my eye swerve past me and then an awful rending crash. Looked back and saw the two planes locked in a death grip, and as I kicked over to avoid another Hun's fire saw both of them go down breaking apart. Scrim didn't see it actually happen but saw it going down afterwards. He said he had shot a Hun, got a good burst into his cockpit, but Hun didn't go down, seemed to nose up and then dive as if under control. More than likely Hun Scrim hit was either killed outright or knocked unconscious and plane was flying wild when it crashed into the Bristol. No one will ever know. The Admiral wild about the picture, danced around in his excitement. (Gives you something to think about when its all over!)"

A group of twin-engined Gotha G-11s lined up at the factory testing airfield ready to go into service.

GERMAN BOMBERS

The salient position of the German front lines, the location of large towns and vital supply centres close to the Allied line and the proximity of the enemy's capital cities gave the Germans three good reasons to make use of aerial bombardment, especially as they had nothing to fear from damaging reprisals. The lay-out of the Front determined the principal targets; concentrations of equipment, supplies and manpower pointing to an imminent offensive were all suitable and constantly accessible objectives; any delay in the arrival of reinforcements from the rear once an attack was under way could have grave military consequences. The Germans thus had a justifiable interest in developing an effective bomber.

The German airforce was therefore supplied with twin-engined aeroplanes from 1916 onwards. One of the most common was the Gotha, a name that for the Allies at least came to be used for all aircraft of this type. They were biplanes, nearly all with wingspans of between 60 and 90 ft., and were usually driven by two 260 horsepower Mercedes engines. Empty, they weighed between 5,300 and 6,400 lb., and were capable of carrying total loads of 2,600 to 4,400 lb. Depending on the amount of fuel on board, the weight of the bombs could vary from 1,300 to 2,200 lb. They could strike effectively at any target located 175 to 375 miles from their bases.

Over the Western Front itself, where the constant presence of Allied fighters had to be taken into account, Gothas were seldom used except at night. However raids against remoter targets such as London were carried out in daylight and in force, especially in 1917.

As well as directing efforts towards the production of the Gotha bombers, the Germans instructed certain aircraft manufacturers to specialise in the development of "giant" planes. As early as 1912 the Russian engineer Sikorsky had pioneered this field with his famous "Ilya Murometz". In the winter of 1914–1915 the Siemens-Schuckert firm produced a 440 horsepower four-engined aircraft. This experiment inaugurated a technical effort which in 1918 culminated in the R-VIII, a biplane with a wing-span of 157 ft., six engines each of 300 horsepower housed in an engine room in the fuselage which could also accommodate the mechanics and from which power was transmitted to the four propellers, an unladen weight of 23,100 lb. and a payload of between 5 and 7 tons including fuel for an eight-hour round trip at about 80 mph. Although the R-VIII was the largest of the "giant" aircraft, a total of 64 aircraft of 20 different types were constructed in this range by the six designated firms. The first of these were used on the Eastern Front at the end of 1916 where they were principally used to bomb stations on the Riga-Petrograd railway line and enemy strongpoints on the island of Œsel. The conception and development of so many diverse types of aircraft presented German engineers with some very difficult technical problems; they had mixed success in overcoming these difficulties, but it is

undeniable that their research alone represented a major technical achievement. The military significance of the airborne giants, on the other hand, was negligible; only twenty were ever used in combat, in which they covered a total of 30,000 miles and dropped just 110 tons of bombs. This may be compared with a total tonnage dropped by all German bombers on Allied targets between March and July 1918 of 2,750 tons, of which 350 tons were dropped in a single week.

The chief targets of the 27 medium bomber squadrons which by the end of the war had been grouped into 8 wings were "sensitive points" in the Allied rear. Dunkirk, Calais, Saint-Omer, Amiens, Châlons, Nancy, railway centres with important marshalling yards all suffered repeated attacks. On 8 October 1917 a squadron of German biplanes also accompanied the attacking infantry on the coast of Flanders, and on 25 April 1918, during the Mount Kemmel offensive, four enemy squadrons comprising almost 200 aircraft took part in the attack.

Paris was not raided by Gothas until 1918 during the night of 30–31 January, on the 8 and 11 March, and 15–16 September. Although they left their mark on the memory of Parisians, these expeditions encountered increasingly stiff opposition from anti-aircraft defence, and ultimately did not inflict enough material or moral damage to justify the resources that the Germans had committed to them. During the whole war the city of Paris, including its suburbs, was hit by 746 projectiles dropped from aircraft which killed 206 people and wounded 603. In contrast, between 23

The largest of the German "giant" bombers: the Siemens-Schuckert R-VIII with a wing-span of 157 ft.

The central fuselage and crew members seen from the right-hand engine gondola, symmetrical with the one seen in the background.
Photographs taken in mid-flight on board a German "giant" bomber.

One of the bomber crew gaining access to the gun position on the upper wing.

The engine and wheels of a giant German bomber shot down in 1918.

Defensive measures: (top), a false airfield near Lunéville, designed to deceive enemy bombers; (far left) an anti-aircraft gun on its revolving stand; (centre) a swivelling searchlight in its emplacement; (centre right) barrage balloons hidden from aerial observation; (far right) experimental emmission of smoke camouflage.

March and 3 August 1918 long-range cannon killed 876 and wounded 256 with just 303 shells.

Because of the lack of a genuine "night fighter" air force, the defence of Paris was chiefly the responsibility of the artillery, aided by listening posts and searchlights. Smoke camouflage was probably more successful at revealing than hiding the target. As for the "false Paris" project which was designed to direct enemy bomb crews from the prime objective, it failed to take any account of the Germans' own nocturnal navigation equipment and the many natural reference points that would guide the bombers to their intended target. In any case, it was implemented too late to be put to the test.

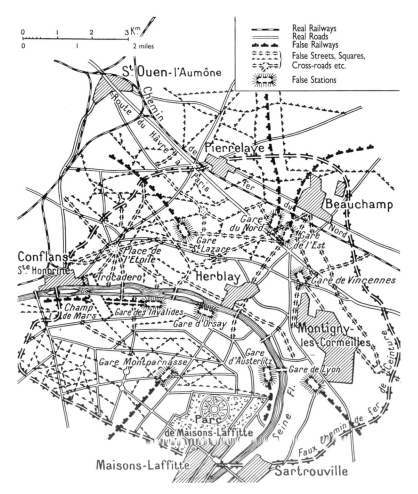

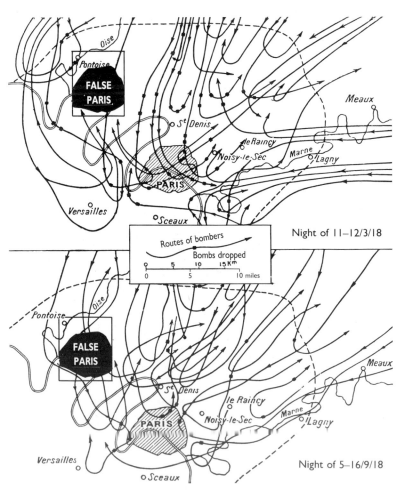

"False Paris" designed and laid out by Jacopozzi.

Two typical air-raids on Paris during 1918.

THE DEFENCE OF LONDON

The German 3rd Bomber Squadron, which was formed in 1917 and based near Ghent, was located only 175 miles from London. After airship attacks on the British capital had been proved a failure this squadron continued the bombing campaign, formations of German bombers attacking London in broad daylight. They were infinitely less vulnerable to anti-aircraft fire, and they also had a very good chance of avoiding the British fighters. It was not far from the coast – where the attackers could first be spotted – to the capital itself and the fighters could not take off instantly, even when kept on permanent alert, much less immediately climb to 10,000 to 13,000 ft. Worse still, having arrived at the same height as the intruders, nine times out of ten the defending fighter pilots could see nothing of them. This is difficult to understand for people who have never flown, but is unquestionably true; an aeroplane has to be directed against an intruder *from the ground* because it is only from the ground that the attacker is constantly visible during a daylight raid.

From a total of 66 fighters scrambled on 5 June 1917, not one managed to make contact with the attacking German force. On 13 June, at midday, 14 Gothas dropped 72 bombs on London, killing and wounding 594 people, and only 5 out of 94 British fighters got anywhere near them. On 7 July, 95 fighters attempted to engage 22 bombers and managed to shoot down two; on 16 July, when 16 Gothas attacked Harwich, none of the 121 fighters sent up met an enemy. But a radical reorganisation of London's aerial defence, under-

Anti-aircraft nets held up by balloons on the outskirts of London. (Cables emphasised by retouching.)

taken from 31 July 1917 under General Ashmore, had an immediate effect. Aeroplanes were kept in the air on recognised patrol routes, and the direction of the enemy was indicated by white arrows

positioned on the ground. The German attacks on 12, 18 and 22 August were repulsed, costing the enemy five bombers. The era of daylight bombing raids on London was over.

On 3 September the Germans switched to night attacks, the first of which got no further than Chatham, where 120 people were killed. On this occasion three Sopwith Camels took off, manoeuvred and landed again without any problems; it was the birth of the night-fighter. At the same time huge anti-aircraft nets were put into position. These were held up by captive balloons at a height of almost 10,000 ft., and forced attacking bombers to use the narrow space between the top of the net and their own "ceiling". The amount of airspace that had to be patrolled by defending fighters was thus considerably reduced. However, it was not until the night of 18–19 December that Major Murlis-Green managed to shoot down a Gotha over the sea. That same night, also for the first time, a "giant" bomber appeared over London. Another on 7 March dropped the first ever "one ton" bomb on the capital, killing 12 people and causing considerable material damage.

A solution to the problem of encountering the enemy was really found only when wireless sets were installed in fighter aircraft. Nevertheless, during the night of 19–20 May, out of 30 or 40 planes that crossed the coast, only 13 managed to reach London; 3 were shot down by fighters and 3 by groundfire, 1 had to land in Essex and 3 others were so badly damaged that they had to crash land in Belgium. Out of 84 defending fighters 14 succeeded in making contact with the enemy. This disaster signalled the end of night raids on London, where bombs had killed 541 people and caused damage estimated at £2 million.

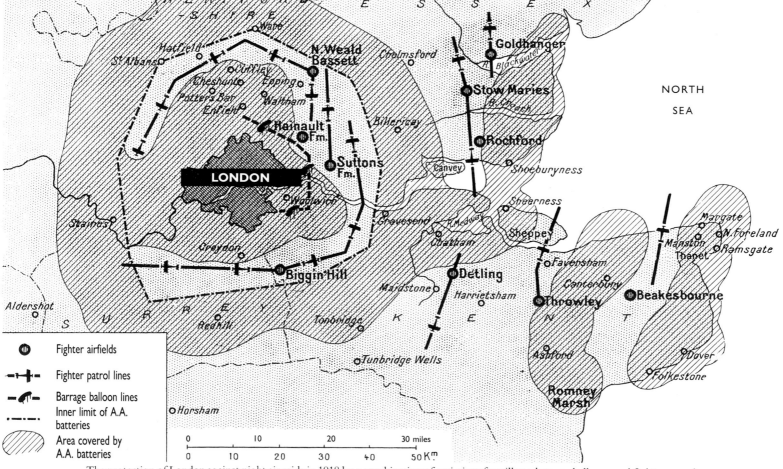

The protection of London against night air raids in 1918 by a combination of anti-aircraft artillery, barrage balloons and fighter aeroplanes.

A Breguet-Michelin B M-IV from the French 5th bomber group (GB-5) at Palesnes-Pierrefonds airfield in August 1916. Note the empty bomb-rack under the lower wing.

ALLIED BOMBING

After the discontinuation of large-scale expeditions by the Voisin bomber units and until the arrival of the Breguet 14s there had been only sporadic French bombing missions, for example the raid on Karlsruhe made in 1916 by the Kervillis unit in twin-engined Caudron G-4s. In 1917 the only raids carried out at all were those made by individuals such as Beauchamp, Daucourt and Mézergues. These aviators ventured out alone in Sopwith biplanes equipped with extra fuel tanks; their bomb load was militarily insignificant.

Then during the winter of 1917–1918 a series of sorties in the two-seater Breguet 14 B-2 demonstrated its pre-eminence. Capable of flying for five hours with a ceiling of about 20,000 ft., these aeroplanes could carry bomb loads of around 500 lb. far behind the enemy lines. Most important of all they were able to defend themselves effectively, and massive daylight bombing raids over the battle zone were carried out by increasingly formidable air units. In the first few weeks of 1918 the German fighter squadrons were too weak to prevent the French bombers from penetrating far behind the front lines; from April, however, the appearance and then the widespread use of the single-seater Fokker D-7 progressively limited offensive operations in daylight to the immediate

area of the Front.

The German attack in March forced the fighters of the French offensive airforce to be thrown into the breach and to concentrate on harassing enemy troops and convoys. The bomber squadrons also intervened in the conflict by machine-gunning

A Breguet-Renault two-seater setting out for the front lines.

and dropping bombs on ground targets, thus adopting the role of rear-guard cavalry while all the time waiting to act as pursuit cavalry six months later in an area stretching from Champagne to Marienburg.

Not until the German attack on the ground had been contained was the Air Division able to revert to its plan of testing the strength and determination of the enemy's aerial defence by large-scale daylight bomber raids. But in May the skies

above Picardy witnessed expeditions involving aeroplanes deployed over fronts of 5 miles or more at altitudes between 13,000 and 16,000 ft.: first 56 single-seater fighters escorting 23 two-seater bombers, then 24 heavy bombers flanked by 64 fighters.

The creation from 15 June of mixed wings, in which a fighter squadron and a daylight bombing squadron were combined under a single commander, was an unsuccessful innovation, soon abandoned, and in August, specific responsibility for protecting bomber units was given to three squadrons of three-seater Caudron R-11s, including the famous C-46 squadron trained by Lecour-Grandmaison. These aircraft could fire in any direction without breaking formation or changing course and therefore provided extremely effective flanking cover for the bombers, which had to remain in very strict formation. Where the R-11s were not available in sufficient numbers, direct protection was provided by Breguet-14s identical to the bombers they were escorting but without bombs. At the same time single-seater fighter aircraft criss-crossed the lines in the air sector where an engagement was taking place; they contributed indirectly to the protection of the expedition by making life harder for the enemy's reconnaissance aircraft and forcing these in turn to demand the assistance of their own fighter pilots.

A group of two-seater Breguet bombers ready for take-off at Sézanne airfield.

Anselme Marchal (†*F*1921),
who flew over Berlin.

General Petain accompanied by Commander Vuillemin
reviewing the American crews of 12 Squadron.

De Beauchamp (†*F*1916) on the right;
Daucourt facing him.

Apart from its strategic role, the Air Division was able to intervene tactically in the ground battle on numerous occasions, for example on 4 June 1918 when two bomber units and a combat group succeeded in halting a German attack in the Salvière valley to the east of the Villers-Cotterêts forest. The contribution of the Air Division on the Marne on 15 July was also crucial: 723 sorties, 24 enemy planes and one Drachen balloon shot down, 46 tons of bombs dropped on the approaches to crossing points and on the footbridges themselves. On 18 July the entire offensive airforce took part in the Mangin attack.

Once the Allies had regained the military initiative, the air division reverted to large-scale raids. On 29 August 250 aeroplanes bombed the area around Anizy-le-Château and Chavignon, dropping 48 tons of bombs. From 8 September the division took part in extremely fierce fighting in the Saint-Mihiel offensive. An expedition against Conflans was set upon by a German fighter unit in a particularly savage attack. During a forty minute battle, 8 aircraft were lost on each side.

The approach of the end was reflected in

An explosion at the Chuignolles depot south-west of Bray on 1 July 1918, caused by a British group bombing from 15,000 ft. on the leader's signal.

heavier and more frequent raids. On 1 November 40 tons of bombs were dropped on troops and convoys; in nine sorties on 3 November, 65 tons of bombs and 107,000 leaflets were dropped, and 30,000 bullets fired in the area around Montgon-Le Chesne.

On 10 November, under commander Vuillemin, 12 Squadron flew to Marienburg, 90 miles from its base, where it machine-gunned and bombarded the retreating troops.

French bomber units were not only handicapped by the geographical position of the front lines, but also by technical inferiority; owing to lack of direction, French industry never succeeded in developing aircraft comparable to the Gotha. After the problems experienced with the Breguet-Michelins, the best French bomber crews (Laurens, Partridge, Coupet, Mahieu, Bizard) continued to attack the enemy rear and Rhineland towns using Voisins identical to those that took part in the 1915 expeditions or even Farmans like the ones used by the Happe unit to raid Rottweil, Freiburg and Habsheim in 1915 and early 1916. The expeditions, in which losses were often

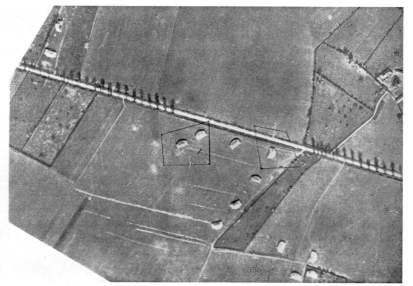

British airforce missions over enemy aerodromes in 1918: verification of damage inflicted by a night raid on the enemy aerodrome at Bazuel. On the right, a picture taken before the operation; on the left, a photograph taken at daybreak the next morning showing smashed aeroplanes and hangars.

A twin-engined Handley Page bomber being loaded with bombs in April 1918 at Cramaille airfield.

A twin-engined Handley-Page bomber as in the poster below.

heavy, even though the raids now took place at night, were rendered almost ineffective by the poor load-carrying capacity of the aircraft; in its first 200 sorties the F-25 unit dropped 40 tons of bombs; while in 41 so-called "reprisal" bombing raids from 1 January 1916 to 1 November 1918, just 16½ tons of explosive were dropped on German targets.

Starved of material resources, French long-range bombing expeditions from 1916 onwards sought mainly to demoralise German opinion by striking at targets which would ordinarily be considered safe from attack.

On 24 September 1916 Capt. de Beauchamp and Lt. Daucourt in Sopwith Camels bombed Essen, probably with little more than 100 lb. of bombs apiece, but having covered a distance of 500 miles behind enemy lines. On 17 November, exactly a month before being killed on the Verdun front, de Beauchamp left Lexeuil (Vosges) in his aeroplane *Ariel*, dropped bombs on Munich, crossed the Alps and landed it Italy near Venice. In 1916 Baumont, Mézergues and Gindre also bombed Essen and Frankfurt, and Marchal set off from Nancy in a Nieuport Special and dropped leaflets on Berlin; unfortunately he had to put down at Cholm, just short of the Russian lines, where he was taken prisoner. Together with Garros, Marchal subsequently escaped, as indeed did Mézergues, who had been forced to land on 22 August after bombing Freiburg.

Of the powerful twin-engined planes that were at last being developed in France, only the Farman F-50 was put into service before the Armistice and even then too late to exert any decisive influence

"What England wants!" A German propaganda poster of the spring of 1918, quoting the British socialist leader Joynson-Hicks: "Day after day we shall repeatedly bomb the industrial districts of the Rhineland with hundreds of aeroplanes until they have been completely destroyed."

on the outcome of the war. In the meantime the Italian Caproni was the only Allied heavy bomber of any significance during earlier campaigns. The two- and three-engined Capronis which took part

in the hopeless assault on the reservoir at Briey could carry between 900 and 1000 lb. of bombs; this can be compared with the 1800 lb. load of the English twin-engined Handley-Page bombers which, on being put into service in 1917, could penetrate 150 to 200 miles behind German lines. Handley-Page bombers, an improved copy of the Gotha, made up the greater part of the British Independent Air Force formed in 1918.

Created for long-distance bombing operations, this autonomous unit led by General Trenchard corresponded to the French First Air Division, though the French force was more closely involved in the battle on the ground. Although the British unit was never a swarm of aircraft blotting out the sun as depicted in German propaganda posters, from June to November the Independent Air Force was nevertheless tenacious in carrying out offensive raids against the Rhineland, and its losses were heavy.

This was because over Germany as well as over London, anti-aircraft defence had made great progress, especially in day and night fighters. Since June 1918 fighters on both sides had been guided to their targets by radio telephone or radio telegraph. Although this development meant that many Handley-Page bombers were lost, it seems that the Germans lost an even greater number of Gothas. From 13 to 30 September, for example, 14 Gothas were shot down at night by the British 151 squadron, which had been brought over to Artois from London. This unit accumulated a tally of 26 victories during the few weeks it was stationed in France and suffered no losses at the hands of the enemy.

A squadron of single-seater fighters stationed inside Germany is warned of an Allied bombing raid.

Rickenbacker.

Pinsard

Ball (1896–†*F*1917)

Coiffard (1892–†*F*1918)

Boyau (1883–†*F*1918)

Piccio

Haegelen

Lufbery (†*F*1918)

Marinovitch (1900–*F*1919)

Bourjade (1890–1924)

ALLIED ACES

High personal scores were at least in part a matter of being in the right place at the right time; many of the highest German scores, for, instance were obtained on the Russian front, but there is no doubt that they captured the public's attention. Of the French aces, Fonck (73 victories), Guynemer (54), Nungesser (43) and Dorme (23) have all been pictured on other pages. Others who shot down more than 20 enemy aeroplanes in the course of the conflict include Guérin (23), Boyau (35) and Coiffard (34), who were killed in action; Madon (41), Bourjade (28), Marinovitch (22), Pinsard who escaped from internment in Switzerland (27), Haegelen (22) and Deuillin (20), who survived the war, but of whom at least three were killed in later air accidents.

The British pilot Captain Ball was killed after

shooting down 43 enemy aircraft. The American ace Major Raoul Lufbery, who was brought up in France, was the hero and mascot of the La Fayette squadron, and died after his 17th victory. Frank Luke, another American, notched up 18. The American Capt. Rickenbacker finished the war with 26 officially acknowledged "kills". Major Baracca shot down 34 Austrian aircraft before himself being brought down by a bullet fired from the ground. Other Italian aces, Lt. Col. Piccio and Lts. Scaroni and Olivari accumulated totals of 25, 26 and 18 victories respectively. And lastly there is Lt. the Chevalier Willy Coppens de Houlthulst, the hero of the Belgian airforce, who triumphed in combat 36 times. The combat techniques employed by British pilots explained not only the great losses they suffered but also the glittering rise to fame of many of their aces. Although the British air command always refused to announce an official number of victories and

was unwilling to establish a "league table" of fighter pilots, some names stand out with that of Ball: Captain Mannock, killed after 73 victories, Major Bishop, who survived with 72 (both shown on earlier pages), Captain McCudden and Captain Fullard, who had shot down 54 and 48 German aircraft respectively when the war ended. The Canadian pilot Major Bishop is believed to have notched up 25 victories in 12 days.

Official German statistics attribute 80 victories to the Red Baron, Manfred von Richthofen, who was killed on 21 April 1918, and 60 to Lt. Ude, who was the foremost German ace at the time of the Armistice and survived to become a noted stunt pilot. Records indicate that seven German pilots shot down more than 40 Allied aircraft and sixteen shot down more than 30. Of the 72 airmen who received the highest distinction, the award with the French name "Pour le mérite", also known as the "Blue Max", 27 were killed.

Baracca (†*F*1918)

Deuillin (1890–†*F*1923)

Coppens

Heurtaux

Madon

A squadron of Capronis at Pordenone airfield (autumn 1916).

A formidable Italian bomber: the Caproni triplane, type 41, equipped with three 300 h.p. engines.

THE ITALIAN AIR FORCE AT WAR

It will be remembered that in 1911 the Italian air force was the first to be confronted with the realities of war in the air. The bombing and reconnaissance missions undertaken by Piazza and Moïzo on the ill-defined Libyan front probably had little in common with those carried out five years later by squadrons of multi-engined Capronis, but the experience had borne fruit and when Italy entered the war in Europe she already possessed an air strategy and airmen who could carry it out.

The Italian effort was not insignificant either. The number of aeroplanes built between 1915 and 1918 – about 12,000 – bore no relation to the quantities churned out by France, Britain and Germany, but we should remember that Italy's resources were smaller and the supply of raw materials more unreliable.

At the Armistice, the total strength of the "military air corps" was 74,000 men and about 5,000 officers; in the units on active service, the reserves and the training schools there was a combined total of 6,000 aircraft. About 1,000 "wings" were issued every month. The Italian air force claimed 643 victories and estimated its losses at 300 pilots and observers killed in combat and 1,300 killed in accidents, of which 500 were lost in the battle zone.

In liaison with ground forces, Italian squadrons carried out the same tasks as the French air force. As for the Italian fighter pilots, Piccio and Scaroni survived the war, but Commander Francesco Baracca, who scored 34 victories, was killed by a

bullet fired from the ground during the battle of the Piave while machine-gunning Austrian troops. Such interventions in the ground battle were frequently carried out by very large numbers of Italian aircraft. On 23 May 1917, 130 planes took part in the offensive; on 19 August 208 aircraft intervened on the Rombon front by the sea; on 24 August, the day Monte Santo was taken, 233 aircraft were used. Indeed the air force shared with the army many of the dangers of the Italian campaign, bombing passes, attacking con-

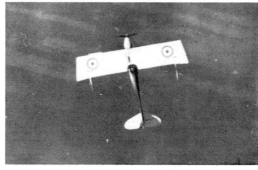

Gabriele d'Annunzio's two-seater.

voys and resupplying isolated detachments of troops stationed in inaccessible mountain areas.

Bombing expeditions were also carried out with effect from August 1915 in increasingly powerful multi-engined Caproni aircraft. On 21 June 1916, 34 daylight bombers attacked Pergine. The development of the 350 horsepower Caproni ushered in night-time bombing in January 1917. Pola was one of the most frequent targets: on 2, 8 and 9 August it was hit by 20 tons of bombs, and in September it was attacked constantly. On 4 October four multi-engined aircraft left Milan on a bombing raid which took them via the south of

Italy and over 260 miles of water to Kotor in Yugoslavia. When at the end of December the enemy responded by repeatedly bombing Treviso, Venice and Padua, Italian squadrons successfully attacked enemy airfields.

Caproni aircraft also served on the French front. An Italian bomber unit was stationed in France, where it launched attacks against the reservoir at Briey, Saint-Quentin, Lorraine and even Friedrichshafen. Between February and July 1918 it made 56 sorties and dropped 164 tons of explosives.

Lastly, we should also mention the amazing expedition made by the "Serenissime" squadron commanded by d'Annunzio on 9 August 1918, when thousands of leaflets were dropped over Vienna. The mission was successfully completed between 6.30 am and 12.40 pm; the aircraft involved – a two-seater and seven single-seaters – circled above the capital of the dual monarchy for twenty minutes before returning to base via Graz and Laibach. The Austro-Hungarian air force was, however, by no means an insignificant opponent. Leaving aside those occasions when the German air force supported them in major offensives – just as British and French squadrons came to the aid of the Italians – the Austro-Hungarian airmen made up in determination for what they lacked in technical advantage. Like Baracca, their greatest fighter ace Brumowsky scored a total of 34 victories. The Italian front frequently witnessed skirmishes between the opposing air forces which turned into full-scale battles: over Treviso on 26 December 1917, for example, the Austrians sent out 35 aircraft on two successive raids and lost 11, 3 of which were shot down by Lt. Scaroni.

The raid on Vienna (9 August 1918) made by the Italian squadron "Serenissime" led by Commander d'Annunzio. Left, the shower of leaflets dropped on the Australian capital; right, the crews that took part in the raid; in the middle, Gabriele d'Annunzio.

Left: General Sarrail, French commander-in-chief on the Salonika front, before his first flight. Right: a giant Sikorsky biplane with a crew of seven on the Russian front in autumn 1915. It had four engines on the lower wings, each driving a tractor propeller and streamlined fuel tanks between cabin and upper wing.

A French squadron on the Serbian front in 1915.

OTHER THEATRES

From the Dardanelles to Rumania, from Palestine to Mesopotamia, in Aden, India and East Africa, on the shores of the Red Sea and in the attack on Arkhangelsk, aeroplanes and seaplanes cooperated with the armies on the ground and with naval forces.

The vast area covered by the Eastern Front and the relative scarcity of Russian aircraft – despite help from the Western Allies – led to a very particular type of aerial warfare: daylight bombing over extremely great distances, long-range reconnaissance and, when an offensive was under way, liaison between columns of troops that might sometimes be hundreds of miles apart.

In terms of military aviation the most important of these secondary theatres of war after the Russian front was Macedonia. On 24 November 1915 the French airforce took up its position on the Salonika front and was to continue its opera-

tions there until it broke through to Üskub as part of the final offensive push launched by General Franchet d'Espèrey. For almost three years the bomber squadrons performed valuable work in this hostile mountainous environment: they attacked Guevgueli and Monastir in raids involving up to 32 bombers, and 16 aircraft bombarded the railway station at Strumitza. A special bombing mission against Smyrna was carried out successfully on 28 February 1916; seven aircraft were transported by sea to a point close to the target, from where they set out to attack the city and then flew 360 miles back to Salonika via Mytilene, Imbros, Lesbos or Mudros.

From the autumn of 1917 the Turkish airforce, which included many German units, became more aggressive. It was on this front that Costes, who soon had ten victories under his belt, first made a name for himself. No doubt he often encountered Lt. Eschwege, the best known German ace on the Mediterranean front. Eschwege had shot down twenty Allied aircraft when he

was finally killed in a trap sprung by some British balloonists. Knowing that he habitually attacked observation balloons, they placed a dummy in an observer's basket together with a powerful explosive device. When Eschwege's plane swooped down on this target and was about to fire at it, the bomb was detonated electronically from the ground and the Albatross was blown apart.

From July 1916 the British air force in the Middle East was at first organised into a brigade and then evolved into a much larger unit operating out of formidable bases in Egypt. Thirteen squadrons were refitted and coordinated from here, 3 on the Macedonian front, 3 in Mesopotamia and 7 in Palestine.

At the end of 1914 several British seaplanes made incursions along the coast of German East Africa. The mouth of the river Rufiji had been fortified by the crew of the cruiser *Konigsberg* which had sailed upriver to avoid detection by the enemy. The seaplanes revealed the ship's position and directed artillery fire on to her.

The airforce of the dual monarchy. Left: an Austrian observation biplane makes a forced landing in a cornfield on the Serbian front. Centre: a two-seater bomber about to take off. Right: airmen taking an oath of loyalty in the field on the accession of the Emperor Charles.

One of the British scout-airships put into service in the autumn of 1914, using an aeroplane fuselage as a gondola.

Front section of the gondola on the CM-14 airship *Caussin*, put into service in 1918. The gondola was made of duralumin, the gun was a 47mm cannon.

AIRSHIPS AT SEA

Airships played an important role in the war at sea, since seaplanes were still incapable of covering extensive areas, and proved an effective weapon in the struggle against German submarines. The British immediately understood the value of constant maritime surveillance by aircraft that could hover for long periods over the water and remain stationary if need be; on 5 August 1914 an English airship was already engaged in naval reconnaissance. Using an old Willows envelope and an aircraft fuselage as a makeshift gondola, a new light airship was improvised which had a gas capacity of 63,500 cu. ft. and was to be the prototype for a whole series of balloons christened "blimps". In 1916 these were replaced by "Sea Scouts", of which more than 50 were constructed. The balloons were cheap and quick to produce, and airship bases sprang up all along the English coast, organised into 19 "centres" and 12 stations without hangars where the dirigibles were moored like captive balloons. Twin-engined "coastal patrollers" were also brought into service, soon to be followed by the far more powerful "North Sea" type.

A "North Sea" airship transferring personnel at sea.

A three-lobed Astra airship coming to the aid of a seaplane off Bizerta.

By the time of the Armistice the British navy possessed 103 dirigibles compared with 7 at the beginning of the war. In total these aircraft had patrolled 2,587,000 miles in 83,160 hours; 339 hours in 1915, 7,078 in 1916; 22,389 in 1917; and 53,354 in 1918. Between June 1917 and October 1918 56 airships carried out 9,059 patrols and 2,210 escort missions. Losses were practically non-existent and almost all due to accidents.

The value of their operations was incalculable: reconnaissance, coastal surveillance, escorting convoys and hunting submarines were just some of the roles filled.

In France naval ballooning dated from 1916. In that year a little Zodiac scout balloon was constructed for reconnaissance purposes, and military observation balloons were attached to the naval service, while airship centres were set up in metropolitan France, on the south shore of the Mediterranean, and at Corfu.

About 45 airships were in service in 1917–1918, and about fifteen more were ready to be deployed at the time of the Armistice. These aircraft were mainly Zodiacs (VZ scouts with a capacity of 100,000 to 105,000 cu. ft. and two 80 horsepower Renault engines, ZDs with a 175,000 cu. ft. capacity) or Astras (AT cruisers with a capacity of

Two flexible Zodiac Z D airships of 1917 with a gas capacity of 210,000 cu. ft.

An Italian dirigible, which has been shot down, is photographed as it sinks.

Left: an American convoy seen from an Astra-Torrès escort airship off the Atlantic coast of France in summer 1918. Right: a dramatic battle with a submarine in the North Sea. The dirigible from which this photograph was taken has located a submarine and alerted the submarine chasers on the surface, which are dropping depth-charges in their wake. A large patch of oil, visible in front of and to the left of the ship coming from the right, proves that the target has been hit.

210,000 to 425,000 cu. ft.). In addition the Chalais-Meudon establishment supplied several rapid airships with 210,000 cu. ft. capacity. All these French dirigibles had two engines.

Eight AT and ZD airships flew without incident from Aubagne to Africa, seven to Algiers and one to Bizerta. The *AT-6* was, on 15 November 1917, the first airship to cross the Mediterranean.

These units of the French navy made 1,128 sorties in 1917 and stayed in the air for 4,164 hours. In 1918 they made 2,201 sorties clocking up 12,133 flying hours in journeys totalling 528,000 miles. Apart from the loss of a T type Chalais-Meudon airship which caught fire mysteriously over the Mediterranean before it had entered service, and the destruction of a scout balloon which exploded after colliding with the cliffs at Le Havre, only the airships *AT-5* and *AT-8* were lost. Only on the latter occasion were any crewmen killed. The dirigibles had a dual role to play: first, they hunted and destroyed mines and submarines; second, they escorted convoys of

A British coastal patrol airship, sinking in the North Sea after being shot down in flames. (Photograph taken from a German seaplane.)

ships coming from the Eastern Mediterranean or America. French airships spotted and attacked more than 60 submarines and destroyed over 100 floating mines. Like the British they also located and picked up survivors from torpedoed ships or from seaplanes in distress.

The development of semi-rigid airships suitable for use at high altitudes was an Italian speciality. As well as naval surveillance missions, dirigibles of this type carried out 258 bombing raids on military targets.

The French navy between 1917 and 1918 also turned some 80 ships into "balloon carriers" by equipping them with specially adapted Caquot captive balloons. Observers who manned these balloons, in the three months from May to June 1918, in addition to normal surveillance duties, destroyed 20 mines and located and attacked 6 submarines. One captive balloon, towed by the *Asie*, spent twenty-five days in the air escorting a convoy of sailing vessels from Royan to the Azores, a remarkable show of endurance not only by the observers but by the balloon itself.

Airships in liaison with the fleet at sea. Left: the German fleet sets off towards England, shadowed by a Zeppelin.
Right: the fleet returning to its base on 19 August 1916 after the indecisive battle of Jutland.

The French naval airforce base at Saint-Trojan on the island of Oleron in 1918.

Aerial observation at sea. A Sopwith *Camel* taking off from a pontoon towed at 36 knots.

A German seaplane hands over a message to the submarine U 35 in the Mediterranean

NAVAL AIR SERVICES

Unlike the British Royal Naval Air Service, which began the war as an organised force with more than 50 seaplanes, not counting land planes and airships, the French naval airforce began virtually from scratch, with just 8 aircraft, in 1914.

By 1916 its strength had grown to 156 aircraft and by November 1918 to a total of 1,264; manpower had correspondingly increased from 200 to 11,000. By the end of the war naval air stations were spaced no more than 60 miles apart on the Channel and Atlantic coasts, and 120 miles apart on the Mediterranean coasts of France, Algeria and Tunisia.

French seaplanes could be stationed from Flanders to the mouth of the Senegal river or from Portugal to Moúdhros.

Because the organisation of the naval airforce took second place to the demands of the battle-front, progress was necessarily very gradual. In January 1915 stations were formed at Boulogne and Le Havre to help protect the English convoys

The steamer *Audax* torpedoed in the North Sea.

that plied the Channel. In May of the same year the stations at La Pallice, Toulon and Bizerta were already in existence. Soon French seaplanes were taking part in operations at Venice, Brindisi and Salonika.

Most of the aircraft had hulls, and engines of 100 to 160 h.p.; they went out to sea in pairs; patrolling an area of up to 30 or 40 miles from the coast in which they protected shipping against enemy submarines, carrying out no less than ninety attacks on submarines in the last eight months of 1917 alone. Although these attacks rarely resulted in the complete destruction of the submarine, they prevented the enemy from operating close to the coasts. This escort and protection work was unrewarding and monotonous, but it was not without its dangers. Breakdowns over the open sea were fatal or nearly fatal on more than one occasion. Sub-lieutenant Lenglet and Petty Officer Dien drifted on the high seas for 267 hours from 2 to 13 July 1918 aboard their FBA 11.4 before eventually reaching Piana bay on Corsica, while Chief Petty Officer Guérin and Sub-lieutenant Richer drifted for more than 80 hours in January 1918 before being rescued.

Dunkirk witnessed the genesis of fighter sea-planes and served as a base right up to the end of the war. A skirmish took place here on 26 May 1917 between four French FBA seaplanes with hulls and four German fighter seaplanes with floats, which resulted in the loss or capture of all the French crews. Sub-lieutenant Teste, who for a long time had thwarted all German attempts to shoot him down, was taken aboard a German torpedo boat but later managed to escape, and became one of the Allies' greatest naval pilots.

Royal Naval Air Service squadrons were also based at Dunkirk and, together with those at Dover, policed the Straits and attacked the enemy without respite, taking part in very tough engage-ments at Ostend and Zeebrugge. Large F-3 sea-planes with hulls, powered by two 720 horse-power engines and armed with five machine-guns, carried out offensive patrols up and down

Captain E.A. Mossop's seaplane burning on the surface of the sea. (Photograph taken from one of the attacking German seaplanes.)

the Channel, during which they surprised and shot down two Zeppelins.

The larger German naval airships mounted regular patrols to protect German maritime bases against surprise attack when the weather was favourable. (Inclement weather not only pre-vented Zeppelins from taking to the air but also made British naval assaults unlikely.) 10 Zeppe-lins took part in reconnaissance expeditions be-fore the battle of the Skagerrak; before the sortie of 9 August 1916 eight Zeppelins provided long-distance protection and sweeping reconnaissance, giving the German naval command a considerable tactical advantage.

Although the British quickly showed interest in the possibility of aircraft-carriers (by July 1918 70 aeroplanes were operating either from ships' bridges or gun-turrets) only one small aircraft-carrier, the Engadine, took part in the actual battle of Jutland, and even then only one aeroplane managed to take off in the course of the skirmish, unfortunately with little effect.

The attack on the British submarine "C25" on 6 July 1918 in the North Sea. (Top) one of the German seaplanes attacking the submarine while a second photographs the scene as it turns back towards the target. (Bottom) German seaplane photographs its own bombs exploding around the submarine, which nevertheless managed to reach the coast.

The pilot of a wrecked German seaplane clings to the float of his sinking aircraft while awaiting rescue.

Presenting arms at Saint-Pol-sur-Mer in honour of Guynemer after his disappearance (20 November 1917). Lieutenant Fonck and Captain Hertaux, who is leaning on two sticks, stand in front of the line of flags being saluted by the General commanding the army.

.THE EFFECT OF AVIATION ON THE WAR

Commander Orthlieb, author of *L'Aéronautique – hier, demain* (*Aviation yesterday and tomorrow*) wrote that "the true miracle of the war in the air was observation". This is tantamount to saying that the airforce demonstrated its usefulness not through its own exploits but through the services it rendered to the armies on the ground. Strategic and tactical reconnaissance, front line surveillance, range-finding, pinpointing targets in liaison with the artillery – all the tasks that formerly had been carried out by the captive balloons – to which were added liaison with the infantry during offensives, aerial photography and the methodical plotting out of the battle zone on maps, the study of the enemy's defences, damage checking and snapshots that revealed the progress of battles as they unfolded. The primary function of fighter aeroplanes, when not going their own way and engaging in mutual destruction, was in this view to create favourable conditions for reconnaissance and observation work.

Such duties must be contrasted with the various offensive roles available to an airforce: intervention in the battle on the ground and bombing raids against more distant targets. The effectiveness of such operations in the Great War has often been questioned, even though there were some indisputable successes, notably those of the French First Air Division and the British Independent Air Force. As far as long-distance bombing is concerned, it is hard to believe that such expeditions affected the outcome of the war in any way, however frequent and dogged they may have been. At the very most it could be argued that the German attacks on England kept a sizeable part of the British airforce away from the main theatre of war, and that the equipment and manpower the British devoted to combating this threat was totally out of proportion to the size of the attacking force or the military value of the target. What is more, when we compare the tonnage of bombs dropped from aircraft with the tonnage of explosives detonated on the battlefield, we come to the conclusion that aerial bombing may have had an effect on enemy morale but

was rarely effective in causing material damage. During the war as a whole, German bombers dropped some 27,386 tons of explosives, which represented well over a million individual bombs; the average weight of a single projectile was rather less than 50 lbs. Aeroplanes were not "machines that hastened the end of the war". On the other hand they certainly helped to do so. Ultimately an aeroplane was a powerful expendable weapon like any other.

Logically this meant heavy expenditure in air crews, since the rate of attrition of men both through accident and through enemy action was just as high as that of the flying machines them-

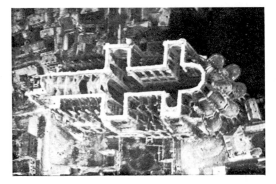

An airman's view of Saint-Quéntin cathedral at the end of the war. The roof has collapsed and the ruined walls form the outline of the cross of Lorraine.

The final mission. A French two-seater, also decorated with the cross of Lorraine and carrying on its wing strut a white flag of truce, waits to take the bearer of the Armistice terms, the German Commander von Geyer, to Spa.

selves and it took a great deal of time and money to train up the volunteers who made up the air crews. There are no uniformly agreed national statistics, but it seems that between all the belligerents some 30,000 to 40,000 airmen were killed or incapacitated in combat, and another 12,000 to 15,000 in accidents or training. Losses seem to be equally divided between killed and injured. This figure may be compared with that of 47,000 which represents the total number of aircrew belonging to the three main powers still flying at the end of the war.

But in addition to the aircrews themselves there were back-up crews of 20 to 30 men per aeroplane who carried out service, maintenance, supply and administrative duties, and yet others engaged in training, procurement and planning.

The total strength of the French airforce by the end of the war was getting on for 150,000 officers and men, out of which only about 16,000 were actually "flying personnel". Great Britain had 20,100 pilots and observers and the proportion of "tail" was approximately the same. (The German airforce was even more "tail-heavy" as her flying crews had been eroded to 11,000 men.)

Above all, aviation contributed to a great wearing down of resources by consuming raw materials and industrial manpower. The French air industry employed 186,000 workers on 2 November 1918. The two sides had turned out a combined total of nearly 200,000 aircraft and 250,000 engines between 1914 and 1918. To finish with a total of 3,608 front-line machines (15,342 total) on the day of the Armistice, France had had to produce 67,982 aeroplanes and 85,317 engines in four years, while Britain, which ended the war with 3,300 front-line machines out of a total of 22,171 on charge, had built 55,093 aircraft and 40,449 engines, and bought 3,000 and 17,000 more, mostly from France. The rate of attrition increased constantly and for the last six months of the war it actually exceeded half of the new equipment being sent to the front every month. Germany had constructed nearly 48,000 aeroplanes and 41,000 engines between 1914 and 1918 alone, and ended the war with just 14,731 aircraft, 3,000 of which were in the front-line; given that she was virtually isolated from the rest of the world, it is not surprising that she was the first to crack under the strain.

A two-seater reconnaissance and observation plane of 1915 and 1916: the Caudron G-4 with two 80 h.p. Rhone engines.

THE EFFECT OF THE WAR ON AVIATION

The best single-seaters in service at the end of the war were equipped with 220 to 300 h.p. engines and could fly at speeds of 120 to 135 mph. at 13,000 ft., a height they reached in twelve to fifteen minutes. Their ceiling was in the region of 26,000 ft. In order to appreciate these performance levels fully, we should remember that on the

A bold experiment: a two-seater Spad of 1915 with the observer's cockpit in front of the propeller.

eve of hostilities a "125 mph. aircraft" was feasible only as a specially built racing aeroplane designed purely for speed and having absolutely no practical use. The best two-seaters in service at the beginning of 1916 – which showed marked improvements over the various models of August 1914 – had engines generating 130 to 200 h.p., a speed of 75 to 80 mph. at 6,500 ft., and could easily climb to over 13,000 ft. In 1918, 110 mph. and a ceiling of 21,300 ft. were the normal performance levels of 250–350 h.p. observation

A three-seater Letort with two Hispano-Suiza engines about to set out on patrol on the Somme front in May 1918.

British single-seater fighters. (Left) the de Havilland DH-2, the only single-seater fighter with a "pusher" propeller and completely clear forward vision put into service during the war. (Right) the single-seater S E 5 with a Hispano-Suiza engine and four propeller blades, a characteristic of English aircraft from 1917.

The Fokker Dr. I single-seater fighter triplane.

Friedrichshafen twin-engined bomber.

planes. A series of two-seater fighters and long-distance reconnaissance aircraft were already under construction, capable of attaining speeds close to 130 mph. The twin-engined Farman F-50, a 440 h.p. bomber that entered service during the last autumn of the war, could reach speeds of 90 mph. at 6,500 ft. with a ceiling of 15,500 ft., even with a bomb load of 1,800 lb.

Such indisputable progress was to a great extent the result of the continuous development of ever more powerful engines. French two-seater reconnaissance aircraft and German heavy bombers had even begun to run up against the problem of maintaining power at high altitudes. In general, the engines built at the end of the war – especially in France where progress had been more striking than anywhere else – bore no relation to those fitted to the aircraft of 1914. Above all, the powerful water-cooled engine had made its appearance and been widely accepted.

Lastly, of course, the need for mass production of military hardware led to the development of truly commercial design, manufacture and testing procedures. Aircraft manufacturing companies

Twin machine-guns on a single-seater Pfalz.

had been formed and there had been a radical rethinking of the design and construction of aeroplanes. As a result of constant use and trial of aircraft over the battle field, new techniques were defined or created. The equipment needed for observation work, to record information and to relay or broadcast data over long distances, opened up the hitherto unexplored areas of aerial photography and radio communication. On a more general level, more men had taken to the air than ever before; tens of thousands of servicemen had become acquainted with the new technology at first hand. Man might have won mastery of the air, but aviation now had a grip on mankind. The war in the air had been given the widest possible publicity, and the attention of young people the world over was firmly directed upon the new element. What use could peace make of all these developments born of war, suited to war and explained by war? What proportion could it retain of a progress which had been determined entirely by military considerations? This was the fundamental problem that had to be addressed at the end of 1918.

Industrial mass production during the war: a stockpile of Hispano-Suiza engines.

CHAPTER V

THE POST-WAR YEARS

1919–1938

The aviation industry at the end of the Great War had no doubts about its capabilities. It emerged from the struggle with a prestige and power that it believed it could consider its own for ever.

The development of combat flying had given birth to an industry of mass production. In France alone in a few months more than 7,300 aircraft of a single type were built; of a single type of engine 20,300. If one considers the promise that civil aviation had shown even before the war, it would seem that this new technical and industrial force should have been capable of rapid redirection to new ends. However one must remember that the war had taken the aeroplane as it was in 1914, had adjusted it in haste – always in haste – to ever more demanding tasks, but to tasks from which risk was never excluded. It was thus inevitable that the war should have brought only quantitative changes in its efficiency.

In 1919 the aircraft industry embarked on a struggle of which the immense difficulties were at first barely suspected, namely to solve the problems of technical advance under the conditions of everyday life, while at the same time justifying the demands that it was going to make on the public purse by proving its usefulness.

The year 1919 saw the proudest responses to this challenge; immediately the aeroplane, the flying boat and the airship all showed off their new powers, as if wanting to demonstrate by ocean crossings and long journeys that the world belonged to them. But even by 1932, thirteen years later, it was by no means clear that their promises had been kept.

Through all the pages of this last chapter it is the twin efforts of justification and of improvement that are most clearly felt. With varying degress of pertinacity and courage all ground was cleared, all paths trodden. By mass-transport, by rapid communications, by aerial photography, by the aid given to exploration, by the new unity lent to the great empires, by the linking of under-developed countries with centres of industrial

expansion, by the creation of a new sport and a new tourism, the aeroplane and the flying-boat tried to prove their value to humanity. But in 1932 no less than in 1912 the industry that built them and flew them drew practically all its resources from the State, and the State is always most interested in preserving its real and potential capacity for war.

The strenuous efforts that had been made since 1919 to improve the techniques of aviation had not, by 1932, freed the aeroplane from its original weakness; lift was still directly proportional to airspeed. Cruising speeds of less than 125 mph were being accompanied by landing speeds of close on 65 mph, which placed severe limitations on the use of aircraft, poorly compensated for by an insufficient decrease in overall journey times, especially when account was taken of the tendency to build airfields further from city centres.

But from 1932 to 1938 the aeroplane, without altering in any of its essentials, passed to a new order of performance. Supercharged engines, variable pitch propellers and retractable undercarriages were the main causes of a significant increase in the cruising speeds of airliners. These in 1938 varied from 160 up to 215 mph., the speed of which for example the four-engined long-haul De Havilland Albatross (shown above) was capable. At the same time landing speeds, thanks to the use of various "high-lift" devices remained in the vicinity of 65 mph. Thus the constraints stayed the same, but the gains in time were enormous.

This very real progress should have resulted in a decisive improvement in operating costs on which a healthy industry, capable of normal growth, could be based. Instead it led to the creation of an aerial arsenal, the direct result – throughout the world – of preponderantly military aircraft construction programmes; in 1938 the aircraft industry had become daily more artificial in its development even as its technique became more remarkable.

It is fair to say, however, that alongside this

forced development a courageous and highly deserving band of seekers – scientists, technicians, inventors, test-pilots – continued to explore the stoney by-ways, dedicating a large part of their activities to the aviation of the future.

The autogiro, sadly handicapped since La Cierva succumbed to a flying accident, still had not eliminated its two most serious defects: speed – for equal power – still inferior to that of the aeroplane, and poor handling at low speeds, which led to too many serious accidents while landing. On the other hand the helicopter – which shares many of its characteristics – appeared capable of being fitted for everyday use much more quickly than was believed possible.

Man was also at last methodically and courageously pursuing the exploration which should give him effective mastery of the atmosphere and even the lower levels of the stratosphere, to 35,000 or 40,000 ft. The way was being prepared for an era of long-distance transport, at speeds of 300 mph. and more, over trans-oceanic or trans-continental distances of 3,000 to 6,000 miles; the day was also being brought forward of aerial navigation for sport or pleasure where the energy of atmospheric currents would be more and more consciously exploited and of which the astonishing cross-country flights of German gliders over pre-set circuits on given dates had already given a foretaste.

Man had not even hesitated to study with scientific detachment the falling of his own body, whether to understand better its behaviour when subjected to rapid changes of altitude, or whether to learn to guide controlled descents. It was to experiments of this sort – even if directed to the provision of public spectacles – that the lives were given in 1937 of the American Clem Sohn, who steered his fall by the use of little ribbed wings, and in 1938 of the Frenchman Williams, who jumping from 37,000 ft. delayed opening his parachute until he was 300 ft. from the ground and landed – that time – without mishap.

One of three De Havilland DH-4 military aircraft converted to 3-seater executive transports for British delegates to the Peace Conference.

The cabin of the civil version of the DH-4.

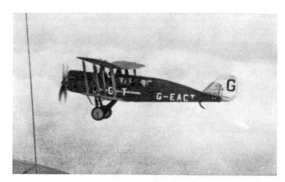

One of the first English aircraft on the London–Paris run, almost identical to the diplomatic aircraft at left but with national registration letters.

The Caudron C-23 leaving Paris for Brussels on 10 February 1919 with passengers seated in the open air.

A Bleriot-Spad of the strike-breaking Paris–London postal service; the pilot Casale is seen talking to M. P-E. Flandin, Under-Secretary of State for Air, and Col. Saconney.

Inside the first Goliath on the Paris–London and Paris–Brussels routes; on the right, M. Henri Farman.

THE FIRST AIRLINES

Transport services provided an obvious employment for the demobilised air-forces. Many aircraft, particularly French and British, were used to ferry delegates to the Peace Conference while others were deployed on relief work. Two bomber groups, GB5 and GB9, were from 20 January 1919 given the task of restocking those parts of Northern France where movement on the ground was still difficult with such items as condensed milk, medical supplies and post, moving in two and a half months and three hundred trips some thirty-six tons of freight.

On 5 February the German company "Deutsche Luftreederei" became the world's first internal airline with the inauguration of its service from Berlin to Leipzig and Weimar; on the 8th the first international service, between Paris and London, was opened by the Farman company. A Farman F-60 bomber, of which the vast size and shape of the fuselage made it an obvious choice for such an adaptation, was piloted to London by Lucien Bossoutrot on that day, carrying eleven passen-

gers and a mechanic, and returned on the 9th. On the 12th the same crew carried thirteen passengers to Brussels, including M. and Mme. Henri Farman and a photographer for "L'Illustration", and again returned on the following day.

Two days later a converted Caudron C-23 carried five passengers in rather less comfort over the same route. Shortly after, on 1 March the "Luftreederei" added Berlin–Hamburg to its network.

Great Britain, to whom the London–Paris link was obviously of primary importance, opened this route on 25 August with a service supplied by "Aircraft Transport and Travel Ltd.". On the same day Mr. G. Holt Thomas, the president of that company and one of the pioneers of civil aviation, called a meeting at The Hague, from which arose on 28 August the International Air Traffic Association (IATA), still the main union of international airline companies. In September the "Compagnie des Messageries Aériennes" extended its Paris–Lille–Brussels route to London, and was shortly joined on the route by the "Transaérienne" specialising in postal freight.

The extreme interest shown in the Paris–

London link was mainly due to the collapse of the sea ferry system as a result of the war, and many considered that the aeroplane would show to increased advantage over longer distances. In March 1919 M. P-G. Latécoère began test flights for a postal service between France and Morocco, and on 13 July the first aircraft – a converted Salmson 2-seater – of the Toulouse–Rabat–Casablanca service left Toulouse.

At that date the French air navigation service under Col. Saconney had already worked out in detail policies towards commercial aviation which covered the definition of territories, the creation of airlines and airports – the word dates from this period – modifications to the aircraft themselves, and the relationship between the companies and the State, including a system of subsidies. France was thus the first country in the world to study this problem in its entirety; when the railwaymen's strike broke out in February 1920 the air services which could be improvised as a result, in particular for the transport of letters between Paris, London, Brussels, Strasbourg, Lyons, Marseilles and Bordeaux, demonstrated the practical value of such a system.

A civil version of the Farman F-60 bomber; a twin-engined Goliath taking off. (Note that the pilot's cockpit has been raised, freeing the whole forward part of the fuselage for the passenger cabin.)

The departure from the aerodrome of Toulouse-Montaudran, at 0630 in the morning of 13 July 1919, of the Salmson 2-seater which inaugurated the regular service between Toulouse and Casablanca.

Left and right: the Curtiss NC-4 which first crossed the Atlantic in May 1919 by way of the Azores. Centre: its captain Lt. Cdr. Read of the US Navy.

THE FIRST ATLANTIC CROSSINGS

The state of any art has always been demonstrated by performances that stretch its boundaries to the limit. The war, with its immediate, daily tasks had placed an effective embargo on any mere proofs of technical ability such as long-distance or record-breaking flights. At the same time it was clear that the aeroplane, the flying-boat and the airship, although unchanged in their essentials since 1914, had in the last four years greatly increased their capabilities, just as their roles had increased. At the beginning of 1919 an obvious test of these capabilities was available – the crossing of the Atlantic.

One after another, from mid-May to mid-July, the flying-boat, the aeroplane, and finally the airship, accepted this challenge, and succeeded.

In the last months of the war, the United States Navy and Curtiss had built flying-boats for offshore patrolling, the NC class, standing for Navy-Curtiss, although they were obviously inspired by the twin-engined British F-2. The range of these machines seemed sufficient for a crossing of the North Atlantic via Newfoundland and the Azores. Three aircraft were chosen: *NC-1, NC-3* and *NC-4*. Each was equipped with three American 400 h.p. Liberty engines with traction propellers; to the *NC-4* a fourth Liberty with a pusher propeller was added behind the central motor.

The three flying-boats left Trepassey Bay, in Newfoundland, at 1600 hours on 16 May; at 1328 on the 17th the *NC-4*, with the extra engine, had reached Horta in the Azores. The *NC-3* and *NC-1*

had had to put down on the sea before sighting land; immediately rescued by surface craft, which the US Navy had stationed over the length of the route, they were towed, one to Punta Delgada, the other to level with Corvo, where it sank. On 27 May the *NC-4*, which had reached Punta Delgada a week before, touched down at Lisbon; on the 30th it was at El Ferrol, and on the 31st it reached its final goal of Plymouth.

McKenzie Grieve (left) and Hawker, a near success.

The well-merited success of this big flying-boat, and its crew of six, led by Lt. Cdr. Read, was in a great measure due to the organisation devoted to the exercise, and to the quality of the equipment on board the *NC-4*: radio-navigation gear capable of picking up a destroyer at 90 miles and a shore-station at over 600 miles, radio-communication to 300 miles and radio-telephone to 25, and a wealth of navigational instruments of which many had been designed by a yet unknown

naval flyer – a Lt. Cdr. Byrd. This was no wild venture but the methodical use of a machine which, thanks to its marine hull and its multiple engines was capable of offering its crew a very acceptable degree of security. It should be noted also that the longest leg accomplished was of less than 1400 miles.

At the very moment of the *NC-4*'s departure another aeroplane was being prepared to hazard the 1900 miles from St John's, Newfoundland, to the coast of Ireland for a prize offered by the Daily Mail; at 1755 on 17 May Hawker and Grieve set out in their single-engined Sopwith. Next day, having covered some 1,250 miles, a failure of the cooling system forced them to ditch alongside the Danish steamer *Mary*, which took them on board. However, having no radio, the ship could not announce their rescue until it neared the English coast some eight days later. On the 27th London gave an enthusiastic welcome to the rescued pair, and the Daily Mail awarded them a consolation prize of £5,000.

The prize itself was to be won shortly after by Alcock and Brown. On 14 June these two left St John's at 1628 in a Vickers Vimy equipped with radio and two 360 hp. Rolls Royce engines. After a flight, helped by a tail-wind, of 15 hours and 57 minutes Alcock reached the coast of Ireland at Clifden and, mistaking a bog for a smooth green field, up-ended the big aircraft on landing. The 1,900 miles had been covered at nearly 120 mph., and a third of the 860 gallons of petrol carried still remained on board.

The airship now entered the lists. As early as 1916 the British, emulating the Zeppelins, had built two rigid airships of 880,000 cu. ft. capacity;

The Vickers Vimy of Alcock and Brown at Clifden, Ireland, on 15 June 1919, after the first non-stop crossing.

Alcock (†*F*1919) and Brown, left, in London.

Grl. Maitland (†*F*1921)

The British airship R-34, which in July 1919 first crossed the Atlantic in both directions.

Major Scott (†*F*1930)

in 1917 two more of nearly 1,000,000 cu. ft., and then two of 1,400,000 cu. ft., all with wooden frameworks. But the *R-33* and *R-34* were not designed until after the giant *L-33* and *L-49* of the German Navy had been shot down in England and in France, and so may have also benefited from a study of German technology. The *R-34* was 660 ft. long, and contained nearly 2,000,000 cu. ft. of gas in 19 compartments. Driven by five Sunbeam engines each of 270 h.p., it weighed 31 tons empty and could carry a payload of 25 tons under the most favourable conditions.

The *R-34* took off from East Fortune, in Scotland, at 0230 on 2 July 1919, a place and date that had been chosen before the Armistice was signed, carrying in addition to its crew of six officers and twenty-one other ranks three passengers, among whom were General Maitland, head of the Royal Air Force, and an American observer, Major Pritchard.

The airship, commanded by Major Scott, carried 16 tons of fuel, 1½ tons of oil and 3½ tons of ballast; the engines were designed to give a cruising speed in still air of 47 mph. This, taking into account the adverse conditions expected, gave an estimated flight-time of one hundred hours, which should have left some 5 tons of fuel in reserve on arrival, enough for an additional thirty hours flying; in fact when, at 1500 on 6 July, the *R-34* arrived over Mineola, there remained on board only sufficent fuel for another forty minutes. The landing at Mineola was supervised from the ground by Major Pritchard, who himself had landed earlier by parachute.

In constant touch with ships and shore-stations, using cloud observation, long-range forecasts and local meteorological bulletins to adjust its route, plotting its position by day and night by radio-navigation "fixes", stopping to repair in flight minor break-downs of the engines, the *R-34* was truly navigating. The enormous detour which Scott decided to make on 5 July to avoid a storm that was affecting all the south of Nova Scotia is only the most striking example of this.

On 10 July, at 0555, carrying only 15 tons of fuel in view of the shorter length of the southern route and of the favourable prevailing winds, the *R-34* set off again, reaching Pulham, in East Anglia, without incident, at 0757 on 13 July, after a flight of seventy-four hours.

Just three years after the North Atlantic the South Atlantic was also conquered by the aeroplane. The delay can undoubtedly be attributed to the absence at that date of an aircraft industry in the countries most directly interested in such a link: Portugal, Spain and the Latin-American Republics. Indeed it was with British equipment that a Portuguese team finally attempted, and with admirable pertinacity eventually succeeded in completing, the crossing.

On the morning of 30 March 1922 Cdr. Sacadura Cabral, pilot, and Vice-Admiral Gago Coutinho, navigator, left Lisbon in a Fairey F-3 seaplane, with a 360 h.p. Rolls Royce engine. This was a standard machine modified to have a larger wing-area and fitted with floats suitable to its all-up weight of over 3 tons. In eight and a half hours the Lusitania, as it was named, reached Las Palmas. Delayed in the Canaries by bad weather until 4 April, the aviators flew that day in ten hours to St Vincent in the Cape Verde Islands, where the storm again held them up. On the 18th

they left Porto Praia, in the south of the archipelago, heading for the island of Fernando de Noronha. A refuelling stop was made at St Paul's Rock as contrary winds did not allow this difficult leg over 1,500 miles to be completed without a break. The *Lusitania*, while moored to the rock, was overwhelmed by the waves, and destroyed.

On 11 May Cabral and Coutinho, in a second Fairey, set out from Fernando de Noronha, did a U-turn over St Paul where their journey had been interrupted, and headed once again for the Brazilian coast. This time engine failure forced them to put down on the sea, where eight hours later they were rescued by a British ship; unfortunately the aircraft was severely damaged during the attempts to get it on board.

On 5 June, in a third seaplane, Cabral and Coutinho flew from Fernando to Pernambuco; on the 17th they moored in the bay of Rio de Janeiro.

This crossing, despite its setbacks, was a triumph of aerial navigation; Admiral Coutinho, then aged 52, had brought to the enterprise all his specialised experience of surveying and of astronomical observation; smoke bombs for the calculation of drift, a specially designed sextant, afterwards copied by flyers throughout the world, observation tables meticulously prepared for all eventualities, these were the pre-requisites of a finally successful navigational exercise.

Admiral Gago Coutinho continued to take a most active interest in ocean crossings by aircraft; early in 1931 he was on board the giant 12-engined Dornier Do-X when it flew from Lisbon to Rio de Janeiro. Sacadura Cabral was sadly lost at sea, on 14 November 1924, while ferrying a seaplane from Holland to Portugal.

The Fairey seaplane in which Coutinho and Cabral began the first crossing of the South Atlantic

Sacadura Cabral (†*F*1924) and Gago Coutinho, right.

Vedrines landing on the roof of Galeries Lafayette in central Paris, on 19 January 1919.

Godefroy flying through the Arc de Triomphe on 7 August 1919.

SOME NOTABLE EXPLOITS

In 1914 Galeries Lafayette, the large Paris store, had offered a prize of 25,000 francs to the first pilot to land an aircraft on the roof, 92 ft. by 40 ft., of their shop in Boulevard Haussmann. As this roof was surrounded by a 3 ft. high balustrade so that an aircraft could only reach it at stalling speed, it was amazing that there had been no general outcry against the offering of a prize for such a dangerous exploit. Nevertheless since the prize had still not been claimed by 1919 the popular war-ace Jules Vedrines decided to go for it. In a slow and highly manoeuvrable Caudron G-3 he practised landing on a 65 ft. square which he had had marked out on an airfield, and then on 19 January 1919 made the attempt. Skimming the balustrade he braked hard on the special surface of sandbags which he had had prepared, but even with the ground crew hanging on to both wings he crashed into the lift housings at the left of the picture, completely destroying his aircraft, but remaining himself unscathed.

Sadly he did not live to enjoy his prize. Three months later on a flight from Paris to Rome an engine failed on his twin-engined C-23, and he was killed attempting an emergency landing at Saint Rambert d'Albon. The people of Paris gave him a public funeral.

The same year saw an equally futile and dangerous feat. At 0730 on 7 August the military pilot Godefroy, piqued at what he considered insufficient recognition given to the Air Force in the Victory Parade on 14 July, flew through the 48 ft. wide arch of the Arc de Triomphe in a Nieuport single-seater with a wing-span of 30 ft.

A more laudable feat took place on 30 July 1921, when the Swiss aviator Francois Durafour landed on the vast snowfield that marks the Dome pass, just below the Vallot Observatory. As he was landing Durafour was hit by a violent gust of wind, and had to summon up all his skill and experience as a pilot to stop himself from slipping into the crevasse on the edge of the pass. Helped by several climbers, Durafour was able to drag his aircraft to the edge of the snowfield and set off again towards Chamonix.

Durafour having landed on the Dôme Pass under the summit of Mont Blanc on 30 July 1921.

The crew of the Farman "Goliath" about to leave Paris (11 August 1919) and salvaging equipment at Koufra (16 August 1919). Group picture left to right: Lt. Boussot, observer, Lt. Guillemot, radio operator, Capt. Bizard, navigator, Léon Coupet, mechanic, Lucien Coupet, co-pilot, Bossoutrot, pilot, Mulot and Jousse, mechanics.

PIONEERING NEW ROUTES

At the beginning of 1919 Roget and Coli had flown across the Mediterranean and back again in twenty-four hours, but it was not until 18 June that a French air crew set out to try to reach French West Africa, when Lt. Lemaître and his mechanic Guichard took off from Villacoublay in a Breguet 14 B-2. On the stretch between Mogador and St Louis Guichard bravely tried to repair the mal-functioning engine in mid flight but only succeeded in making the problem worse, and they were obliged to put down at Port-Etienne on the edge of Lévrier bay. The aircraft while taxiing on the soft sand rolled over gently; neither of the crew was hurt.

It was left to a flying boat piloted by Lt. Cdr. Lefranc to make the first complete air journey from France to Dakar, which he did between 28 November 1919 and 14 February 1920 in a Renault G-L with a 300 h.p. engine, travelling via the Canary Islands.

The first trials of the twin-engined Farman Goliath on the Paris to Brussels and Paris to London routes confirmed the remarkable performance of what was at that time one of the most successful aeroplanes ever constructed. This huge biplane with a wing-span of 92 ft. was driven by two 270 h.p. Salmson engines and had shown that it was capable of carrying very heavy loads. Overall it weighed 5 tons and could climb to a height of 6,500 ft. in 23 minutes. On 5 May

Bossoutrot had taken a Goliath to 16,700 ft. with 24 passengers aboard. It cruised at about 70 mph. It was therefore easy to see why the Farman company wanted to try out the Goliath on the West African route which Lemaître had not managed to complete.

Having reached Casablanca the crew waited for three patrol boats which had been made available to take up positions along the African coastline. On 14 August the Goliath reached Mogador, and at 1600 on the 15th it set out for Dakar, expecting to reach there by 0700 the next morning. The day came and went with no sign of the aeroplane. Search parties were organised; all over the world newspapers featured the aircraft's disappearance. A week later a telegram sent by Bossoutrot from Dagana told the world that the crew was safe.

According to Captain Bizard's log book, at 0645 on 16 August the right-hand propeller fell off without warning, having ruptured its bolts. By 0735 the remaining engine was so hot that Bossoutrot was forced to land on the beach. The aircraft slid into the ocean and was broken up by the waves. The crew salvaged some equipment and provisions and built themselves a shelter among the dunes. They had not managed to bring the wireless set ashore, and so had no idea of their exact position; being cut off from the land by lagoons, they decided to strike out towards the south during the night.

On 17 August, suffering from extreme physical exhaustion and racked by thirst, they stopped after walking for about 13 miles. They had seen no sign of human habitation and had been unable

to cross the lagoons. They decided to get back to the wrecked aeroplane and await rescue.

On 21 August two natives appeared; the next day the Emir of Trarza was alerted at Mederdrah, and arrived with his Arab scouts.

The accident to the Goliath had been almost exactly paralleled three months earlier when on 20 May 1919 a British four-engined Handley Page V1500 piloted by Major Darley and Lt. Kilburn, with Lt. Murray as observer, and three mechanics, returning from a courtesy visit to Spain lost its right rear propeller and part of a wing over the sea off Biarritz. It also crash landed on the beach and ran on into the sea, from which the crew had to be rescued by rowing boats, losing the aeroplane and nearly all their possessions.

The first air crossing of the Sahara proper was an expedition organised by the highest authorities in French West Africa who had in mind a regular air service across the desert. Preparations for the expedition included the setting up and provisioning of 14 stop-over and rescue points between Biskra and Timbuktu, fully staffed by mechanics and equipped with tow trucks, spare parts and wireless stations.

Three officers were chosen for the crossing; Commander Vuillemin, Captain Mézergues and Lt. Dagnaux set off from Paris on 26 February 1920 in three Breguet 16 Bn-2s with 300 h.p. Renault engines.

Only Vuillemin reached the Ahaggar, to be met by an Algerian squadron and General Laperrine, an immensely experienced Saharan veteran.

On 18 February two aeroplanes left Tamanraset

Sergeant-major Bernard's wrecked plane after its crash landing near Tin Zaouaten. (February 1920)

General Laperrine's grave, marked by a wheel and his kepi.

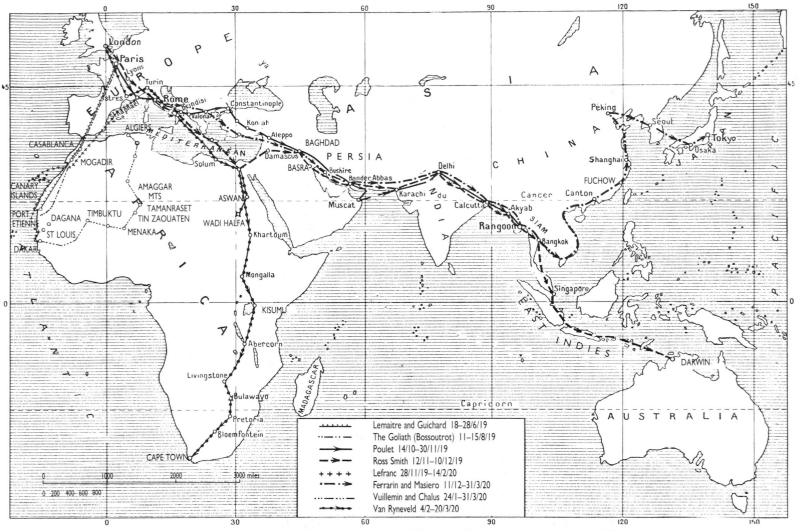

The great intercontinental journeys made in 1919 and 1920 between Europe, Asia, Australia and Africa.

piloted by Vuillemin, accompanied by Chalus, and by Sergeant-major Bernard carrying General Laperrine and the mechanic Vasselin. Timbuktu should have been reached by nightfall, but it was not until ten days later that Vuillemin and Chalus were known to have landed safely on 19 February at Mcnaka, having last sighted the other plane in bad weather close to Tin Zaouaten.

On 22 March, when all hope of finding the lost aviators in the second plane had been given up, the wreck of Bernard's aeroplane was spotted by a patrol south of Tin Zaouaten. Bernard and Vasselin were alive but exhausted; General Laperrine had died on 5 March of injuries sustained during the crash. Vuillemin and Chalus, however, eventually succeeded in carrying out their mission, touching down at Dakar at 1030 on 31 March.

Between the autumn of 1919 and the spring of 1920 three other long-distance air routes were pioneered. On 14 October 1919 Poulet and Benoît left Issy-les-Moulineaux for Melbourne in a twin-engined 160 h.p. Caudron G-4. This aircraft was not robust enough to take them all the way, but they managed to reach Rangoon in 47 days. It was a British air crew that finally made the entire journey: having left London on the 12 November, a powerful twin-engined 720 h.p. Vickers Vimy arrived in Darwin on the 10 December. The aviators who flew this amazing mission – Ross Smith and his brother K.M. Smith, with a radio-telegraphist and a mechanic – won a prize of £10,000 from the Australian government.

Together with her dominions, Great Britain led the way in opening up transcontinental air routes. Soon afterwards, and with a great deal of hard preparatory work on the ground, the London to Cape Town via Cairo route was inaugurated. After unsuccessful attempts to fly all the way had been made by Brackley, Cockerell and Browne, Colonel Van Ryneveld left London on 4 February and reached the Cape on 20 March. En route he had written off two aeroplanes, one in Upper Egypt and another at Bulawayo, where the South African Confederation had a third plane sent on to him so that he could reach his goal.

But perhaps the most ambitious expedition of all was made by the Italians: the Rome to Tokyo route. There were some difficulties in setting up supply centres along this route, but eventually the two aeroplanes taking part in the expedition, S V A's piloted by Ferrarin and Masiero, were able to set out on the 11 February; on the 31 May Ferrarin landed in the Japanese capital one hour ahead of Masiero.

Ferrarin is welcomed by a Japanese crowd on his arrival in Tokyo.

Ross Smith's plane on the race-course at Singapore.

225

Sadi Lecointe's Nieuport, winner of the Gordon-Bennett cup, at Etampes on 28 September 1920. This plane was the first to exceed 300 kph. (186.3 mph., 20 October 1920).

Kirsch, the winner of the Deutsch de la Meurthe Cup, taking off in his Nieuport monoplane at Etampes on 1 October 1921.

SPEED TRIALS 1919–1921

The keenly contested pre-war trials had left Prévot holding the Gordon Bennett Cup with a speed of 124.5 mph. while Gilbert held the Deutsch Cup with 96.6 mph. In 1919 there were numerous contenders for this second trophy,

Bernard de Romanet with Louis Blériot and Lauga in front of his Spad-Herbemont at Buc (October 1920).

contested individually every time a new challenge was made. On 15 October 1919 Sadi Lecointe, flying a specially adapted Spad-XX, completed the circuit at 153.5 mph. Six days later Bernard de Romanet, a renowned wartime pilot with 18 victories to his credit, brought the record up to 166.8 mph. in a modified Nieuport-29. But because he had not exceeded the original record by a margin of 10% as the rules stipulated, Sadi Lecointe was still officially the record holder.

Rivalry between these two pilots, whose planes were both fitted with the Hispano-Suiza 300 h.p. engine, continued throughout the following year, with intermittent challenges from a third ex-fighter pilot, Casale. The following official performances were recorded: 171.3 mph. on 7 February by Sadi Lecointe in a Nieuport; 176.2 mph. on 28 February by Casale in a Spad; 181.7 mph. on 10 October by Romanet in a Spad; 184.2 mph. and 188.0 mph. on 11 and 20 October by Sadi Lecointe in his Nieuport, breaking the 300 kph. (186.3 mph.) barrier.

On 4 November, Romanet beat this record by 4 mph.; on 12 December Sadi Lecointe again took the lead with a speed of 193.4 mph.

These trials were no doubt motivated by the approach of the Gordon Bennett Cup meeting, held at the Etampes circuit on 28 September 1920. The winner was Sadi Lecointe who covered the 300 km. course at 168.6 mph., thus retaining the cup for France. None of the other contestants stayed the course, the need to maintain an engine at maximum output proving too much for most competitors. However, certain American aeroplanes at that meeting, in particular the Dayton-Wright monoplane with variable wing curvature, retractable wheels and no wing struts, pointed the way forward in aircraft design.

The Deutsch de la Meurthe Cup saw another French victory on 1 October 1921 by Kirsch, who covered the course at 172.8 mph. in a Nieuport-Delage with a 320 hp. Hispano-Suiza engine. However, five days earlier Sadi Lecointe had increased the basic speed record to 205.0 mph. in

a similar machine. In fact, assured of victory by the successive elimination of his rivals, Kirsch had deliberately kept to a prudent speed. The Italian pilot Brackpapa covered the first 100 km. at 185.7 mph. in a 700 h.p. Fiat biplane (a world record) but was then obliged to land with engine trouble. The English pilot James, flying his *Bamel Mars*, noticed that part of his fuselage had peeled away

Sadi Lecointe in front of his Nieuport-Hispano speed-trial monoplane in 1921.

in mid flight and put down hurriedly. Sadi Lecointe's propeller shattered in the air, and he was slightly injured during his forced landing. Speeds in the region of 200 mph. posed new problems for aircraft designers and manufacturers; more than one life was to be lost in trying to resolve these difficulties, the first accident occurring on the 23 September 1921 when Bernard de Romanet was killed in a de Monge monoplane, the fuselage of which ripped open in mid-air.

The Dayton-Wright monoplane with retractable wheels and variable wing curvature at Etampes airfield during the 1920 Gordon-Bennett Cup meeting.

The "tail-less" Simplex speed plane designed by M. Arnoux and tested at Etampes in 1923 by Madon.

Triplane built by Clément for Sardier at Combegrasse.

Maneyrol in his Peyret glider with wings in tandem.

Thoret's Hanriot seaplane on a Corsican beach in 1925, after a 3½ hour flight made without power.

The Rhön in 1922. Between the glider *Greif* which is lying on the ground and the monoplane hovering far up in the sky is Martens' glider *Vampyr* which stayed airborne for 64 minutes.

GLIDERS AND GLIDING AEROPLANES

The German airforce after the war found its freedom severely curtailed by the terms of the peace treaty, and began to learn again the lessons of the great Lilienthal. In 1920 their first air meeting at Rhön was attended by twenty-four gliders. The best glides, which were not helped by poor launches, covered 2,000 yds. and lasted just over 2 minutes, dropping 1100 ft. in the process. In 1922 a better organised meeting assembled 45 gliders; Martens stayed in the air for 32 minutes, and Klemperer remained airborne in a low-wing monoplane for 13 minutes, executing figures of eight, and climbing 300 ft.

These experiments attracted wide attention. The French Aeronautical Association organised a meeting in August 1922 at Combegrasse, but the site was unfortunate since it only permitted flights lasting 2 to 5 minutes.

The third Rhön meeting, in 1922, produced some truly astonishing performances. Martens stayed airborne for 1 hour and 4 minutes in his glider *Vampyr* while Nenzen remained in the air for 3 hours and 10 minutes in the same aircraft,

climbing to a height of 1200 ft. above his starting point. Fokker's glider remained airborne for 12 minutes with a passenger aboard.

Several weeks later at a British meeting at Itford Hill the French pilot Maneyrol flew for 3 hours and 12 minutes in a Peyret glider with wings in tandem, while the British pilot, Major Grey, used the uplift created by the same gust of wind to keep a makeshift glider composed of an old and heavy two-seater aircraft fuselage and the wings of a Fokker D-7 fighter in the air for more than an hour. These experiences confirmed that the length of a flight was determined by the strength and constancy of the uplifting winds. Indeed, on 29 January 1923 Maneyrol stayed airborne for 8 hours and 4 minutes over the cliffs at Vauville, while near Biskra in Algeria, Barbot flew for 8 hours and 30 minutes in a Dewoitine glider, climbing 1,770 ft. higher than the summit of Mount Delouatt. On 11 May Schulze upped the record to 8 hours and 42 minutes at Rossitten on the Baltic coast.

Earlier the same year, on 3 January, Lt. Thoret had carried out an even more startling experiment near Biskra. While flying a two-seater Hanriot HD-14 with an 80 h.p. engine, he had shut down his engine above Mount Delouatt in the upward air current created by the impact of the north wind against the sheer rock face, and there he had

hovered for 7 hours and 3 minutes despite the strong gusts and turbulence.

These experiments demonstrated one of the most undeniable qualities of gliding; its educational value. Thoret therefore sought suitable "training areas" where aeroplanes could be profitably used as gliders, and found perfect conditions over the Alpilles hills near Istres in Provence, where the biggest military flying school in France had been established. Here on 27 August 1924 he hovered in mid-air without power for 9 hours and 4 minutes in an 80 h.p. Hanriot. On 24 January 1925 he began training sessions, regularly achieving un-powered flights of more than 8 hours in a 2-stroke machine. Lt. Thoret's research into the long-distance effect of air turbulence caused by objects projecting into the path of the wind convinced him that an aviator could make upward air currents work in his favour if he were able to forecast where they would occur for any given wind direction, just as he could learn to avoid turbulence that could slow him down or prove dangerous. He gave a convincing demonstration of the way in which air currents could be used on 24 September, when he flew without power for 3 hours and 33 minutes covering a tortuous 40 km. long aerial route over Corsica in a Hanriot fitted with floats and weighing over a ton.

Berliner testing his helicopter in the
United States.

Œhmichen's first helicopter, partially lifted by a
balloon, in flight in 1921.

The blades of Pescara's helicopter wrapped around each
other after a sudden jamming of the propeller shaft.

Bothezat's helicopter with four six-bladed rotors
hovering at Dayton in 1922.

Œhmichen's No. 2 helicopter, piloted by the inventor,
hovering at Valentigney.

HELICOPTERS AND AUTOGIROS

Pescara's No. 3 helicopter, piloted by the inventor,
lifting off at Issy in 1923.

The inventors of the helicopter were to take advantage of certain features in the development of aeroplanes that had become widespread since 1919. These included lightweight engines, better constructed airframes built of new materials, and safer, more reliable bearings. Indeed Œhmichen in France, Pescara (an Italian living in Spain) and Berliner in the United States had been researching into and building flying machines that were powered by aircraft engines but relied on rotating wings, or rotors, to lift them into the air, from as early as 1920.

In order to solve the problem of the helicopter, Œhmichen attached a balloon containing 5000 cu. ft. of gas to his helicopter No.1, thereby lightening the machine by 155 lb. and guaranteeing more stability. In these conditions the machine could lift a total weight of 587 lb. It had two propellers of 21 ft. diameter, and a small Dutheil and Chambers 25 h.p. engine. Trials began on 15 January 1921.

Pescara's Mark 2-R helicopter with a 160 h.p. Rhône engine weighed 1750 lb. when loaded and was exhibited in Paris in 1921. The inventor having made contact there with French technical services built his Pescara No.3 in 1992 with a 180 h.p. Hispano engine. The machine weighed one ton and was able to hover in the same spot for more than a minute at a height of one metre; in January 1924, it managed to remain in the air for 10 minutes and 10 seconds.

Œhmichen's second helicopter dispensed with the balloon and instead used four lifting rotors,

four small propellers on a vertical axis (so-called "manoeuvring propellers"), a stabilising gyroscope and movable steering flaps which also prevented the machine from spinning. In total it weighed 1,870 lb. and was driven by a 120 h.p. Rhône engine. From 6 November 1922 to 15 January 1923 the Œhmichen No.2 made about thirty flights at altitudes ranging from 3 to 10 ft. It covered a distance of about 90 yards on the ground and stayed in the air for 2 minutes and 37 seconds. In 1924 it regularly climbed to 20 or 25 ft. when fitted with a 180 h.p. engine, and nearer the ground it covered one kilometre (1,093 yds.) in 7 minutes and 40 seconds on a closed circuit.

Since late 1922 Bothezat had been experimenting in the United States with a helicopter lifted by four rotors with six blades each, a machine that proved to be very stable.

One of La Cierva's first autogiros with 5 blades on the
lifting rotor.

All these experiments led to the helicopter being accepted as a new type of flying machine, and from 1 April 1924 performance records were officially recognised. By the end of the year Pescara held the record for flying over a certain distance in a straight line (805 yds.), and Œhmichen held the altitude record for a helicopter carrying loads of 100 and 200 kilos, which was 3 ft. It was not until the end of 1930 that these performances were bettered.

At the beginning of 1923 Europe learned the results of the first experiments carried out by a young Spanish engineer, Juan de La Cierva, with a flying machine that its inventor christened the "autogiro". This name derived from the fact that the lifting rotor system, though apparently similar to that of a helicopter, was not connected to the engine. The autogiro's engine drove a normal tractor propeller, and when the machine had picked up enough speed the larger lifting rotor would start to revolve under the influence of the slipstream; after a little while the lifting rotor would turn at a rate sufficient to sustain flight. Once airborne the autogiro could carry out the same manoeuvres as any aeroplane, and was able to land with almost no forward speed.

La Cierva's first autogiro piloted by flying officer Gomez Spencer, completed a circuit of 4 km. (4,375 yds.) in 3 minutes and 30 seconds at the Cuatro Vientos aerodrome near Madrid on 31 January 1923; it also proved that it could manoeuvre as freely as any aeroplane.

On 12 December 1924 a C-6 type autogiro piloted by Lieutenant Loriga, driven by a 110 h.p. engine and weighing 1,720 lb. flew between the aerodromes of Cuatro Vientos and Getafe, a distance of 12 km.

Lieutenant Maitland and his Curtiss biplane (September 1922).

Lt. Rittenhouse on the float of the Curtiss which won the Schneider Cup in (1923).

A U.S. Navy racing Curtiss in September 1923; on board is Lt. Brow, the first man to exceed 400 kph. in the air.

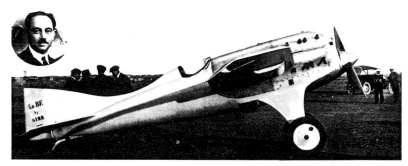

The Bernard-Ferbois in which Bonnet established his air speed record on 11 December 1924. This record stood until 1932.

AIR SPEED IN THE UNITED STATES

In 1920 American airmen had gone to France and learned a thing or two about air speed. The pupil was soon to outstrip the teacher and the successive challenges for the Pulitzer trophy illustrated the Americans' rapid progress in this field.

In 1921 the race was won on 3 November by Bert Acosta with a speed of 176.4 mph. In 1922, when the Deutsch Cup was won by Lasne with a speed of 179,7 mph. Lieutenant Maughan won the Pulitzer in a 400 h.p. Curtiss with the astonishing average speed of 207.7 mph. over 250 km. (155 miles). This result was confirmed on 18 October when Brigadier-General Mitchell set a new speed record of 222.8 mph. A few weeks later Sadi Lecointe, in his Nieuport-Hispano, reached 211.8 mph., then 216.1, and on 15 February 1923 took the record again with a superb average speed of 232.9 mph. French technical prowess, it seemed, still reigned supreme. The

French were very much mistaken however, because these American successes were the result of a general trend in design and construction towards lighter, sleeker and above all faster planes, and the Americans were soon to provide decisive proof of the superior speed of their aeroplanes in European competitions. The 1922 Schneider Cup winner – the English pilot Baird who flew a superb Supermarine-Napier with a hull – was roundly beaten by two U.S. navy seaplanes at Cowes in 1923. On 28 September Lieutenant Rittenhouse took the record to 176.9 mph. in a 465 h.p. 500 lb. Curtiss float plane. In second place was Lieutenant Irvine in a similar aircraft with a speed of 173.4 mph. Baird came third at 151.3 mph.

Eight days later the Pulitzer trophy was won over a course of 200 km. (124.2 miles) by Lieutenant Williams with a speed of 243.6 mph. Brow came second with 241.6 mph. An epic struggle between Williams and Brow then ensued. Brow was the first to exceed 400 kph. (248.4 mph.) when on 2 November he reached a speed of 257.1 mph. The record was then broken four times by

each pilot alternately; by 4 November Williams held the record at 266.4 mph. The Curtiss aircraft used in these trials were driven by 507 h.p. engines weighed 2,100 lb. fully loaded and had a wing area of 148 sq. ft.

But American technical superiority was once again threatened by the French. Thirteen months later, on 11 December 1924 Sergeant-major Bonnet took the speed record up to 278.3 mph. at Istres in a Bernard-Ferbois monoplane designed and built by the engineer Hubert. It had thick wings without struts and a wing area of 116 sq. ft. and was driven by a 600 h.p. Hispano-Suiza engine; the metal Levasseur propeller was similar to one Redd had made for the Americans; aircraft designers were borrowing each other's techniques.

In 1923 France also won back the altitude record from the United States. On 30 October, flying a Nieuport-Delage special with a wingspan of 46 ft. and a surface area of 366 sq. ft., Sadi Lecointe climbed to a height of 36,555 ft. in 1½ hours, thereby beating by nearly 2,000 ft. the record set by MacReady.

Left: helped by Dr. Garsaux, Sadi Lecointe emerges from the pressure-chamber in which he has just "ascended" to 39,000 ft. in preparation for his record-breaking flight. Right: the Nieuport-Delage that broke the altitude record (36,000 ft.) and the pilot, Sadi Lecointe. Note the extremely long wings.

The successful air show at Buc: the aeroplanes standing in line, the hot-air balloons and the crowd (9th October 1920).

PUBLIC AIR SHOWS

From 1919 the Aeronautical Exhibition at Amsterdam was an occasion for sporting trials for the aerial fraternity. In 1920 Monaco hosted its first post-war air meeting in which seaplanes played a major part. The same year saw the Royal Air Force's first "aerial extravaganza" at Hendon, and its varied and colourful display inaugurated a tradition. Then at Antwerp, during a lengthy air fair, Fronval made a name for himself as a virtuoso pilot in competition with Robin and Pinsard; Nungesser thrilled the crowd by simulating aerial combats with the Belgian aviator Van Cotthem; hot-air balloons, the ancestors of aeroplanes, were sent up too, emphasising the link between the two forms of aerial navigation. It was, however, the Buc air show held on 8–10 October 1920 which provided the perfect model for future "air propaganda" drives. At this show airships and balloons of all shapes and sizes pro-

vided a magnificent spectacle and demonstrated that they were an established and accepted part of the life of a modern people. At the Blériot aerodrome at Buc the Aéro-Club de France, presented manned flight in all its diversity to a huge crowd. There were performance trials and displays of military aircraft as well as a demonstration of aerial manoeuvres carried out by naval airships. Capazza and Dollfus made an exciting descent in a parachute-balloon. Then there were aerial photography competitions, ascents in hot-air balloons, handicap races, tests of skill in handling aeroplanes and precision in landing them, and several attempts on the speed record, which were always thrilling and on two occasions successful. Lastly, there was also a very effective marketing exercise in which the public could see passengers leaving for London or Brussels aboard transport planes; five hours later these passengers returned after a short stop at their destination.

In 1921 the propaganda effort spread from Paris to the provinces. Country shows were often

organised on a shoestring budget, and an essential ingredient was always parachute descents, usually made by women. At this stage Lt. Robin, a wartime pilot and virtuoso airman, suggested that a society for aeronautical propaganda should be formed to organise air shows around France with the aim of presenting a true picture of modern flying while at the same time pulling in the crowds with well planned shows. These aerial demonstrations would emphasise the safety of well constructed aeroplanes used in a responsible manner. After this it should be relatively easy to persuade ordinary people to take a trip in an aeroplane, airship, or balloon. From 1922 this society, run jointly by Robin and Finat, put on 18 air shows; at Bourges 350 people took to the air for the first time.

In 1924 the society organised 50 meetings; in the same year Finat and Knipping formed the "Society for the Development of Aviation" which organised 22 meetings in the provinces and the spectacular Vincennes Air Fair.

A performing acrobat dangling from an aeroplane during one of the first Vincennes air shows.

Charles Robin (1894–†F1926)

The first rally held by the Aéro-Club de France the "104 to the 104". A Goliath about to land on the field where the rally is being held, by a hotel 104 km. from Paris.

At the second rally Lt. Robin's little Caudron C-68 is towed towards the hotel on Berck beach. The aeroplane's wings have been folded back.

PRIVATE FLYING

1920 saw the appearance of two new aeroplanes for private flying: the two-seater Potez with a 50 h.p. engine, and the 40 h.p. single-seater Avro that flew non-stop from London to Turin in May.

Barbot's Dewoitine motor-plane fitted with a 16 hp. Clerget engine about to cross the Straits of Dover.

Shortly after, the engineer and pilot de Pischof produced his bizarre "aerial motorcycle", whose 18 h.p. motor focused attention on the possibilities of smaller engines. At the same time Thoret's experiments with gliding pointed the way to small "motor-gliders", which were basically gliders but equipped with lightweight engines. On 6 May 1923 Barbot crossed the Channel and returned in a good example of this type of aircraft,

the Dewoitine D-7. On 15 July of the same year Coupet won the "motor-glider" race organised by the *Petit Parisien* newspaper in a little Farman with a 16 h.p. Salmson engine; his aircraft flew at 38.5 mph. over a circuit of 300 km. (186.3 miles), and had an unloaded weight of less than 220 lb.

However, the dangers and limitations of such naturally fragile hybrid machines soon became apparent. Indeed even as good a pilot as Maneyrol was killed in one of these aircraft in 1923. A safer and more permanent future lay ahead for light private aircraft equipped with normal-sized engines, such as the Caudron C-68, a biplane with a 50 h.p. engine and folding wings, which won the Brussels air competition in 1922. It was for aeroplanes such as these, and for larger aircraft as well, that the state-aided Aéro-Club de France organised meetings, rallies and competitions.

On 18 June 1922 the Aéro-Club de France held its first air rally which went down in the history of French aviation as the "104 to the 104" rally. The venue was a hotel 104 km. along the Paris-Granville road, and 34 aeroplanes duly gathered in a neighbouring field. Among these were four Farman-Goliaths which brought to a total of 104 those who attended the event. Mr. Laurent-Eynac, the Under-Secretary of State for Aviation, presided at the lunch, which was followed by an improvised dance on the lawn of the hotel. This entertaining day out, repeated every year from

then on, proved very favourable publicity for amateur aviation.

In 1924 the club's competition was won by Labouchère in a Potez-VIII with a 50 h.p. engine; in the same year a group of these machines toured the whole of France. At the same time Paumier was trying out an amphibian Schreck, as a possi-

A flying motorcycle: de Pischof's biplane with an 18 hp. Clerget engine, piloted by the inventor in 1920.

ble solution to the amateur aviator's problem of never having enough free space to land on, while in order further to reduce the aeroplane's dependence on the aerodrome, in 1921 Tampier designed and built an aeroplane-automobile which travelled along roads using a 10 h.p. automobile engine separate from the aircraft engine, and made its own way to the Grand-Palais Exhibition in November.

Private flying by amphibian: Emile Paumier in a Schreck-17 ending the round-France circuit in 1924.

Tampier's aeroplane-automobile driving along the Rue Royale with its wings folded during the spring of 1922; when used as an automobile it proceeded tail-first.

Left: The cabin-gondola of the Zeppelin *Nordstem*, which was subsequently delivered to France. Centre: the *Bodensee*, which the *Nordstem* was a sister-ship, and which inaugurated a regular service between Friedrichshafen on Lake Constance, Berlin and Scandinavia on 24 August 1919. Right; the Zeppelin L-72 also delivered to France, where it was known as the *Dixmude*, in front of its hangar at Cues-Pierrefeu.

AIRSHIP DISASTERS

The two-way transatlantic journey made by the R-34 had proved the aptitude of the rigid dirigible for long-distance navigation. At the same time the first regular short-haul services, entrusted after the war, in Italy and Germany, to lighter-than-air machines, added to the value of this demonstration; particularly the astonishing achievements of the little airship *Bodensee*, which by the end of 1919 had transported without accident between Lake Constance and Berlin, nearly three thousand passengers and forty tons of mail.

In 1920 the *Nordstern*, sister of the *Bodensee*, carried out its trials between Lake Constance and Sweden before being delivered to France.

The long-distance capability was of great interest to the United States, as much from the commercial point of view as from that of military reconnaissance on the high seas. The Americans therefore pressed ahead with the construction of the *ZR-1* in America, which was not completed until 1923, and commissioned the building of the *ZR-2* at Cardington in England. On 23 June 1921 this airship, under its English name the *R-38*, set out on its maiden voyage. On 24 August "the greatest airship in the world" ruptured and exploded over the river Humber not far from Hull. 44 of the 49 men aboard perished; among them was Air-Commodore E.M. Maitland, who had made the Atlantic crossing in the *R-34*. The disaster was probably caused by weaknesses in the

metal framework, certain parts of which had already been reinforced; when this gave way the gas compartments were tore open, and the contents ignited by the engines.

The airship *Los Angeles*, with American airforce insignia, over New York.

This catastrophe came shortly after the loss of the R-34, which had been destroyed in a storm on

30 January 1921 while moored at its home station. British enthusiasm for airships waned considerably and a plan to exploit the transcontinental air routes of the Empire using the rigid airships *R-36* and *R-37* was dropped, even though the airships themselves were completed. The destruction of the R-38 also led to an American decision to have a large rigid airship built in Germany under the terms agreed in the peace treaty. This was the *ZR-3*, containing 2,470,000 cu. ft. of gas, 656 ft. long and driven by five 100 h.p. Maybach engines. Manned by a German crew led by Dr. Eckener, the *ZR-3* left Friedrichshafen on 12 October 1924 and arrived in Lakehurst on the 15th, having dropped a bag of post in the Azores on the way. Filled with helium and used by the American navy for training purposes, the airship was rechristened the *Los Angeles*.

Meanwhile another large German rigid airship, the *L-72*, which had been delivered to France and christened *Dixmude*, had been confined to its hangar at Cuers-Pierrefeu near Marseilles. From 2 August 1923 however it undertook a series of journeys round France and between France, Algeria and Tunisia, including one that lasted 118 hours, under the command of Lt. Cdr. du Plessis de Grénedan. The striking success of these was abruptly ended by the catastrophe of 21 December. Nobody is sure exactly what happened, but on that night witnesses on Sicily reported seeing the flash of an explosion in the sky; the commander's body was later washed up on a beach near Sciacca. All France was shocked and saddened not

The burnt-out wreck of the British-airship R-38 lying in the Humber off Hull.

The *R-33* returns to Pulham 29 hours after being torn from its mooring mast; (inset), the nose of the airship left on the mast after the accident.

The *Shenandoah* back in its hangar at Lakehurst 9 hours after being ripped from its mooring mast in a storm on 16 January 1924.

only by the number of victims – all 51 crew members perished in the disaster – but also by the anguished uncertainty of what had happened after the airship left the gulf of Gabès and disappeared over the sea.

Rigid airships did however possess one major safety advantage over flexible ones, of which the successful amputation of the *Zeppelin-V* in 1909 had been the first demonstration. Various other incidents and even a major disaster were paradoxically to confirm this characteristic.

On 16 January 1924 the American rigid airship *Shenandoah* was ripped from its mooring mast at Lakehurst by a wind gusting at more than 60 mph. Despite sustaining a large gash in its forward section, the airship was brought under control by a skeleton crew who managed to bring it back to Lakehurst.

A similar mishap occurred one year later in England. On 16 April 1925 the *R-33* was torn away from its mooring mast at Pulham by the wind. The front section of the airship collapsed completely, but again, a skeleton crew consisting of one officer and a few men succeeded in guiding the striken dirigible back to its departure station 29 hours later, despite the fact that it had been blown all the way to Holland.

On 3 September the *Shenandoah* was caught in a violent storm over the Ohio river and broke into three pieces in mid-air. The main gondola immediately crashed to the ground killing eight people. The rear gondola also came down heavily but without too much damage, and 21 members of the crew walked unharmed from the wreckage; only one was injured. Four people died in the propeller gondolas. The front section however actually floated on like a free balloon; when it eventually landed only one person was hurt and six people escaped without a scratch. Out of a total of 43 passengers, only 14 died and 2 were injured. The use of helium rather than hydrogen to fill the gas-bags had eliminated the risk of a conflagration similar to those that had completely devastated the R-38 and the *Dixmunde*, and the cellular design inherent in rigid airships had allowed at least parts of the airship to survive an accident that would have totally destroyed a flexible craft.

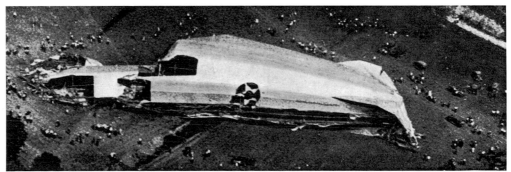

The wreck of the *Shenandoah* on 3 September 1925. Left: the forward section which came down separately from the rest of the airship. (Right): The rear section after the crash. 21 people escaped unhurt from this part of the airship. Altogether there were 29 survivors.

ACROSS THE UNITED STATES

The vast and politically unified territory of the United States presented aerial navigation with a favourable testing ground. Even before the war was over, the U.S. government had launched a study into the feasibility of an air mail service; and on 15 May 1918 the New York–Washington air mail link was established.

Very soon the U.S. Mail assumed responsibility for the experiment. It then proceeded to open up new mail routes across the continent and adapted the air service to each new link, often over difficult or dangerous terrain. First of all the relatively easy path across the central belt of the country was pioneered with night flights, and then the New York to Chicago route was opened up despite the obstacle of the Alleghany mountains. By 1926 the U.S. Mail was in a position to sell the service off to private enterprise. It had successfully established a true aerial road across

A de Havilland military biplane built in the United States and used from 1919 by the U.S. Air Mail Service. A photograph taken at Schenectady after the first experiments in long distance wireless telegraphy.

The Fokker T-2 used by MacReady and Kelly for the first non-stop trans-American flight in 1923.

Mac Ready and Kelly with their aircraft. Parachutes were standard American military issue from 1924.

America, punctuated by airfields and used constantly by air traffic that was in permanent wireless contact with the ground.

Despite all these carefully orchestrated efforts, the air mail service was of course still unable to demonstrate its speed and long range capability over the entire width of the American continent, that is to say over the full 3,000 miles, because it was obliged to operate a realistic service. That sort of journey still required a fully fledged expedition. So it was that on 2 May 1923 two of the American airforce's best pilots, Lts. J.A. Mac Ready and Oakley G. Kelly, set off from Mineola (New York) aboard a Fokker T-2 with a 400 h.p. Liberty engine on a non-stop flight to San Diego. They reached California the next day having covered 2,540 miles at 108 mph. One year later Lt. Maughan crossed America by air between dawn and dusk on the same day, 23 June 1924. He flew from New York to San Francisco in a Curtiss single-seater PW-8, covering 2,698 m. in 21 hr and 44 min, with an actual flying time of 18 hr. and 12 min.

Lt. R.L. Maughan and the Curtiss single-seater in which he flew from New York to San Francisco between dawn and dusk on the same day. The 450 hp. Curtiss engine drove one of the first Reed duralumin propellers.

THE FIRST AERIAL CIRCUMNAVIGATION OF THE WORLD

The first round the world flight was completed in 1924. It was accomplished by Americans, not as just another long-distance flight but as a thoroughly organised and meticulously planned expedition carried out by three crews flying as a group.

After lengthy preparations involving meteorological studies, the establishment of bases along the route stocked with supplies and spare parts, and the careful selection and testing of equipment, four aeroplanes took off from Santa Monica (California) on 17 March. These were Douglas DT-2s, robust biplanes equipped with Liberty engines, that could easily be turned into seaplanes by replacing the wheels with floats. The expedition was led by Major Martin, who was backed up by the three team leaders Lts. Smith, Wade and Nelson; Lts. Arnold, Ogden and Harding accompanied them as volunteer mechanics. There was only one professionally qualified mechanic, Sergeant Harvey, who travelled in Major Martin's plane. Unfortunately this aircraft developed engine trouble during the Seward to Chignik leg of the journey, and was then completely wrecked when it collided with a mountain in the mist. Martin and Harvey were unhurt, but it took them ten days' hard walking to reach Port Moller. The three other planes, which had been fitted with floats since leaving Seattle, had left Dutch Harbour on 3 May; Smith was now leading the expedition. By 22 May the aviators had reached Japan; on 16 June they had got to Saigon; on 1 July they were in Calcutta. On 14 July, having made a special effort to get to France by Bastille day, they touched down in Paris. 5 August saw the arrival of Smith and Nelson in Reykjavik. Wade had been forced to put down on the sea between the Orkneys and Horna Fjord and was subsequently picked up by a trawler; unfortunately his aircraft, which was intact when he had dropped out of the expedition, was damaged while being hoisted aboard the cruiser *Richmond*. Nelson and Smith arrived in Labrador on 31 August. On 9 September the three crews landed in Washington; Wade had rejoined his companions in another aeroplane in Nova Scotia. The aviators had covered 30,777 miles in 175 days, a period of six months having originally been envisaged for the whole journey. In 66 days they had flown for 351 hours at a speed of 85 mph. Their engines had been changed five times and their wings twice at pre-arranged points along the route. An incredible technical and navigational feat had been accomplished.

At the very same moment an equally courageous if less highly organised journey was being undertaken by the British S. Ldr. Mac-Laren, who set off from Calshot on 25 March 1924 aboard a Vickers amphibian to try to fly round the globe. His first plane sank near Akyab on the coast of Burma, and a second was lost in the Pacific at Nikolski in the Aleutians on the 3 August.

The three Douglasses of the round the world flight seen over France.

The aviators welcomed back to America by the naval authorities. On the left is Lowell Smith, the leader of the expedition. In the middle, shaking hands with the admiral, is Nelson. Between them are Lts. Arnold and Harding, who acted as mechanics on the trip.

Nelson and Smith's aeroplanes, the *Chicago* and the *New Orleans*, touch down in American waters at Indian Harbour (Labrador), five and a half months after leaving Santa Monica (California).

The two seaplanes of Amundsen's expedition on the pack-ice 158 miles from the North Pole. On the left, the *N-24*. In the middle the *N-25* flies the Norwegian flag. On a relatively flat section of the pack-ice formed by "young ice", the expedition members on the right are busy digging a take-off strip.

AMUNDSEN'S 1925 EXPEDITION

The American aeroplanes that made the first round the world trip had used a northerly route to get from Europe to the United States. During this stage of the journey ice and snow prevented them from reaching Angmagssalik on the east coast of Greenland as they had originally intended, and instead forced them to make a perilous non-stop flight between Reykjavik and Frederiksdal on its southern tip. However, aeroplanes were soon to be faced with far more hostile conditions when the great Norwegian explorer Amundsen made a bid to reach the North Pole by air. Helped by public subscription and a $85,000 gift from the American J.W. Ellsworth, Roald Amundsen chose to make the expedition in a Dornier-Wal seaplane, whose broad flat-bottomed hull stabilised by floats which were an integral part of the airframe seemed to him to be ideal both for putting down normally on the sea and for landing on the polar ice fields. Two such aircraft were built in Italy at Marina di Pisa. Each plane was fitted with two 360 h.p. Rolls-Royce engines and was elaborately equipped with all the gear that its three man crew would require.

The aeroplanes, christened the *N-24* and the *N-25*, were put through their paces at Ny Aalesund (Spitzbergen) and on 21 May 1925 finally set off at 1710. On board the *N-25* were Lt. Cdr. Rijser-Larsen, the pilot, Amundsen, the navigator and head of the expedition, and the German

mechanic Feucht. On board the *N-24* were Lt. Cdr. Dietrichson, the pilot, Omdal, the mechanic, and Lincoln Ellsworth, the son of Amundsen's American backer, who came along as an observer. In total four Norwegians, an American and a German. Take-off was difficult; their carrying capacity was 6,820 lb. and all up weight 14,080 lb. on setting out for the Pole.

The two aeroplanes flew together in brilliant sunshine, first of all in a completely clear sky and then above a sea of clouds. A fairly strong side wind blew them off course, nobody knew exactly by how much. At 0115 on 22 May the *N-25* flew over a small stretch of water, the only surface on which the crew could be sure of landing safely since their departure from Spitzbergen. Since the rear engine was overheating, more than half of their fuel was gone and they had no idea of where they were, the crew decided to land and subsequently did so without incident. The *N-24* also touched down and Dietrichson manoeuvred his aircraft on to the ice; his hull had been torn open when he took off and was now letting in water at an alarming rate. The aviators discovered that they had come down at a position 87°43′ north and 10°20′ west of Greenwich; they were 158 miles from the pole. They had reached this point eight hours after leaving an inhabited village and flying due north for 620 miles. Twenty years earlier such a feat would have been possible only in adventure stories.

But the greatest part of the adventure was the return trip. It is hard to imagine the courage and discipline the crews demonstrated in digging a flat

runway in the snow, transferring petrol and supplies on to the *N-25*, and finally preparing the heavy seaplane for take-off on the ice. On 15 June the six men crowded into the aeroplane and at 1030 Rijser-Larsen succeeded in getting the aircraft into the air. They set course for Spitzbergen, knowing that there was little chance of their surviving if they failed to reach the island. After a flight lasting less than eight hours but frequently made perilous by patches of fog, mountains were sighted in the distance. The *N-25* was heading straight for its intended destination, the northern cape of North-East Land. But before the aeroplane could reach the coast, an aileron jammed. The crew had to put down on the sea. By guiding the aircraft with its engines, the pilot managed to reach a sheltered bay. There the necessary repair was done and the aeroplane was directed towards a ship that the crew had sighted, the *Sjoliv*, which towed the *N-25* south. On 17 June Amundsen and his companions reached King's Bay, where there had been very real fears for their safety.

The expedition had proved the absence of land in the area of the Arctic explored by the crews. At the point where they had touched down, the explorers had taken acoustic soundings of the ocean floor and revealed a depth of 12,300 ft. Most of all, Amundsen was now thoroughly convinced of the valuable contribution aviation could make to polar exploration. At the same time he had experienced at first hand the dangers faced by both aeroplanes and seaplanes operating at such latitudes. From then on the great Norwegian's thoughts turned to airships.

The *N-25*, flying up Oslo fjord on 5 July 1925 to a reception in the Norwegian capital after the expedition.

Rijser-Larsen, pilot of the *N-25*.

The explorers dragging blocks of ice by sledge to fill up crevasses in the runway they are constructing.

Commander Byrd's Fokker FVII *Josephine Ford* reappears over the frozen peaks around Ny Aalesund on 9 May 1926 after the first successful attempt to reach the North Pole by air. Amundsen is standing in the foreground with his back to the camera, waiting to congratulate the American aviators.

THE NORTH POLE CONQUERED BY AIR

Less than a year after he had set out from Spitzbergen in a seaplane, Amundsen was once more planning an Arctic expedition. This time he planned to take off from King's Bay on board a semi-rigid airship.

Helped again by the Ellsworth family, Amundsen had had this dirigible, the *Norge*, constructed specially for the expedition in Italy. It had been designed and was captained by Colonel Nobile and carried a crew of twelve. On board also were Lincoln Ellsworth and Rijser-Larsen, Amundsen's previous companions. The *Norge* was a well built airship 269 ft. long, filled with 677,500 cu. ft. of gas, and powered by three 260 h.p. Maybach engines. It left Rome on 10 April, and reached Spitzbergen on 7 May, where it was sheltered in a specially built roofless hangar on King's Bay.

An aeroplane had preceded the airship to Spitzbergen; the Fokker F-VII *Josephine Ford*, fitted with three 230 h.p. air-cooled Wright engines and skis, was being made ready to attempt a transpolar flight. Its crew were Lt. Cdr. Richard E. Byrd, head of the expedition and navigator, and the great pilot Floyd Bennett. The aircraft weighed 5 tons and take-off on skis was by no means easy, but after several aborted attempts, the three-engined plane took to the air majestically at 0030 on 9 May 1926, carrying nearly 660 gallons of petrol, enough to keep it airborne for

23 hours. At four minutes past nine in the morning Byrd flew over the North Pole and circled for fourteen minutes over that point, which he was the first to reach by air. He touched down at King's Bay at half past four in the afternoon. The aeroplane had been constantly helped by changes in the direction of the wind, especially on its return journey, and as a result had been able to cover about 1550 miles in 16 hours.

Two days later Amundsen and his companions took off from King's Bay in the *Norge*. On 12 May, in perfectly still weather, the airship reached the pole. Photographs were taken and flags were thrown down. Then the airship set a course for Point Barrow, since the expedition also involved crossing the Arctic ice cap. At this point the *Norge* was caught in a freezing fog; not having sufficient ballast to avoid this icy mist, the airship continued in these conditions for 1,350 miles. Deposits of ice and hoar frost started to accumulate, especially on the front of the envelope; these weighed the airship down and made steering difficult. Soon they were posing a real threat to its safety. Chunks of ice were breaking off and being thrown by the propellers into the airship's skin. It became impossible to receive meteorological data because the radio mast was so heavily encrusted with ice. Nobile deliberately flew very low, keeping to the coldest layer of the air immediately above the pack-ice. Even so, when the skin was deflated later it was found to have more than a ton of ice still adhering to it.

On 14 May at half past three in the morning the

airship skirted Cape Prince of Wales and at 0800 it came to rest at Teller, a few kilometres northwest of Nome in Alaska. The Arctic ice cap had been crossed for the first time: 3,415 miles (2,748 as the crow flies) in 68½ hours.

Two years later the *Norge's* journey was to be repeated by a single-engined aeroplane, a Lockheed Vega fitted with a 230 h.p. Wright engine and a wooden fuselage that kept in the heat. This time the journey was made in the opposite direction, from America to Europe. The great Australian explorer Wilkins and his pilot Eielson left from Point Barrow in Alaska on 15 April 1928. On 20 April they completed the 50 miles which separated them from Green Harbour. The flight to Grant Land the most northerly part of Ellesmere Island, and their last landmark, was uneventful, but soon after a thick patch of freezing fog forced Wilkins to depart from his intended route and to make a detour round the pole. The temperature outside the aircraft went down to −46°C. After covering 2175 miles in 20 hours they arrived the next day in northern Spitzbergen. Here, at Dødmansoeira, they were delayed for four days by a terrible snow-storm. On 20 April they completed the 50 miles which separated them from Green Harbour.

The Lockhead was not equipped with wireless, but its abundant navigational aids – six different types of compass, two sextants and a drift indicator – had ensured precise control of the route and allowed the aviators to make valuable comparative readings on their instruments.

Wilkins and Eielson's Lockheed Vega puts down on the snows of Green Harbour on 28 April 1928 after its flight from Point Barrow (Alaska).

Preparations for Amundsen's 1926 expedition: the *Norge* is sheltered in an open-topped hangar at Ny Aalesund (Spitzbergen).

The French Moroccan Campaign. Left: a shelter built in the shape of a cross with a magazine at its centre protects from the wind five Breguet-14s, one of which is a hospital aircraft with a red cross painted on its fuselage. Right: a wounded man being evacuated in a hospital aeroplane.

MILITARY AVIATION IN THE COLONIES

During the war the airforces had proved invaluable in keeping watch over vast expanses of colonial territory, thus acting as a kind of aerial police force. From 1919 French squadrons based in West Africa and Indochina established a network of air routes across these territories. Although these were military units, the tasks they performed were essentially peaceful. The air units based in Morocco and Syria, however, found themselves involved in military operations in 1925 and 1926.

Bombing raids in both of these countries against a highly mobile enemy that fully exploited the nature of the terrain were largely ineffective, but the usefulness of the airforce in liaison with other units of the military was far greater, either by resupplying outposts that had been surrounded and which could not have held out otherwise, or by evacuating the wounded in relative comfort and with a speed hitherto unimaginable. More than 500 men in Morocco and 200 in Syria owed their lives to this prompt method of evacuation. French losses of aircrew, however, were heavy, due mainly to sniper fire from mountain peaks aimed at low-flying aircraft.

Great Britain also realised early on the value of aviation, both as an important tool in binding her

The Spanish Moroccan campaign. A steamer carrying aircraft arriving at Cebadilla in the summer of 1925.

Empire closer together, and as a useful, effective and relatively cheap way of policing territory and dealing quickly with flash-points. The great journeys of 1919, from London to the Cape, to India and to Australia, underlined the military and political importance of these routes and were followed by an immense clearing and building effort on the ground. For several years British squadrons stationed in Egypt undertook the Cairo to the Cape journey as part of their annual training schedule. In certain parts of the Empire where reconnaissance and even combat were necessary, the airforce was frequently placed under the direct control of the local high command, and other military units subordinated to it. The squadrons based in Mesopotamia and on the north-west frontier of India saw constant service, and the routes plied by large seaplanes along the Persian Gulf and the Red Sea from Port Said to Aden, Colombo, Calcutta and Singapore had considerable prestige value as well as proving to be useful training experiences for their crews, who were faced with new tasks in very diverse climates. An interesting aspect of British colonial aviation at this period was the development of "troop transports", huge multi-engined aircraft whose enormous fuselage could accommodate twenty to thirty fully equipped soldiers. These aeroplanes could fly troops in a matter of hours to any point on the globe where their presence might be required.

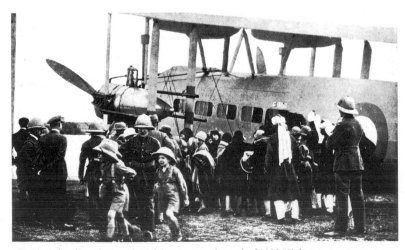

During the disturbances in Afghanistan at the end of 1928 Vickers troop transports were brought in from India to evacuate British residents.

A squadron of Royal Air Force Faireys flying up the Nile during a journey from Cairo to the Cape, undertaken as a training exercise.

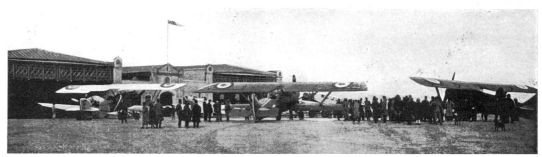

Left top and bottom: the first Tokyo to Paris flight; Abé, Kawachi and (standing) their mechanics in their two Breguet-19s. Top centre: Costes and Rignot at Le Bourget after their record journey to Jask. Top right: a mishap on the Paris–Tokyo flight of 1924: Pelletier smiling at rescuers coming to cut him free from the wreckage; Bésin, sitting on the fuselage, is unbuttoning his flying suit. Bottom right: the Paris–Teheran–Paris planes at the Teheran aerodrome.

GREAT JOURNEYS OF 1924–1926

Between 25 April and 9 June 1924 Lt. Pelletier-Doisy and his mechanic Sgt. Bésin captured the attention of the world's press by flying from Paris to Tokyo. Their aircraft as far as Shanghai was a new Breguet 19 with a 400 h.p. Lorraine engine. Unfortunately this ended its career in a ditch on Shanghai's Kiang Wang race-course and the journey had to be completed in an aged Breguet 14 loaned by the Chinese Government. Japan returned the visit, and the earlier one of Ferrarin and Masiero, in 1925 when on 28 September two Breguet 19s with Lorraine engines piloted by Abe and Kawachi arrived at Le Bourget, having left Tokyo on 25 July. They went on to visit London and Rome.

1925 saw too a resurgence of interest in the opening up of Africa by the colonial powers. An expedition in two large Blériot 115s with four 180 h.p. engines, which included such famous names as Pelletier-Doisy, Le Prieur, Vuillemin and Dagnaux, left Buc on 19 January and crossed the Sahara from Colomb Béchar to Gao between 28 January and 5 February. The expedition came to a tragic end on 7 February when one of the aircraft crashed on taking-off from Sao, killing the wireless operator and injuring his companions.

On 3 February Captains Lemaître and Arrachart flew from Etampes to Timbuktoo via Dakar in a Breguet 19 with a 480 h.p. Renault engine. From there they turned back towards France but misread the tracks on the ground and were blown off course by strong winds. Running out of petrol they had to make a forced landing in the desert. They were quickly rescued, however, and were back in Paris by 24 March.

Later the same year, between 10 and 12 August, Arrachart with Carol as co-pilot made a famous trans-European trip in a Potez 25 with a 450 h.p. Lorraine engine. The trip lasted a mere 66 hours, of which 39 hours were spent in the air. Despite storms and torrential rain they flew at an average speed of 118 mph. along a route that took in Belgrade, Istanbul, Bucharest, Moscow, Warsaw and Copenhagen.

Finally, towards the end of the year, a group flight headed by Dagnaux and comprising three Breguet-19s and a Potez-25, each fitted with a different make of engine, flew from Paris to Teheran and back.

Belgium too showed interest in pioneering a route to her African possessions. On 12 February 1925 Roger, de Bruycker and Thieffry set off from Brussels in a three-engined aeroplane built by the Belgian aircraft construction company; they reached Léopoldville on 3 April. One year later, between 9 March and 12 April, Sergeant Verhaegen and Lts. Medaets and Coppens flew from Brussels to Kinshasa and back via the Nile valley, covering a distance of 11000 miles at 121 mph. in a Breguet-19 with a Hispano engine.

On 12 October 1926 two single-engined French naval seaplanes, a Liouré-Olivier II-13. Jupiter and a CAMS-37, left Marseilles to reconnoitre a suitable air route to Madagascar.

During their flight from Etampes to Timbuktoo in 1925 Lemaître and Arrachart had established a new distance record of 1966 miles between Etampes and Villa Cisneros. The engine manufacturer Renault offered a cup for the greatest non-stop distance accomplished in 1926. The record was broken several times during the year as a result, firstly by the Arrachart brothers on 26–27 June who flew 2,673 miles from Paris to Basra in a Potez 28 with a 550 h.p. Renault engine. Next, on 14–15 July Girier and Dordilly flew 2,929 miles from Paris to Omsk in a Breguet 19 with a 500 h.p. Hispano Suiza engine. On 31 August–1 September, again in a Breguet-19 fitted this time with a 500 h.p. Farman with a reduction gear engine, Challe and Weiser increased the record to 3213 miles with a trip from Paris to Bandar Abbas. However, it was Dieudonné Costes, a great military pilot and also the chief pilot for the Breguet company, who took the definitive record at the end of the year: on 28–2 October Costes and Ringot flew non-stop from Paris to Jask in a Breguet-Hispano similar to that of the Paris-Omsk flight, covering 3,351 miles in 32 hours. The Breguet's carrying capacity had steadily increased: the empty weight of the Paris-Jask plane was just one third of the total weight with which Costes took off from Le Bourget.

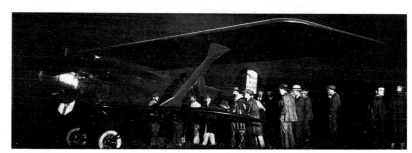

The record breaking Breguet 19s of 1926. Left: Costes' with 500 hp. Hispano Suiza engine. Right: Challe and Weiser's with 500 hp. Farman engine.

TWO FLYING-BOAT EPICS

The greatest and probably the most significant aerial expedition of 1925, however, was the one accomplished by Commander de Pinedo and his mechanic Campanelli. Singlehandedly in a small Savoia S-16 *ter* flying-boat with a 450 h.p. Lorraine engine, these two aviators covered an astonishing distance of 34,000 miles from Sesto Calende to Australia, round the western, southern and eastern coasts of Australia, up via the Philippines to Japan, and then back to Rome by the coasts of China and Indochina. Apart from ensuring that there would be adequate supplies of fuel and oil along the route, they made no preparation on the ground. Their engine was changed only once, in Tokyo, after they had completed 23,000 miles.

The journey was divided into three stages. The first, from Italy to Melbourne via the Persian Gulf and India, included a flight across the Indian subcontinent (683 miles from Bombay to Cocanada) and was made between 20 April and 9 June. In total 30 flying days were needed to cover 14,300 miles. As far as Australia the Italian crew had kept to fairly well established air routes, where spare parts were always in plentiful supply. But the Melbourne to China leg via New Guinea, the Moluccas, the Celebes, the Philippines and Taiwan was entirely virgin territory for aerial navigation. Despite this fact, de Pinedo and Campanelli left Melbourne on 16 July and Brisbane on 6 August, and arrived at the Kasumiga Ura naval airforce base near Tokyo on 26 September. They had covered 8,700 miles, hopping from island to island and from open bays to hazardous ports; the hull had been damaged at Manila and almost all repair work had been done by the crew themselves.

The return to Europe was even more amazing: the 11,000 miles separating Tokyo and Rome were covered between 17 October and 7 November, 21 days, of which 18 were spent in the air. The average length of each flight was therefore over 600 miles. A triumphant welcome awaited the aviators in Italy. Commander de Pinedo and Campanelli had made the longest air journey in history. In a little seaplane with a wooden hull and canvas wings weighing less than three tons fully loaded, they had covered their route in 68 stages and 350 flying hours. Along the way they had been exposed to a wide range of often very hostile atmospheric and climatic conditions, but they had triumphed over all the obstacles in their path and had given the most conclusive demonstration yet of the scope and versatility of the aeroplane.

Meanwhile, on the other side of the world the American naval airforce was spending a great deal of time and effort in establishing a link between the U.S.A. and Hawaii. On the 31 August 1925 two large Packard flying boats with twin 950 h.p. engines set out for Hawaii from San Francisco. One of them broke down 300 miles off the American coast and was rescued immediately. The other captained by Cdr. John Rodgers, the leader of the expedition, was also forced to put down the next day for lack of fuel 2,200 miles from San Francisco and less than 300 miles from its intended destination. Even though twelve naval vessels had been posted along the route and radio contact had been maintained constantly, the search parties that were immediately dispatched could find no trace of the missing aircraft. Nine days passed before the seaplane was sighted by a submarine just 15 miles off the island of Kauai, where it had drifted with the aid of a sail made out of the canvas that covered the wings. The crew of four men, despite the considerable hardships they had endured, refused to leave their aircraft before they had anchored it in the harbour.

It was not until 28–29 June 1927 that the first successful non-stop flight from San Francisco to Honolulu was finally made. Lt. Maitland, the pilot, and Lt. Hegenberger, the navigator, covered a distance of 2,422 miles in 25 hours and 49 minutes in a three-engined 690 h.p. Fokker landplane.

De Pinedo and his mechanic Campanelli aboard their Savoia S-16 *ter* driven by a French Lorraine engine.

Commander Rodger's PN-7 flying boat which flew from San Francisco to Hawaii in 1925, finishing its journey by drifting for nine days towards its destination. The barrels of fuel in the foreground represent the total capacity of its tanks.

Maitland and Hegenberger's three-engined Fokker leaving for Honolulu which it reached in 25 hr. and 49 min. It is seen here flying over the quays of San Francisco, several minutes after leaving Oakland airport

The *Oiseau Blanc* a few minutes after take-off following the Seine near Gennevilliers. The undercarriage had already been jettisoned, and the plane is heading for the sea.

1927: YEAR OF THE ATLANTIC

The long distance records of 1926, all set by Frenchmen, had opened up new possibilities for aviation. However, these expeditions ended up at Asian destinations which gave the public at large only a hazy idea of the sheer distance involved. Crossing the great oceans was seen as a far more impressive and exciting feat. On 21 September 1926 Fonck had crashed tragically while taking off from New York in a bid to fly to Paris. In December wide publicity was given to the fact that another French crew was about to attempt the Paris–New York crossing.

On the night of the 7–8 May 1927 a solemn atmosphere reigned at Le Bourget airport. In a bare room adjoining the hangar two military beds had been prepared; towards 2 o'clock in the morning two men came into this room: they were Coli and Nungesser, the aviators who were going to attempt the transatlantic flight. A witness to the scene wrote:

"Nungesser was calm yet visibly moved. He spoke little and his cheeks were flushed. He lay on one of the beds for most of the time. Coli was equally calm, more reserved than usual, and meticulous in his preparations. His expressive face with the legendary black monocle that covered the eye he had lost during the war seemed more sharply defined than usual as he stood there in khaki coloured jacket and trousers . . . Instinctively everybody talked in low voices. I could not take my eyes off these two men who were so conscious of the dangers they faced and who seemed so noble, as if they were detached from the ordinary flow of life . . . "

At 21 minutes past five, seven minutes after the aeroplane had been wheeled out of its hangar, Nungesser took off in 46 seconds, climbed rapidly and veered off into the distance. The undercarriage was no longer required and was jettisoned as the aircraft followed the Seine towards the sea. And so Coli and Nungesser set out for America in the *Oiseau Blanc*. At four minutes past six their aerial escort saw them cross the French coast above Étretat.

Thirty hours' silence followed. Nobody reported seeing the plane over Ireland. Then, on Monday the 9th, between midday and five

François Coli and Charles Nungesser in the *Oiseau Blanc*.

o'clock in the afternoon, various sightings were reported: the *Oiseau Blanc* had passed over Newfoundland, then Halifax, then Boston and had finally touched down in New York. The evening papers brought out numerous special editions which were snapped up by the crowds, especially after the announcement that Coli and Nungesser had put down in New York harbour. One newspaper even purported to relay the exact words of the aviators as they climbed out of their aeroplane, exhausted but triumphant, in America.

Contradictions in these reports soon became apparent. One by one the telegrams were shown to be fraudulent and meaningless. In the Chamber the French Air Minister denounced what he called a remarkable case of "collective illusion". Searches were organised, but it soon became clear that the two airmen had vanished without trace.

Just before setting out on this tragic flight, one of the two men had remarked to the chief mechanic "If we disappear you'll tell them that our expedition was well prepared, won't you?" This was the truth. Since there was no seaplane with the desired range available, Coli and Nungesser had opted for a tried and tested naval aeroplane, a Levasseur with a rigid fuselage. Detailed fuel-consumption tests had been carried out. Total weight on take-off was 11,066 lb., a quite reasonable load for 650 sq. ft. of wing surface. The aeroplane was fitted with an over-size metal propeller and had a discardable undercarriage with specially designed wheels. All this foresight and technology, complemented by the absolute determination and courage of the aviators, had nevertheless ended in tragedy.

L'Atlantique est traversé
Ils sont arrivés à 16 h. 50
NUNGESSER ET COLI
ont amerri en rade de New=York

One of the headlines of a Parisian newspaper published on the 9th May 1927 announcing the false news of the French crew's arrival in New York.

The Ryan *Spirit of St. Louis* with a 220 hp. Wright engine during its flight from Saint Louis to New York.

Lindbergh and Ryan technicians at San Diego.

NEW YORK TO PARIS: LINDBERGH

The aviator whom the newspapers still called the "flying fool" left Roosevelt Field on Long Island at 1252 (Paris time). He was sighted at Halifax at 1440, at Cape Race (Newfoundland) at 2355, and over the Atlantic by two ships located 600 and 500 miles west of Ireland. At 1720 he reached the Irish coast at Smerwick Harbour. At this point the importance of Lindbergh's achievement suddenly became apparent and the Parisian crowds rushed to Le Bourget to welcome him. At 2025 Lindbergh's plane was sighted over Cherbourg. From ten o'clock a vast crowd started to press against the railings around the aerodrome. At 2215 the soft drone of a descending aircraft could be heard in the sky and moments later the ghost-like silhouette of the *Spirit of St. Louis* came into view. Fully illuminated by the ground lights, this aeroplane that had flown right across the ocean landed and came to rest. At the same moment a tide of 200,000 spectators surged forward, trampling down the railings that restrained them in an spontaneous attempt to get closer to Lindbergh and share his glory.

Next day the full story of the first solo transatlantic crossing became known. Lindbergh had set out on the strength of favourable weather reports, and had been helped along by tail-winds over the first 1,250 miles of his journey. He had then had to fly in rain, fog and cloud, constantly changing his altitude from anywhere between 11,500 ft. and sea level. The most anxious moment of the trip occurred during the small hours of 21 May when black ice began to form on the wings and imposed an extra burden on the aircraft. However, the weather improved as Lindbergh approached Ireland, and he crossed the Irish coast 3 miles from the point he had intended.

Measured in a straight line, his journey covered 3633 miles and constituted a new world record. The actual distance travelled by the aeroplane was nearer 3,415 miles, which Lindbergh completed in 33 hours and thirty minutes, averaging 117 mph. 71 gallons of fuel were left in the *Spirit of St. Louis'* tanks when it landed, which would have allowed it to cover a further 750 miles. A little monoplane driven by a 220 h.p. engine had been able to beat the Paris–Jask distance record recently established by Costes and Rignot in a 600 h.p. aircraft not by 250 but by 1000 miles.

Who was the pilot who made this remarkable journey? He was by no means a mere novice, still less a "flying fool". In May 1927 Charles Lindbergh was not yet 26. A pilot officer in the American army air force, he acquired a reputation as a brave and dashing young airman who had already made two successful descents by parachute from stricken aeroplanes. In 1925 he had left the army and worked as a pilot on the Chicago to Saint Louis run for a company under contract to U.S. Mail, making nightly deliveries which he felt duty bound to carry out whatever the weather. The risks he ran by flying in such conditions were enormous; twice at the end of 1926 he had been caught in thick fog and had had to bail out of his aeroplane at night, thus bringing up to four the total number of escapes by parachute, which remained a record until 1932.

When he decided to embark on the transatlantic expedition, friends in Saint Louis helped him to raise the quite modest sum needed to charter an aeroplane; he chose a monoplane of a type unknown in Europe, a Ryan, whose air-worthiness had been tested on difficult shorter-range routes in the United States, in particular up and down the Pacific coast. With an empty weight of 2255 lb. to 325 sq. ft. of wing surface, the aeroplane took off from Long Island weighing 5300 lb. The engine was a 220 h.p. air-cooled Wright model

with 9 cylinders arranged in the shape of a star. During the journey which lasted 33½ hours it consumed 305 of the 376 gallons of petrol in the fuel tanks and less than 4 gallons of oil.

The Ryan's instrument panel assembled the greatest number of steering and navigational devices yet to confront a single pilot in one plane. Owing to a device pioneered in France by Badin and manufactured under licence in the United States, Lindbergh had been able to fly for hours through the darkness and fog without once having to look for any external features that would give him an idea of the aircraft's position. This device was especially valuable to him because he could only see what was going on in front of the aeroplane through a periscope, since a very large fuel tank was located directly in front of the cockpit. A new type of compass had also made it easier for him to stick to the correct course.

Lindbergh's success was rich in practical lessons for the aeronautical industry. But most of all this remarkable expedition had a deep human significance for the people of Paris. Their homage was spontaneous, enthusiastic and affectionate. The memory of Coli and Nungesser made their acclaim even more emotional. Lindbergh was conscious of this immense popular feeling, and he was equal to the welcome he received. At the Élysée, the Aéro-Club de France, with Blériot and Madame Nungesser, even among the French aviators who at first begrudged his tremendous success, the conqueror of the Atlantic everywhere showed himself to be an unaffected, and generally upstanding young man as he was ushered into Parisian society by the accomplished U.S. ambassador Myron T. Herrick.

On 28 May, one week after his triumphant night landing, Charles A. Lindbergh, Knight of the Legion of Honour, left Paris. As he flew low over the French capital, he dropped a message of thanks pinned to a flag.

Charles Lindbergh and Louis Blériot in 1927.

Police, firemen and volunteers protecting Lindbergh's aeroplane from the stampeding crowd.

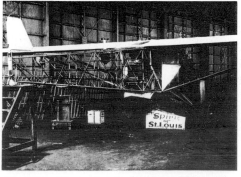

The *Spirit of St. Louis* stripped at Le Bourget: the new wind-powered compass is clearly visible.

The cockpit: joystick, fuel cocks and instrument panel.

Arrival of Chamberlin and Levine at Le Bourget on the 30 June 1927 after flying from Berlin in the Bellanca that made the New York to Eisleben crossing.

Top: Byrd's three-engined Fokker *America* on its take-off ramp at Long Island, New York. Bottom: the *America* on the beach at Ver-sur-Mer.

CHAMBERLIN, BYRD AND BROCK AND SCHLEE

The excitement of Lindbergh's triumph had not yet died down when another aeroplane took off for Europe from Roosevelt Field on the 4 June. The aircraft was a Bellanca with the same specifications and engine as Lindbergh's Ryan, flown by the great pilot Clarence D. Chamberlin and carrying the first ever transatlantic passenger, Charles Levine.

This time Paris was not the ultimate destination. By choosing Paris as a landing place, Lindbergh had ensured worldwide publicity for his flight, and had also won the Orteig prize which was worth $25,000. Chamberlin did not stand to win any prizes, and he let it be known from the outset that a mere repetition of Lindbergh's route would not satisfy him. He hoped to go as far beyond Paris as his petrol would allow, a presumptious ambition, perhaps, but nonetheless on the morning of the 6 June he landed at Eisleben some 100 miles south-west of Berlin. He had beaten by 400 miles at least the distance record that Lindbergh had just set in the *Spirit of St. Louis*.

The third aerial transatlantic crossing from New York to Europe was concluded at half past two in the morning on 1 July 1927. This time the journey had been made by four men in a large three-engined transport plane, and had taken 40 hours. They had also nearly died battling against rain and fog on a pitch-black night.

At dawn on the 29 June, the three-engined Fokker *America*, with 220 h.p. Wright engines, was wheeled out on to the specially constructed take-off ramp at Roosevelt Field. Four airmen took their places in the aircraft: Acosta and Balchen, the pilots, Noville, the wireless operator, and Richard E. Byrd, leader of the expedition and the first man to have flown over the North Pole. The aircraft weighed an enormous 15,950 lb. for 720 sq. ft. of wing surface.

At 7 o'clock in the evening on 31 June Byrd signalled his position over Land's End to Cherbourg, which he believed he was approaching. At this point there was a deviation from the intended route – later found to be the result of a faulty instrument – and the aeroplane began to fly due south. Eventually Byrd was informed of this error by wireless off Ushant, and he turned east towards Brest; at half past eight Paris was ready to welcome the crew.

Night had fallen over Le Bourget airport. It had started to rain. The *America* had passed over Saint-Brieuc at 2019; Byrd would be in Paris by midnight. It began to rain even harder. At half past midnight the loud-speakers announced that Le Bourget wireless station had started receiving signals from the *America*; Five minutes later the signals were said to be getting more and more distinct. Ground-lights and search-lights were turned on at full power, though their effect was considerably reduced by the pouring rain. Rockets were sent up, which momentarily revealed an airfield that looked more like a marshy bog. The spectators were asked to remain absolutely silent in order to hear the approaching aircraft. How-

ever, the sudden stillness of the crowd merely accentuated the total silence in the sky.

At five minutes past one in the morning the wireless station at Le Bourget received a message that was not broadcast to the crowd: Byrd was asking for an airfield, any airfield. Soon afterwards there was an S.O.S. signal, which gradually grew fainter and fainter and then died out altogether. The crowd waited silently and expectantly; the sense of crisis had affected everybody.

By two o'clock in the morning the *America* had run out of fuel and the crew prepared for an emergency landing. They had spotted a lighthouse and the sea, and Byrd decided to put down in the water rather than risk the aircraft on the land, where all sorts of hazardous obstacles were probably hidden in the darkness. After a difficult touch-down during which the wheels were ripped off, the fuselage hit the shelving beach and the crew scrambled ashore in a rubber dinghy. They had come down at Ver-sur-Mer (Calvados) where they were warmly welcomed, and the post office at Ver was the first to process letters that had come from America by air.

On 27–28 August Brock and Schlee accomplished another successful Atlantic crossing, and on 12 October Haldeman and Miss Elder put down on the sea near a steamer and were picked up north-east of the Azores.

1927, the "year of the Atlantic", had witnessed four and a half successful crossings from west to east and five failed attempts in which the aircraft and their crews had disappeared, two from Europe and three from America, a total of 14 missing airmen.

Left: at Ver-sur-Mer on 1 July 1927. From left to right: Noville, Byrd, Acosta, Balchen. Centre: Fonck's Sikorsky in flames at Roosevelt Field after the failure of his bid to cross the Atlantic on 21 September 1926. The mechanic Islamov and the radio operator Clavier were burned alive. Right: the Archbishop of Cardiff blessing the Saint-Raphaël (lost over the Atlantic on 27 August 1927) at Upavon. Princess Löwenstein-Wertheim is on the left in flying kit. Colonel Minchin and Captain Leslie Hamilton were the crew.

A Boeing mail plane, with a cabin for three passengers, at 10,000 ft. over the Ruby Mountains on the San Francisco–New York run in 1928.

The Air Union fleet at Le Bourget airport in 1929 on the company's tenth anniversary. Left and right: twin-engined Blériots and Lioré-Oliviers from the "Golden Ray" Paris–London service. Centre and extreme right: Breguets used on the Paris–Marseilles and Paris–Geneva routes and two Farman F-190 monoplanes.

AIR LINES IN THE 1920s

While long-distance expeditions and records demonstrated the increased technical possibilities and endurance capabilities of various aircraft, heavily subsidised air transport enterprises were making their mark in the fields of international trade and travel.

One example was the Franco-Rumanian air service which from 1920 and 1921 developed the Paris–Prague–Warsaw and Paris–Prague–Bucharest–Constantinople air routes pioneered by Deuillin. Opposition from the German authorities, who refused to open their air-space to aeroplanes that were technically superior to aircraft from the German airforce, which had deliberately been weakened under the terms of the

peace treaty, was not overcome until 1926 however, when a joint Paris to Berlin service was inaugurated by the Farman and Luft Hansa companies. This latter company enjoyed a monopoly in air transport across Germany and operated an extremely well organised domestic network within the Reich.

The years 1926 and 1927 saw a decisive turnaround in the way the commercial air service was run in the United States also. From 1926 the U.S. government decided to hand over the operation of various air mail routes covering 5,300 miles to private companies. The following year the 2,800 mile New York–Chicago–San Francisco air mail route ceased to be run by the state as well. In general, however, as more and more air transport companies sprang up, bigger subsidies were needed to support them since there was not enough freight to keep them all in business. A way ahead for the air transport industry only gradually developed as air carriers made agreements to pool their efforts and it was not until aircraft had developed to the stage of being able to exploit the long distance routes that commercial aviation really came into its own.

A Soviet A.K.I. near Gorokhovetz during the inaugural Moscow–Kazan flight (10 July 1924).

Farman company aeroplanes at Le Bourget. In the front is a four-engined Jabiru, behind it are single-engined planes with 500 hp. Farman engines.

A Dornier-Superwal seaplane in service with Italian carriers in 1928.

The first arrival of a German commercial aircraft at Le Bourget in 1926.

A Blériot-Spad, an aeroplane in service with various French long distance carriers.

A Savoia-Marchetti S-55 seaplane used by Italian air companies in the Mediterranean.

Cleaning an all metal Junkers G-24 belonging to a Swedish company.

A three-engined Imperial Airways Armstrong-Siddeley Argosy over London in 1927.

Left: One of the Loening flying boat bases of Lt. Cdr. Wyatt's expedition on the Alaskan coast near Ketchikan (1926) Centre: in Tierra del Fuego: Plüschow's seaplane *Silberkondor* moored in a sheltered bay near the Magellan strait. Right: What no human eye had ever seen before; the centre of the Darwin Cordillera on Tierra del Fuego photographed from the air by Plüschow in February 1929 shortly before his tragic death.

PUTTING AIRCRAFT TO USE

Before 1926 there had been plenty of aerial photographs that were not just visually striking or of military value but also some that had been taken from the geographer's point of view. As early as 1919 the French air service had tried to convince the government, civil engineering companies and geographical and scientific researchers of the value of aerial photography in the fields in which they were working. Such techniques were particularly successful in surveys of areas that had been occupied during the war and were now in need of reconstruction, and in town planning exercises.

However it was in areas of the globe that were still remote and practically uncharted and in vast tracts of territory which had been only incompletely visited by explorers that aircraft yielded the most significant results. The American naval airforce's Alaskan expedition of 1926 provided the model for scientific journeys of this nature – alas all too rarely followed since – the sole aim of which was to broaden man's knowledge of a particular corner of the globe.

The expedition involved twelve officers and one hundred men, a supply ship, a specially constructed flat-bottomed boat weighing 250 tons on which the workshops, laboratories and living quarters were located, and three amphibious Loening flying boats. The expedition's cameras were fitted with three lenses and took three shots, one from the vertical and the two others diverging by 35° to the left and right in order to obtain a three dimensional effect. An elaborate wireless communications system ensured the safety of the air crews, who were flying over uninhabited, inaccessible and heavily wooded mountains. In fact there were no accidents or forced landings over the total distance of 50,000 miles covered by the aviators. The expedition, which was led by Lt. Cdr. Wyatt, set out from San Diego and returned there four months later having completed a programme of exploration, photography and map making of forest areas that would have taken a ground-based expedition ten years to carry out.

Aircraft also quickly became the prime means of transport in the far north both of the Old World and the New where climatic conditions had made the construction of roads impractical, but where valuable cargoes of furs which would otherwise have taken months to reach their markets, could now be flown out in a matter of hours. This was particularly true in such areas as Finland and Canada where an abundance of lakes could serve as ready-made landing grounds.

The aircraft did not only transport the trapped furs either. In Russia aeroplanes were also used to reconnoitre the hunting grounds and direct the hunters to areas where the game was abundant. In this way the sealers of Podkamenaya – Tunguska were able to amass in 14 days in the winter of 1926–1927 the extraordinary total of 50,000 pelts.

In more temperate climates aircraft began to be used to monitor the progress of forest fires, and in agriculture to spray pesticide on to vast areas of crops, an infinitely faster and more effective method of pest-control than spraying from a tractor. Not only did the speed of the aeroplane protect the operator (the pilot) from the effects of the insecticide, but the slipstream caused by the propeller fluttered the leaves of such crops as oranges in such a way as to allow the chemicals to reach all parts of the plants and in particular the undersides of the leaves, which would not have been covered by conventional spraying.

A "Dobrolyet" aircraft from Arkhangelsk, made available to the seal hunters at Podkamennaya Tunguska (62° North), being welcomed by the local Soviets (1926).

A northern air link: a private company seaplane plying the Porjus to Suorva route in Lapland and the hangar at Porjus beyond the Arctic Circle.

Spraying pesticides on an orange plantation near Santa Ana (California)

An aircraft of the U.S. forestry service monitoring the progress of a forest fire.

Survivor from the *Italia* signalling from the "red tent".

The *Italia* at King's Bay on 23 May 1928.

On board the *Italia* above the pack-ice.

THE DRAMA OF THE *ITALIA*

Aerial exploration of the North Pole was to claim more victims in 1928: some of the crew of the airship *Italia* and the rescuers who went to its aid.

The *Italia* was a semi-rigid airship 348 ft. long that held 563,000 cu. ft. of gas. It was an adaptation of the *Norge*, the airship Amundsen had used on his expedition. Three 240 h.p. engines allowed the dirigible to cruise at speeds in the order of 60 mph. The crew numbered 16 and was again led by General Nobile. The expedition, which was subsidised by the Italian government and the city of Milan, intended to survey Lenin Land and to look for the so-called Crocker Land, then to fly on to the pole and to try to land there in order to do oceanographic and magnetic experiments.

Between 15 April and 6 May the *Italia* flew from Milan to King's Bay in Spitzbergen. On 15 May, following a "false start" on the 11th, the airship set off towards North Land (Severnaya Zemlya) but was prevented from reaching its destination by a strong headwind. It returned to King's Bay on 18 May after an exhausting journey of 69 hours.

On the 23rd the *Italia* set off towards the pole, which it reached in 20 hours; the intended landing did not prove possible, and after two hours spent circling the pole a course was set for Spitzbergen. On 25 May at 0600 in the morning a wireless message from the *Italia* reported that it was in considerable difficulty owing to fog and heavy deposits of ice on the envelope. At 10 o'clock the airship reported that it was struggling against a violent west wind.

On 9 June, while search parties were being organised over a wide area, the base ship *Citta di*

Dietrichson, Amundsen and Guilbaud (†*F*1928) and their Latham flying boat at Tromsö (17/18 June 1928).

Milano received a message from a group of survivors. The *Italia* expedition had come to an abrupt end not far from the Foyn islands, off the northeast coast of Spitzbergen, 250 miles ENE of King's Bay, when the airship had crashed into the pack-ice owing to the weight of ice on its envelope. The principle gondola had broken off from the rest of the dirigible on impact; the occupants – nine men including Nobile who was injured in the crash – escaped alive and moreover were left with a few provisions and a wireless set. The rest of the airship, relieved of its weight, immediately flew off again and was carried to a very great height by the strong winds; the seven men it took with it were never seen again.

The comings and goings of the marooned crew and their rescuers across the pack-ice, the news of a terrible tragedy and the triumphs and setbacks of the whole episode kept the world's press occupied for weeks on end. On 20 June Maddalena, who had arrived from Italy in a Savoia-S55 flying boat, discovered six men around the "red tent". On the 22nd both he and the Swede Tornberg, who was flying a Junkers G-24, dropped fresh supplies near the survivors. On the 24th Lundborg managed to land nearby and rescued Nobile; on attempting to make a second landing

he overturned his Fokker C-V aircraft and remained trapped with the *Italia*'s crew until 6 July, when Schyberg succeeded in landing a little Moth with skis and rescued him. Swedish planes also helped Sora and Van Dongen, who were trying to reach the marooned survivors by land. The Russian aviator Chuknovsky took off from an ice-breaker in a Junkers but crash-landed near Cape Platen. On the 12th he was rescued by the same ice-breaker which, thanks to his directions, had already been able to pick up the remaining *Italia* survivors.

None of the main rescue operations had cost any life, a fact largely attributable to organisation and experience, qualities which were particularly evident in the Swedish team led by Captain Tornberg, whose seaplanes set out from Hinlopen some 125 miles away from the Foyn Islands, often surcharged 50% above their theoretical carrying capacity. Apart from supplies for the marooned crew of the airship each aircraft was equipped with a tent, firearms, and provisions that would last its pilot for a month if he were forced to land and make his way back to base across the ice.

The rescue operation did however finally claim some notable victims. A French Latham flying boat captained by Commander Guilbaud had flown from Caudebec to Bergen on 16 June. There it had picked up the great explorer Amundsen, who was anxious to go to the aid of Nobile, together with Lt. Dietrichson, who had accompanied Amundsen on the 1925 expedition. On the 17th the Latham reached Tromsö. On the 18th it left for Spitzbergen in deteriorating weather conditions, but never arrived at its destination. Many weeks later the identification of a wing-float and two petrol tanks confirmed the tragic fate of its distinguished passengers and crew.

Swedish H E-5 seaplanes in King's Bay.

Survivors under the wing of Lundborg's Fokker.

American airmen being trained to use parachutes above San Diego. Left: One has jumped and waits to clear the aeroplane before releasing the parachute; the other stands by the wing-strut of the bomber (1926). Right: an airman about to open an American-style parachute that became standard issue in the British airforce.

PARACHUTES

It is astonishing that during the war the steady loss of thousands of expensively trained servicemen – quite apart from the cost in human terms – did not lead to the widespread use of parachutes for airmen. Although balloonists and some airship crews were sometimes provided with them, very few fighter pilots (and those German) were issued with parachutes.

From 1924 all airmen in the United States army and navy airforces were obliged to wear a parachute, and pilots working on the official mail routes were always provided with them. Parachute drill was never compulsory but the training sessions were so frequent and thorough that many young airmen willingly came forward to make parachute jumps. This repeated proof of the parachute's effectiveness soon inspired absolute confidence in its safety and reliability: 2 lives were saved in 1922, 9 in 1924, and 12 in 1925. At the beginning of 1926 three American pilots, Lts. Barksdale, Hunter and Lindbergh, had each been saved twice by their parachutes. On 6 March Lindbergh had escaped from his aeroplane by parachute when he collided with a foreign body at an altitude of 5,500 ft.; on 2 June, less than three months later, he jumped from a height of 300 ft. from a plane whose controls had failed. In the light of these demonstrations, the British Air Ministry ordered more than 2,000 American-style parachutes in 1926; between 30 June and 31 July these parachutes saved the lives of four airmen. By the 18 August 1926 eight French aviators had bailed out of their aircraft safely using parachutes.

AERIAL ALPINISM

During a remarkable flight from Paris to Venice in a light aircraft, Lt. Thoret (who will be remembered for his prewar experiments in gliding powered aircraft) had to fly over Mont Blanc. On the return journey he also overcame the falling air currents and violent turbulence of the Gondo ravines in Italy. Partly because of these experiences Thoret was engaged by Monsieur Dina to organise air transport from Geneva to the Vallot observatory at an altitude of 14,300 ft. Thoret was able to transport, in just nine flying days and in spite of considerable problems both with his equipment and with the weather, over a ton of material to the observatory by aeroplane and parachute, much of which would have been too heavy to take up the mountain by back-pack.

During this time Thoret had the idea of inaugurating air trips to Mont Blanc, to make the Alpine peaks that had formerly been visited only by mountaineers accessible to airmen and their passengers. Trial runs at the beginning of 1928 showed that such excursions would be of great interest to the general public.

With his usual tenacity, Thoret found an airfield at Passy, set up a committee and a local air-club, interested the regional railway company in his project (promoting Alpine tourism was one of its responsibilities), and signed an agreement with the Air-Union company to provide a shuttle service from Lyons to Geneva for his clients.

Between 25 June and 1 October nearly 550 passengers went on Thoret's excursions. Great attention was paid to safety: the aeroplane could glide down to the airfield it had set off from even from the summit of the mountain at 15,767 ft.; there was therefore no risk of danger from engine failure. Thoret's knowledge and expert handling of air currents stood him in good stead: he even managed to soar over Mont Blanc for 45 minutes in a 260 h.p. aeroplane carrying 5 passengers.

Air-Union pulled out of the project and Thoret subsequently teamed up with M. Potez, one of the main French aircraft designers. In a very short time over a thousand passengers had flown over the Alps, demonstrating the enormous public interest that can be generated in "local flying", when the site is chosen with care.

Thoret circling the Grépon in a Potez-32 with 5 passengers aboard (summer 1929).

An Air-Union Goliath ferrying passengers for Thoret to Geneva in January 1928.

Left: the attempt to cross the Atlantic made by the crews Edzard-Risticz-Knickerbocker and Loose-Koehl-Hünefeld; the two Junkers *Europa* and *Bremen* preparing for take-off at Dessau (14 August 1927). Right: the *Bremen* (Koehl, Hunefeld, Fitzmaurice) taking off from Dublin en route to America (12 April 1928).

THE NORTH ATLANTIC EAST TO WEST, THE SOUTH ATLANTIC NON-STOP, AND THE FIRST CIRCUIT OF THE ATLANTIC

Between 3 and 5 August 1927 Edzard and Risticz increased the endurance record to 52 hours and 12 minutes; the real distance covered by their plane, a 300 h.p. Junkers W-33, was nearly 4,000 miles, both figures sufficient for an east-west transatlantic crossing even against head winds.

Encouraged by this, on 14 August 1927, two identical W-33s, the *Europa* and the *Bremen*, left Dessau. The former soon landed at Bremen, but the latter, manned by Loose, Koehl and Hünefeld, battled on for 22 hours in a fierce storm without managing to break through to the fine weather that was forecast over the Atlantic, before returning to Dessau.

Koehl and his navigator Hünefeld did, however, eventually become the first men to cross the North Atlantic from east to west, but not until the following year, and with the Irish Cdr. Fitz-maurice as the third member of the crew. At 0538 on 12 April 1928 the *Bremen* set out from Dublin after two false starts. Westerly winds retarded the plane all the way and forced it to fly at less than 60 mph., navigation was hindered by fog, snow and problems with the compass, and for most of the crossing the Junkers had to fly almost at sea level, but on 13 April after a flight lasting 36 hours, Koehl reached Greenly island off the coast of Labrador and attempted a risky landing on a frozen lake. The ice gave way and the plane crashed, but the crew was safe.

After Koehl's crossing, and the triumphs and tragedies of 1927, the North Atlantic became a source of fascination for airmen. The amount of space devoted by the newspapers to even the most minor transatlantic attempts, regardless of whether they were seriously and carefully planned or mere frivolous whims, provided the encouragement for several hare-brained schemes. In 1928 alone there were eleven more attempts of which ten were failures. Three aeroplanes were simply too heavy and failed to take off; two seaplanes had to make emergency set-downs and were either picked up or flew back to their starting point. A third gave up its attempt in the

The *Nungesser-Coli* over the jungles of Panama on its round the world journey.

Azores. The Amiot SECM piloted by Idzikowski and Kubala put down on the sea near a ship after flying for 31 hours. An aeroplane that attempted to make the crossing from Canada was forced to land in Greenland. Two planes disappeared without trace. The only success apart from Koehl's was that of the *Friendship*, which left Newfoundland on 17 June, piloted by Stutz and Gordon, accompanied by Miss Amelia Earhart. The *Friendship* was a Fokker F-VIII with three 230 h.p Wright engines and metal floats; it reached the Welse coast at Llanelli in 20 hours and 50 minutes. Guided by its wireless it had covered 2,100 miles in fog and rain at an average speed of just over 100 mph.

In 1929 there were nine attempts and seven failures. A Swiss crew that set out from Lisbon disappeared. An American flying solo in a light aircraft with a 45 h.p. engine was lost over the ocean after setting out from Newfoundland. Franco, Gallarza, Ruíz de Alda and Pérez, the Spanish crew of a twin-engined Dornier Wal seaplane, were rescued at sea after drifting for eight days; their undamaged aircraft was taken aboard the *Eagle*. Idzikowski and Kubala tried

again in the *Marszalek Pilsudski* but had to make an emergency landing on the rocky coastline of the Azores; the aircraft turned over and caught fire; Idzikowski was killed and Kubala injured. Costes and Bellonte, who had set out at the same time as their Polish comrades, showed remarkable self-control by turning back to Europe – even though they were past the Azores – when they discovered that their fuel consumption had exceeded all expectation; they reached Paris without having to make an emergency landing. The only two successful crews both set out from Old Orchard beach in Maine one month apart; both ended up on the north coast of Spain.

The first crossing between Maine and Comillas was made on the 13–14 June by Jean Assolant, pilot, René Lefèvre, navigator, and Armand Lotti, radiotelegraphist. Twenty minutes after setting out in a 600 h.p. Bernard-Hispano called the *Oiseau-Canari*, the crew discovered a stowaway hiding in the fuselage but completed the journey with this extra load covering the 3,415 miles in 29 hours and 20 minutes at an average speed of nearly 117 mph. 50 gallons of fuel were left over.

On 8–9 July Williams and Yancey took 31 hours and 40 minutes to cover almost exactly the same route in a Bellanca with a 230 h.p. Wright engine. They then flew on to Rome, which had been their intended destination.

The journey made by Coutinho and Cabral across the South Atlantic was repeated in 1926 by the Spanish pilot Comandante Franco in a Dornier Wal flying boat with two 450 h.p. Napier engines. Between 22 January and 10 February he and a crew of three travelled from Palos de Moguer to Buenos Aires via the Cape Verde Islands, Fernando de Noronha and Pernambuco. On 16–17 March 1927 the Portuguese Commander Sarmiento de Beires and three other officers, also in a Dornier Wal, flew directly from Bolama in Portuguese Guinea to Fernando de Noronha, a distance of 1,593 miles at an average speed of 88 mph. despite strong headwinds. On 10 April they

Commander Franco's *Plus Ultra* at Buenos Aires.

De Pinedo and his companions on the *Santa Maria*.

Franco's Dornier-Wal *Numancia* rescued after drifting
for a week (29 June 1929).

The *Friendship* (Stutz, Gordon and Miss Earhart) at
Southampton (19 June 1928).

reached Rio de Janeiro. The choice of a flying boat rather than a seaplane appears in both cases to have avoided many of the problems that beset Coutinho and Cabral.

The first French attempt, by Saint-Roman, Mouneyres and Petit, to cross the South Atlantic by air came on 12 May 1927, just four days after the disappearance of Nungesser and Coli and had an equally tragic outcome. A French crew did not succeed on this route until 14 October 1927 when a Breguet-19 like those that had established so many long distance records in 1926, made what was also the first non-stop crossing of the South Atlantic, from Senegal to Brazil, and then an impressive flight around three quarters of the globe. It was flown by Dieudonné Cortes and his navigator Lt. Cdr. de Brix and was named the *Nungesser Coli*.

Shortly before the crossing of Sarmiento de Beires an Italian crew had also flown from Europe to Rio as the prelude to an imaginative circuit of the Atlantic. General the Marquis de Pinedo who in 1925 had flown to Australia and Japan, Commander Del Prete and the mechanic Zacchetti left Sesto Calende in Italy on 8 February 1927 in a Savoia S-55 called the *Santa Maria*, like the famous caravel. This large flying boat, designed by the engineer Marchetti, had twin hulls and two 500 h.p. Isotta-Fraschini engines in tandem. By the 14th it was at Bolama in Portuguese Guinea; on the 16th and 17th de Pinedo attempted to take off several times but was thwarted on each occasion by the heat and the air pressure, even at night. After moving to Porto Praïa, the flying boat eventually took to the air on the 22nd after two more days of fruitless attempts, having been stripped of all excess weight. On the 23rd it reached Fernando de Noronha; then Pernambuco,

Rio and Buenos Aires on 2nd March. From there the *Santa Maria* flew north along rivers and across rain forests via Asunción to Georgetown, in British Guiana, and thence via Colombia and Jamaica to North America. On 29 March de Pinedo landed at New Orleans and set out on an aerial tour of the United States, putting his heavy aircraft down on lakes, rivers and reservoirs, until on 6 April a careless smoker set the aircraft on fire

The type 123 Amiot SECM *Marszalek Pilsudski* flown
by Captains Idzikowski and Kubala

while it was moored on the Roosevelt Reservoir near Phoenix, Arizona.

A *Santa Maria II* was hurriedly sent over by sea from Italy, and between 8 and 25 May de Pinedo and his companions flew 4,350 miles across the eastern U.S.A. and Canada. They left Newfoundland for the Azores on the 23rd, but were forced to put down 200 miles short of their destination on a stormy sea, having exhausted their supply of petrol in the struggle against the bad weather. That evening they were taken in tow by a Portuguese sailing vessel and on the 26th by an Italian steamship; during a journey that

lasted seven days on very rough seas the *Santa Maria II* suffered surprisingly little damage. On 30 May the seaplane was brought to Horta, where it was repaired and set off again on 10 June. After doubling back to the place where they had broken down, de Pinedo set a south-easterly course and reached Punta Delgada. On the 11th the *Santa Maria II* was in Lisbon, and on the 16th it was in Rome.

After his 34,000 mile journey of 1925, this 25,000 round-Atlantic trip was the crowning glory for a pilot-navigator who had few if any equals. Tragically he died in a flying accident in 1933.

At the beginning of 1928 the Italian engineer Marchetti produced a land plane inspired by the large Savoia flying boats which he had built and which had been put to such good use by de Pinedo and others. The Savoia-Marchetti S-64 was really one large thick wing 70 ft. 6 in. across with a total surface area of 645 sq. ft. inside which the aeroplane's thirty petrol tanks were housed. The fuselage was reduced to a tiny egg-shaped cockpit positioned in front of the wing, and the tail-plane was attached to the wing by streamlined struts. The engine was situated on a pylon well above the wing, giving the pusher propeller an exceptional degree of efficiency. Between 31 May and 2 June 1928 the S-64 was kept in the air for 58 hours and 34 minutes by the pilots Del Prete and Ferrarin, covering an estimated 4,760 miles in circuit. After establishing this remarkable world record, the same crew took off from Montecelio on 3 July at 8 o'clock in the evening and landed at Touros in Brazil after a flight lasting 48 hours and 14 minutes. The aircraft had weighed 14,395 lb. full and 5,915 lb. empty. The long-distance record had been increased to 4,463 miles.

Ferrarin and Del Prete's Savoia S-64 on the take-off ramp at Montecelio (3 July 1928).

The *Oiseau Canari* on the beach at Comillas on 15 June 1929.

The Cierva C. 8-II at Le Bourget. Aboard are Juan de la Cierva and Henri Bouché.

Pitcairn autogiros, manufactured under licence in the U.S., over New York.

THE AUTOGIRO COMES OF AGE

On 18 September 1928 a flying machine that was heavier than air but was not an aeroplane crossed the English Channel for the first time. This aircraft, the Cierva C.8.II autogiro, with a 200 h.p. Lynx engine, piloted by its inventor Juan de la Cierva was accompanied on the crossing by a Goliath from the regular London to Paris service. The passengers in the aeroplane were impressed by the autogiro's remarkable stability in flight; it seemed unaffected by air turbulence and gave the impression of being suspended by a piece of elastic in mid air, while the articulated rotors turned horizontally twice a second like a vibrating halo. The crossing, between Lympne and Calais, was made at a height of 4,000 ft. between 1045 and 1103 i.e. 18 minutes for more than 25 miles. The autogiro landed at Saint-Inglevert aerodrome, and flew on to Abbeville and Paris without incident.

The three landings were deliberately varied to show that the autogiro could come in to land at any approach angle between 15° and 80° to the horizontal, making landings in confined spaces as easy as normal ones. The distance between

Juan de la Cierva, (†F1936) the inventor of the autogiro. Note the double articulation of the rotor blades, which are free to move in both vertical and horizontal planes.

touching down and coming to a full stop was never more than 10 ft., though the autogiro always interrupted a steep approach to the ground, glided for a little like an aeroplane, and then let itself drop on to the landing area from a height of 3 to 6 ft. in order to spare its undercarriage excessive wear and tear.

And so the new "aeroplane with rotating wings", which could never fall prey to fatal stalling on its final approach, demonstrated yet again its practical qualities and high speed. However, these successes could not hide the fact that take-off procedures were still laborious. Since the autogiro lacked any means of turning the rotator blades at sufficient speed to give lift while the craft was stationary, a long take-off run was still necessary; if the ground was hard and poorly levelled the rotor blades often collided with the tail. However in 1929 the inventor designed a tail-assembly that deflected the rotor blades, and in the same year the American companies which had acquired the licence to manufacture the autogiro fitted it with a by-pass which transmitted part of the engine power to the rotors – the rotation of the blades became free again as soon as the lifting speed was reached – and these modifications reduced the take-off run to a respectable 10 to 20 yards.

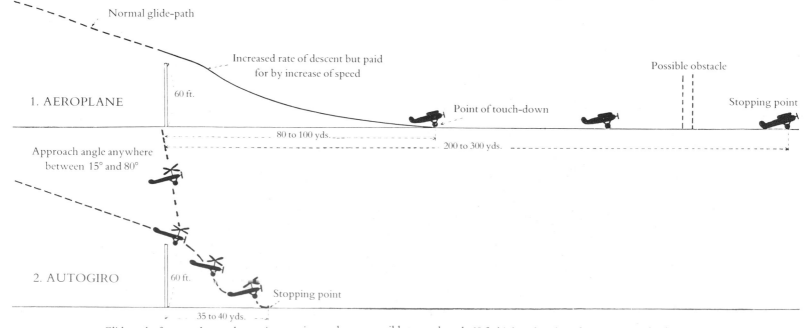

Glide paths for aeroplane and autogiro, passing as close as possible to an obstacle 60 ft. high at the edge of an emergency landing site.
(Key to diagram: I-Aeroplane; normal gliding descent; slight change in direction to steepen approach path, but aircraft increases speed, aeroplane touches down; possible obstacle; stop. II Autogiro, stop.)

The three-engined Fokker *Southern Cross* arriving at Wheeler Field near Honolulu in Hawaii at the end of the first stage of its journey (1 June 1928).

ACROSS THE PACIFIC AND ROUND THE WORLD

By 1927 the 2,350 miles separating San Francisco from the Hawaiian islands had been covered three times by air. Four other air crews had been lost on this route. In 1928 four men, two Australians, Charles Kingsford Smith and Charles T.P. Ulm, and two Americans, Harry W. Lyons and James W. Warner, not only reached Hawaii by air from San Francisco but continued all the way to Australia. The journey was made in a three-engined Fokker cannibalised from two damaged aircraft of that type which had belonged to Wilkins. The three 230 h.p. Wright engines, however, were brand new, and particular attention had been paid to the navigation and wireless equipment, which was designed to make use of radio beacons in California and Hawaii. The all-up weight was nearly 7 tons, more than 20 lb. per sq. ft. of wing area.

This aeroplane, which had been named the *Southern Cross*, left Oakland, San Francisco, on 31 May and landed next day at Honolulu after a flight lasting 27 hours and 27 minutes. The remainder of the journey was divided into two stages, both over areas that had never been crossed before by air. It was 3,117 miles from the island of Kauaï, where the take-off runway was better, to Souva in the Fiji islands. There was no land along the way except for one or two

archipelagos of coral islands. This distance was covered in 32 hours from the 2 to the 4 June. On the second night the *Southern Cross* had run into a tropical rainstorm as it approached the Equator; to avoid this it had deviated from its original route and climbed above the cloud tops, where it was guided by a full moon. When it landed at Souva it still had fuel in its tanks for two more hours' flying. On 8 June the Fokker left Fiji and after a 21 hour flight into a strong headwind landed at Brisbane. The four men had covered nearly 7,500 miles in three stages.

The crew of the *Southern Cross*: From left: J.W. Warner, radio operator, Capt. Ulm, co-pilot, Charles Kingsford Smith, leader and pilot, Lt. H.W. Lyons, navigator.

The first trans-Pacific flight was a remarkable achievement, all the more so as the smallest details of this historic crossing had been broadcast all over the world as and when they actually occurred. Thanks to a wireless system which allowed the *Southern Cross* to remain in constant communication with the ground, and the fact that nothing did go wrong, the public did not see the

expedition as an adventure and perhaps underestimated both the boldness of its execution and the significance of its outcome.

Three months later, Kingsford Smith and Ulm linked Australia and New Zealand for the first time by air: the 1,430 miles between Sydney and Wellington were covered in 14 hours on the 10–11 September 1928. On the return trip on the 14 October the *Southern Cross* was caught in a thick fog; when the crew finally landed at Sydney they had 3 gallons of fuel left.

Even more dramatic was the Southern Cross's first attempt at the Sydney–London leg of what was to become for Kingsford Smith and the aircraft a round-the-world flight. Leaving Sydney on 30 March 1929 the crew, which consisted of Kingsford Smith and Ulm from the Pacific flight, and two newcomers Litchfield and Williams, were forced to put down in the North Australian bush, where they were not discovered until 5 April after a week of frantic searches which cost the lives of more than one would-be rescuer. The flight to London was eventually made in sixteen days between 25 June and 10 July.

Almost a year later on 24 June 1930 Kingsford Smith, this time with a Dutchman, Van Dyck, an Irishman, Saul, and a South African Strannage, left Ireland to reach Newfoundland after a foggy crossing, and, on 26 June, New York. On 4 July 1930 the Southern Cross touched down again in San Francisco two years and thirty-four days, and 33,500 miles, after having left it.

Left: the *Southern Cross* stranded in the North Australian wilderness, 30 miles south of Port George Mission, as it appeared to the first rescue plane to discover it on 5 April 1929. Right: the *Southern Cross* above the skyscrapers of New York on 26 June 1929.

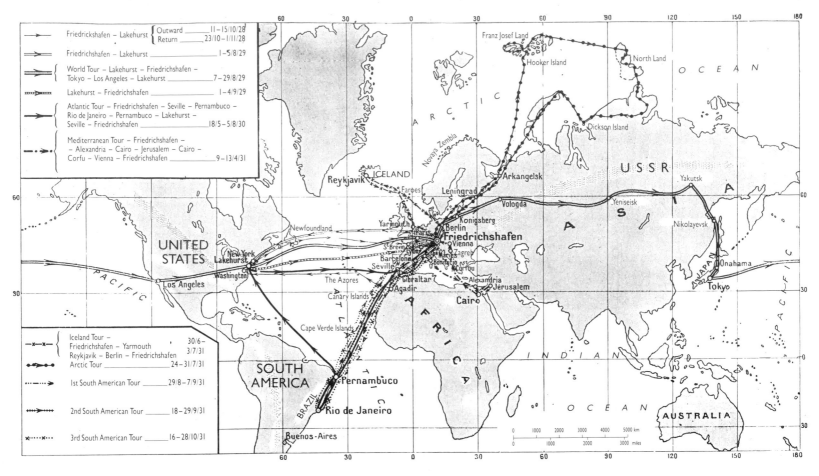

The map legend reads:

- Friedrickshafen – Lakehurst {Outward _____ 11–15/10/28 / Return _____ 23/10–1/11/28}
- Friedrichshafen – Lakehurst _____ 1–5/8/29
- World Tour – Lakehurst – Friedrichshafen – Tokyo – Los Angeles – Lakehurst _____ 7–29/8/29
- Lakehurst – Friedrichshafen _____ 1–4/9/29
- Atlantic Tour – Friedrichshafen – Seville – Pernambuco – Rio de Janeiro – Pernambuco – Lakehurst – Seville – Friedrichshafen _____ 18/5–5/8/30
- Mediterranean Tour – Friedrichshafen – Alexandria – Cairo – Jerusalem – Cairo – Corfu – Vienna – Friedrichshafen _____ 9–13/4/31

- Iceland Tour – Friedrichshafen – Yarmouth 30/6 / Reykjavik – Berlin – Friedrichshafen 3/7/31
- Arctic Tour _____ 24–31/7/31
- 1st South American Tour _____ 29/8–7/9/31
- 2nd South American Tour _____ 18–29/9/31
- 3rd South American Tour _____ 16–28/10/31

The main journeys made by the *Graf Zeppelin* around the world. (The map includes all routes taken up to 1931.)

THE GRAF ZEPPELIN'S WORLD TOUR

In 1926 Germany regained the right to construct large-scale airships for herself. Government support for such a programme was not forthcoming, and the money had to be raised through a nation-wide public subscription that took more than a year to organise, but eventually work began on the *LZ-127*, a rigid airship with a gas capacity of about 3,706,000 cu. ft. The hanger at Friedrichshafen where the *LZ-127* was to be built limited the overall height of the dirigible to 108 ft. The gas envelope measured 100 ft. across and 774 ft. long.

The general structure was made up of 17 light-alloy main sections which divided the airship into 19 separate compartments. 17 of these were filled with small hydrogen-filled envelopes whose total volume came to 2,647,000 cu. ft. The compart-

The *Graf Zeppelin* being moored at Lakehurst.

ments at either end and all along the bottom of the structure contained 12 smaller envelopes with a contained capacity of 1,059,000 cu. ft. These were filled with a specially mixed combustible gas of the same density as air, which gave the airship considerable stability and balance over long distances.

The dirigible was driven by five Maybach 530 h.p. engines which were fuelled either by combustible gas or by benzole, of which the *LZ-127*

Dr. Eckener on the bridge of the *Graf Zeppelin*.

carried an eight ton supply. Behind the bridge and

the navigation and wireless rooms, the main gondola contained a dining room, ten two-berth cabins and a kitchen.

On 11 October 1928 the *LZ-127*, which had been christened the *Graf Zeppelin*, made the first ever scheduled transatlantic flight, under the command of Dr. Eckener with 37 officers and crew, 18 passengers, including three who paid for their places, and 62,000 surcharged letters. It reached Lakehurst via the Azores in 111 hours, despite damage caused by the weather which necessitated on-board repairs. The return journey was made via the northern route, and took 75 hours with 61 people aboard. The following year, between 8 and 29 August, the *Graf Zeppelin* made its celebrated round the world journey in four stages. Besides Dr. Eckener and 39 officers and crew, 14 passengers made the round trip. Four more travelled from Friedrichshafen to Tokyo and three from Tokyo to Los Angeles.

The *Graf Zeppelin* over Rio de Janeiro 25 May 1930

MILITARY AVIATION

For a long time after the war military aviation in the countries that had taken part in the conflict was still heavily influenced by the experiences of 1914–1918. The essential tasks of the wartime squadrons had been liaison, observation and reconnaissance for the benefit of units on the ground. Even when they engaged the enemy directly, fighter planes were primarily supposed to facilitate the work of observers on their side, and frustrate similar work on the enemy side. And when at last offensive aviation was given the task of attacking ground targets, neither daylight nor night-time bombing raids proved really effective and consequently no independent bomber units were set up. As a result in all the countries that fought in the war, subsequent cuts in the size of the air forces were largely achieved by the scrapping of bomber aircraft. The main objective, particularly in France, was the retention of an adequate number of observer aircraft to ensure direct liaison with ground units. Financial constrictions also encouraged the view that larger planes, which were becoming increasingly heavy and more expensive, were mere costly luxuries.

This very conservative doctrine was particularly prevalent in France, and countries which looked to France to help them organise an airforce, or that had military agreements or formal alliances with France, tended to espouse the same philosophy. Although her colonial airforce was faced with more specialised tasks the view prevailed that standard equipment had to be sufficient for its uses too, and for this reason, the French airforce never developed, for example, large troop-carrying planes like the British.

The Italian air force also declined rapidly after 1919, but was resurrected in the 1920s by the Fascists who lavished resources on it. By acquiring licences to build any make of foreign aeroplane or engine which they considered desirable, the young directors of the Italian air programme succeeded in revitalising their own aeronautical industry and re-establishing its independence.

At the same time German aircraft designers, once freed from the technological restrictions placed upon them by the peace treaties, started to build technically advanced civil aircraft which could easily be adapted for military, and particularly offensive, use, an indication that future wars in the air might be fought independently of the conflict on the ground.

Certain other aircraft manufacturers – in Italy,

A squadron of single-seater Boeing military aircraft flying in stacked formation over California.

Sweden and Japan, for instance – also started to build large metal aeroplanes and flying boats which demonstrated the feasibility of "giant" military aircraft. The development of this type of aeroplane meant that it was for the first time theoretically possible to create formidable offensive squadrons capable of destroying entire cities overnight, and it was primarily considerations of cost that prevented the re-organisation of airforces on these principles. In many countries, however, concern grew that neighbouring states might be developing aerial attack forces, although in 1930 these did not in reality exist. These

imaginary squadrons had by 1932 a psychological and political effect which resulted in all air forces receiving increased funding on a scale unthinkable earlier.

Compared with her distant Japanese neighbour across the Pacific, the United States had, at least until 1928, a largely out-of-date airforce, but an elite corps of airmen, whose training both at flying school and in squadron exercises was monitored by aerial photography, and this use of photographs in training gave this still relatively small airforce a high international profile quite out of proportion to its size.

Left: a group of American single-seater Curtiss-Hawk fighters on skis taking part in the 1928 winter manoeuvres at Camp Skeel near Oscoda (Michigan).
Right: a single-seater Bristol-Bulldog fighter in flight above a sea of clouds. The aeroplane is a typical example of trends in British military thinking and aircraft design around 1930: a biplane airframe, maximum all-round views, laterally positioned machine-guns and bomb-racks beneath the lower wings.

Doret in a Dewoitine: left to right, beginning and end of a loop, entering a spin.

AEROBATICS

Two years before the outbreak of the war Pégoud invented aerobatics. The usefulness of these misleadingly termed "aerial acrobatics" was questioned at the time, but it should be remembered that Pégoud's accomplished displays of airmanship were intended simply to demonstrate the inherent safety of a well constructed and properly maintained aircraft.

Left: Doret (left) and Fieseler in front of Doret's aircraft. Right: Udet.

At that time it was widely believed – perhaps with some justification in the case of certain aeroplanes – that if a pilot dived at an angle too close to the vertical, he would be unable ever to lift the nose of the aircraft out of its dive. Pégoud showed that a pilot could return to a normal flight path from any position in the sky, provided, of course, he kept his nerve and left himself a certain amount of room for manoeuvre.

The war immediately justified Pégoud's initiative, and indeed placed ever increasing demands on pilots' handling skills. From the end of 1915,

the motions of fighter combat had become so involved that only specially designed and constructed planes could hope to stand up to stresses several times greater than those of normal flying. As the aeroplanes improved, so too did the qualities and skills of their pilots. At the altitudes where skirmishes between fighters usually took place, any manoeuvre was theoretically possible, though it was still dangerous to climb too sharply at the end of a prolonged dive. Ultimately the pilot, especially in a single-seater, had to "feel" his machine and become one with it. The aircraft in service during the war were comparatively lightweight and their load per square metre of wing surface and per horse-power was relatively small. The physical union of the pilot and his aeroplane was therefore made easier, and in the twenties and thirties the best virtuoso pilots chose aeroplanes very similar to the most advanced fighters of 1918 to give public displays of aerobatics.

The value of a basic knowledge of aerobatics even for ordinary pilots cannot be over estimated. As long as an aeroplane stays in the sky through the power of its engines alone, the pilot must know how to handle the plane safely if those engines should ever fail or if outside forces should divert the aircraft from its normal position of flight. Right up to 1915 "spinning" was thought to be an incurable (and usually fatal) condition simply because it had never been researched or analysed in depth, and no determined effort had ever been made to train pilots how to overcome it in flight. By the end of the war even the most inexperienced pilot knew how to deal with the problem, assuming that he had sufficient altitude.

It is in this light that we should view the aerobatic displays given by the best pilots from the "advanced air school". Without any doubt the finest of these were the countless demonstrations given by Alfred Fronval right up to the time when his plane was in collision with another on the ground; Fronval, who knew more about aerial safety than anyone else, perished in the ensuing fire. In the orange and blue Morane which he handled with such agility it seemed as if he was writing in the sky, a flowing, deceptively easy handwriting that was the hallmark of his masterly style. Even when he consented to take part in quite spectacular stunts, for example on 26 May 1920 when he looped the loop 962 times in 3 hours and 52 minutes, it was with the intention of proving that a well-built aeroplane should be able to handle reputedly dangerous manoeuvres over an indefinite period of time.

The successors of Fronval and Robin, who were both casualties of aviation but not of aerobatic displays, were Doret and Detroyat in France, and Udet, Fieseler and Achgelis in Germany. Detroyat was plainly a pupil of Fronval's; Doret was used to flying heavy aircraft, but in a famous aerial contest with Fieseler he proved that he could quickly adapt to lighter aeroplanes, such as the 110 h.p. Raab-Katzeinstein in which his German rival created or perfected manoeuvres such as flying inverted, outside loops and vertical "S" figures.

Two photographs on the next page give some idea of the pilot's sensations – at least the visual ones – during the execution of spin. They were taken by a German journalist, Willi Ruge, who accompanied Udet on one of his flights. Ruge exposed the plate long enough to obtain a succession of images of the ground taken during a loop, a spin and a stall turn. The camera was attached to the fuselage and directed obliquely forwards and downwards, the shutter could be opened at will and shut again after an exposure lasting anything up to one second.

However suggestive they may be, these visual evocations cannot really give an adequate impression of what an aerobatic display is like. Deafened by the ceaseless roar of the engine, the novice passenger is disoriented by repeated changes in the aircraft's attitude; he is subjected to violent swaying, sudden drops which leave his stomach behind, steep climbs which force him back in his seat, centrifugal forces that would rip him out of the aircraft if he were not restrained by the straps across his shoulders, and an unpleasant sensation of vertigo or nausea if he happens to look away from the direction of a sharp turn or a spin.

The expertise and polish of the airmanship can, however, endow these various manoeuvres with a touch of elegance which even a novice can begin to appreciate. At this point the pilot really starts to reveal the glories of his art to his passenger.

The difficulties of aerobatic displays are of course multiplied if the manoeuvres are carried out in group formation. The American airforce was probably the first to perfect those formation flights involving three or more aircraft which the British in turn used to spectacular effect at Hendon, in particular the long inverted flights in constantly changing formations.

Fieseler half-rolling to the right in a Raab-Katzenstein.

Alfred Fronval (1893–†F1928)

A Lithuanian pilot displaying aerobatic skills over the Niémen.

NATIONAL AIR SHOWS

While the principal attraction at many air shows in the provinces remained an aerobatic display given by highly trained pilots, the increasing role of aeroplanes in national life – particularly in the military – led to the inauguration of national air shows planned on the grand scale.

In Great Britain the Royal Air Force "Pageant" was instituted immediately after the war. This wonderful spectacle, which was planned and run entirely by the R.A.F., had a dual purpose: first of all, it was a way for the military airforce to justify its existence and at the same time give thanks to the general public, who paid for it out of their taxes. Secondly, the organisers made considerable profits from the vast crowds that flocked annually to Hendon to see an excellently run and thoroughly fascinating show; this money went towards charitable causes sponsored by the R.A.F. and a general fund for the consolidation of the air force's resources. The Hendon air show was characterised by elegance and sophistication; the British press called it the "Ascot of the air". Every minute of the display was planned and executed with absolute precision, and relied on the impeccable functioning of an elaborate telephone and wireless signalling system. The preparations and

Above and left: photographs taken during a spin above a crowd of spectators; the spiral gets more pronounced as the rate of rotation increases.

(Above and far right) Coloured smoke trails from aircraft taking part in the Hendon Royal Air Force Pageant in 1931.

rehearsals for the show also provided excellent training for the air units taking part, often selected through competition between various squadrons of the home air force.

A notable characteristic of these "Pageants", later simply called "Displays", was the relatively small number of aeroplanes involved in each event. The number of machines present in the sky at any one time rarely exceeded fifty, yet the displays were still spectacular because the aircraft were always perfectly aligned, the gaps between them remained constant, and they changed formation effortlessly. Up to 1932 the most ambitious French air show was the National Aviation Day at Vincennes. The site was ideal for large crowds and the event itself was a commercial success thanks to the political patronage secured by the organisers and the increasingly important role played by military units in the display, which gave the event more of an official character each year. From 1929, it was run by the Aéro-Club de France, backed by a press cartel, and the focus of the display was always an impressive military fly-past involving massed squadrons.

Formation flying by Hawker-Hart two-seaters at Hendon.

The aerodrome at Hendon during the 1928 Royal Air Force pageant.

Byrd's three-engined Ford being freed from the snow after wintering in the Antarctic (November 1929).

En route to the South Pole, Byrd's trimotor flies over the 15,000 ft. Queen Maud range (28 December 1929).

Carl Ben Eielson and Sir Hubert Wilkins with the Lockheed Vega.

AEROPLANES AT THE SOUTH POLE

The aerial conquest of the Antarctic was brisk and efficient. Much had been learned from polar expeditions to the Arctic, and the reconnaissance by aeroplanes of the South Pole was carried out exclusively by men who had already visited the Arctic regions: Eielson, Wilkins and Byrd.

Aided financially by Mr. Hearst, Sir Hubert Wilkins planned and organised an expedition whose principal aims were scientific: a geographical and cartographical exploration of the area between Deception Island and the Ross Sea, and meteorological observations which would be of benefit to future Antarctic observation stations.

Wilkins again chose Eielson to be his pilot. They prepared two Lockheed Vega aircraft which could be fitted either with skis or floats and which had insulated cabins lagged with heat-retaining material. These aeroplanes were shipped to Deception Island, which was to be the base camp. An auxiliary base stocked from Tasmania had been set up near the Bay of Whales.

On 19 December 1928 Eielson and Wilkins set out from Deception Island on a lengthy reconnaissance flight ranging over 1,200 miles in the direction of Graham Land. On 10 January 1929 they reconnoitred an area of 500 miles around Deception Island; finding no suitable site to establish a more permanent base for an assault on the pole, they returned to the United States.

In the event it was Byrd who first flew over the South Pole. Byrd's team, arrived at the edge of the Ross Ice Shelf on Christmas Day 1928. Five days later a base camp christened "Little America" was set up not far from Amundsen's former camp at Franheim.

The aircraft used on the expedition had been chosen and fitted out by Byrd himself. These were a little 110 h.p. GAC, a Fairchild and a Fokker each with a 425 h.p. engine, and an entirely metal 1,000 h.p. Ford tri-motor which was used on the longest flights, and was the aircraft which ultimately flew over the pole.

On 28 January 1929 Byrd, Balchen who had taken part in Byrd's transatlantic flight, and Harold June, the radiotelegraphist, spent five hours in the Fairchild reconnoitring Mounts Nunataks and Alexandra, which had been discovered by Scott. On 19 and 20 February the Fairchild and the Fokker set out to photograph the Rockefeller range and explore an area east of the Bay of Whales which the crews christened "Mary Byrd Land". On 8 March the geologist Larry Gould in the Fokker with Balchen and the radio-operator Hansen while studying the geography of the Rockefeller range; came down in a violent storm on 16 March, 125 miles from the main base. Byrd and June located them on the 18th, and on the 22nd all five men got back safely to "Little America". The 84 members of the expedition were by then trapped at the base through the Antarctic winter. While outside temperatures plunged to −67°C Byrd and his companions set to work developing films and photographs, plotting route-maps and preparing for the assault on the pole. Sledges carrying fuel and supplies were able to leave on 17 October; by

7 November the aeroplanes had been released from their prison of snow; at 1029 on 28 November Byrd finally set out.

With Byrd in the Ford were Balchen, June and the cameraman Mackinley. As they reached the mountains the aircraft had to dump three sacks of provisions (it was carrying a total of 3 months' supplies) in order to clear a mountain pass 15,000 ft. high and then continue its flight over a plateau at 10,000 ft. The aircraft flew in a wide circle around the South Pole and got back to "Little America" at 2210, after a brief stop at a refuelling station set up at the foot of the mountains, having covered a total of 1,550 miles.

One of the most notable features of Byrd's journey was the permanent liaison by wireless between the mobile and stationary elements of the expedition as well as the contact maintained between the base camp and the outside world. Also the immense value of aerial exploration had been proved as never before; all the photographs, films and geographical, meteorological and geophysical observations of hitherto unexplored regions had been made possible by aeroplanes, which could reach areas that were otherwise inaccessible.

Ironically Ben Eielson, the great pilot who had accompanied Wilkins, lost his life at almost the very moment when Byrd was making his assault on the South Pole; on 9 November 1929 he left Teller in Alaska with his mechanic Earl Borland to go to the aid of a ship trapped in the ice off the northern Siberian coast south of Wrangel Island. In January 1930 the wrecked aeroplane and the bodies of the two airmen were discovered half-buried in snow by a Soviet air rescue mission.

Eielson and Borland's wrecked monoplane half-buried in the Siberian snow, found by search parties in the two aircraft on skis.

Commander Dagnaux' mechanic repairing a damaged Breguet at Broken Hill in 1927.

Native chiefs examining a Transafricaine exploration plane at Niamey in 1930.

OPENING UP THE WORLD

If the majority of the attempts at the great ocean crossings were made for reasons of publicity or personal satisfaction, there were plenty of other flights to Africa, Asia or South America that had a serious scientific or commercial purpose.

On 20 February 1927 the Swiss pilot Mittelholzer touched down at Cape Town at the end of an extraordinary journey made in a Dornier Merkur seaplane with a 500 h.p. engine. He had left Zurich on 7 December the previous year and travelled south by way of the Nile valley, the Great Lakes and other less secure landing places, collecting valuable scientific data as he did so. His travelling companions were the geologist Heim and the geographer Gouzy, who had ample opportunity to observe and record information both in the air and on the ground.

The most remarkable, though perhaps least commercial, of the trans-African trips were made by British aviators. Between 28 September 1927 Lt. Bentley flew from London to the Cape in a little Moth aeroplane with an 80 h.p. engine, and 1928 saw similar journeys in lightweight planes by Lt. Murdoch, Lady Heath, Bentley and Mrs. Bentley, and the astonishing solo flight from London to the Cape and back made by Lady Bailey in her Moth.

Between 17 November 1927 and 31 May 1928 Sir Alan Cobham, accompanied by Lady Cobham and a six man crew, completed the first round-Africa flight in a twin-engined 1,300 h.p. Short. On 2 March 1928 Mauler, Baud and their wireless operator Cohendy set out on a return journey from Paris to the Cape. They arrived back in France on 7 September having covered 16,000 miles without once changing the 120 h.p. Salmson engine in their little Caudron biplane. Between 5 September and 26 October the Portuguese Captains Ramos and Viegas, each aboard a 450 h.p. Vickers, flew from Lisbon to Lourenço Marques.

All these journeys led to the establishment of improved air-strips and better facilities at existing landing places. The Belgians in particular made great progress in the Congo: by 1927 the twice monthly service from Boma to N'Gulé had been extended as far as Elisabethville, 1,400 miles from the coast.

At the same time as Britain was developing the Cape to Cairo route, France was planning an air link between Paris and Madagascar via the Congo; the Belgian government naturally took a great interest in this project. In 1928 the Compagnie Transafricaine d'Aviation run by Dagnaux began to organise a link between Algeria and the Congo via Chad. Between 29 January and 29 March 1929 Richard's preliminary expedition in a Farman 190-Titan piloted by Lallouette reconnoitred the first stage of the intended route as far as Fort Lamy. By the end of the year crews were already making remarkable journeys between France and Madagascar in the latest Farman-190 cargo planes fitted with 200-250 h.p. air-cooled Salmson or Titan engines. The first of these flights, which were fully endorsed by the French Air Ministry since they were air mail services, was organised by Captain Goulette. Accompanied by Marches-seau and Bourgeois (pilot and navigator) he flew from Paris to Madagascar between 17 and 27 October 1929. The crowning achievement came when Goulette established the first air link with Réunion Island between 28 October and 5 November. It seemed that the trans-African air route was now a reality, at least for small single-engined aeroplanes. However, the mishaps that occurred during the return journey: engine trouble over the Mozambique channel near Juan de Nova Island where Marchesseau managed to put down safely, an aeroplane turned over on take-off on the poorly surfaced landing strip at Elisabethville, and lastly a forced landing and the subsequent rescue of the crew in the Tanezrouft area of the Sahara, quickly dispelled any over-confidence that might have arisen.

The harsh realities and risks of flying over Africa were further highlighted when Caillol, Roux and Dodement disappeared on 13 January 1930 near Brazzaville on a return flight from Madagascar; they had made the outward journey in 20 days in an F-190 with a Lorraine engine. Two months later the skeletons of the three unfortunate airmen were discovered in the jungle not far from the river Kasai.

In 1924 Van den Hoop had flown in a single-engined Fokker from Amsterdam to the Dutch East Indies in 54 days. But it was an American businessman, Van Lear Black, who first demonstrated the full potential of multi-engined cargo planes on the Dutch East Indies route. In the spring of 1927 he chartered a powerful Fokker F-VII-3m with three 400 h.p. Jupiter engines from the Dutch air company KLM, left Amster-

Left: Neguès' Schreck flying boat moored in the old port at Naples during a French test flight prior to the establishment of an air service between Marseilles and Beirut, the first leg on the journey to the Orient. Right: the first of five mail planes operated by KLM and piloted by Koppen and Kengen lands at Tjililitan airport in the Dutch East Indies on 25 September 1928, twelve days after leaving Amsterdam.

Left: an Aéropostale plane being repaired after breaking down 25 miles from Cape Juby. Right: Meimoz'
Latécoère-28 at Natal after the first South Atlantic air mail flight.

dam on 15 June, and returned on 23 July after spending a week in the East Indies and covering 18,500 miles in 27 flying days.

In October of the same year another three-engined Fokker F-VII-3m, this time fitted with Siddeley-Puma 185 h.p. engines, flew from Amsterdam to Batavia between the 1st and the 10th and then returned between the 17th and the 28th. The crew consisted of the pilots Lt. Koppen of the military air force, Fryns of the KLM company and the mechanic Elleman.

On both the outward and return journeys the plane carried a considerable number of surcharged letters; the potential profit on postage between the East Indies and Amsterdam was considerable, since the fastest mail-ships took 30 to 35 days to make the same journey. In order to prove this commercially five successive journeys were made in September and October 1928 by Fokker F-VIII-3m aircraft with 185 h.p. Siddeley-Lynx engines. Three of these flights were successful, the average flight time being 12 days; two aeroplanes were damaged on inadequate runways along the route. The weight of the surcharged post carried by these planes varied between 415 and 650 lb.; this first regular air mail service still excites considerable philatelic interest.

The programme submitted to the French government on 7 September 1918 by Pierre Latécoère had envisaged an aero-maritime service between France and South America via Morocco and French West Africa. It was, however, ten years before the project finally took shape. On 1 June 1925, an air mail service was inaugurated between Casablanca and Dakar, but the next link lay across the ocean. After several unsuccessful attempts to establish a seaplane service over the 500 miles separating Saint-Louis from the Cape Verde Islands, the Compagnie Aéropostale decided to use express despatch-vessels for the whole ocean crossing and then to switch back to aeroplanes between Natal and Buenos Aires. But the crossing alone took nearly five days, imposing a severe delay on the service. Even so post was delivered from France to Argentina – a distance of 8,000 miles – in an average of ten days. This was an impressive performance achieved by continuous relay flying both day and night between Toulouse and Saint-Louis on one side of the Atlantic and Natal and Buenos Aires on the other.

Despite this improvement, the Aéropostale was still failing to honour its contracts and was at risk from competitors as long as it continued to use maritime carriers to transport mail across the Atlantic. Despairing of ever obtaining the large flying boats considered indispensable for the crossing, Aéropostale took a gamble in 1930 by using a fast Latécoère-28 with a 600 h.p. Hispano-Suiza engine, an aeroplane that had already been used successfully on land routes, fitted with floats.

The first flight was astonishingly successful. On 12 May Mermoz, the pilot, Dabry, the navigator, and Gimié, the radiotelegraphist, left Saint-Louis with 286 lb. of post that had left Toulouse on the 11th at 0510; on the 13th at 0810 they arrived at Natal after covering 1,970 miles nonstop, and incidentally breaking the distance record for seaplanes. Much more important was the fact that the post from France reached Buenos Aires on 14 May at 1935 and Santiago de Chile on the 15th at 1330.

The return journey was less triumphant. 450 miles from Saint-Louis Mermoz was forced to put down at sea near one of the rescue ships that were strung out along the route just as they had been on the outward flight. The seaplane was damaged and sank, but the crew were picked up uninjured; the technical difficulties involved in an Atlantic crossing had evidently not been resolved. There was nothing wrong with the navigational techniques or the crews, but single-engined planes fitted with floats were still not equal to the task.

Air links with South America were also of great interest to civil aviation companies in the United States. In 1928 U.S. mail planes were already flying to Central America along the Pacific coastline. Then two large companies which were initially rivals, the NYRBA and Pan American Airways, started services that ran down both the Pacific and Atlantic coasts, the huge aerial circuit being completed by regular flights across the Andes.

Left: a Sikorsky amphibian carrying 8 passengers and piloted by Colonel Lindbergh is escorted by single-seater American fighters over the Panama Canal zone during the inauguration of a regular air service between North and South America at the beginning of 1929. Right: Colonel Lindbergh flying the same route two years later in a Sikorsky amphibian with 40 passengers.

The long-distance Breguet-Hispano *Question Mark* taking off from Le Bourget on 1 September 1930.

PARIS–NEW YORK DIRECT

Between 27 and 29 September 1929, Dieudonné Costes and his navigator mechanic Bellonte increased the record for flying non-stop in a straight line to 4,909 miles when they flew from Paris to Tsitsihar in Manchuria, beating del Prete and Ferrarin's record journey from Italy to Brazil by over 400 miles. The aeroplane in which the new record was set was not a particularly new model, merely the latest refinement of the long-distance Breguets which had been setting records since 1924. However, whereas the Breguet that had flown from Paris to Jask in 1926 had weighed 9,152 lb. and carried 682 gallons of petrol for a 550 h.p. Hispano-Suiza engine, the Paris-Tsitsihar Breguet, which bore the famous *Question Mark* insignia, had taken off with a total weight of 13,530 lb. and 1,140 gallons of fuel. The same make of aero-engine with an extra 75–100 h.p. had been enough to lift the additional two tons. Increases in the wing area, which had gone up from 570 to 645 sq. ft. and the distance between the upper and lower wings, which had been separated by an additional 15¾″, had contributed to this improvement in performance.

When Costes returned to Paris from Peking he immediately started making plans for an even more ambitious journey: Paris to New York.

Costes and Bellonte refused to be affected by the hyperbole generated by the press which surrounded their projected departure and were strong-minded enough to wait calmly and patiently for favourable weather. They kept in close and frequent contact with the French National Meteorological Office, and they took its forecasts seriously. During the afternoon of 31 August the forecast was good, with tail winds predicted for at least the first half of the crossing and Costes decided to make the attempt. The *Question Mark* weighed 14,740 lb. on take-off, over half a ton more than on the Tsitsihar flight, although Costes had decided to dispense with extra fuel tanks, so the fuel capacity was the same as it had been then.

Le Bourget airfield was not really suitable for a long-distance departure since it had neither a runway nor a raised launching ramp of any kind. Nevertheless Costes managed to get away at 1054 on 1 September 1930 even though the trolley inserted beneath the tail-plane to support the aircraft at a more advantageous angle came off prematurely.

The cockpit of the "Question Mark": the pilot's seat (top) and the navigator's (bottom) seen from above.

A traditional ticker-tape welcome in New York for the French aviators on 3 September 1930.

Maurice Bellonte and Dieudonné Costes, after the first non-stop Paris to New York crossing of the Atlantic.

37 hours and 18 minutes later, at 1912 New York time on the 2nd, the *Question Mark* appeared blood red in the evening sunlight over Curtiss Field, where it landed. There were still 99 gallons of petrol in the fuel tanks. Three years and three months after Lindbergh's non-stop flight from New York to Paris, a great European crew finally returned his visit in equally spectacular style.

The crossing had been followed with keen interest and excitement. Huge crowds gathered in the Place de la Concorde in Paris, heightening the sense of occasion. Thanks to wireless, the Paris crowd could actually hear the tumultuous welcome given to Costes and Bellonte by the American crowd nearly 4,000 miles away. The French aviators could themselves be heard confirming their arrival in the United States. They were fêted in New York and then flew on to Dallas.

Special great circle navigation charts prepared by the great engineer Kahn had replaced lengthy nautical calculations with simple diagrams and greatly facilitated the navigator's task during the flight. Bellonte was fully acquainted with the navigational chart of the route, which had been drawn out in 1928, and made maximum use of it during the crossing. He was able to plot on the chart the seventeen astronomical observations that he made in the course of the flight, and by the last one, which he calculated from the position of the sun at 1255 on 2 September, he was able to announce to Costes that they would sight land at 1400; at 1402 precisely the *Question Mark* crossed the coast which was barely visible through the mist and rain.

What conclusions could be drawn from this great feat of airmanship? Far from heralding the inauguration of a regular air service across the North Atlantic, it merely highlighted the difficulties and dangers of the route, an impression that became firmly rooted in Costes' mind.

The crew had had to wait all summer for suitable weather conditions before making the crossing in a single-engined aircraft of the most up-to-date design, and even then they had ventured out only with the reassurance of constant forecasts provided by the National Meteorological Office. Even then the crossing had been far from easy. Costes and Bellonte had run into fog and rain over America and had very nearly failed to reach their destination. The broadest stretch of the Atlantic Ocean had been crossed for the first time from east to west. But the furrow opened up by the French aviators had closed again just as rapidly behind them.

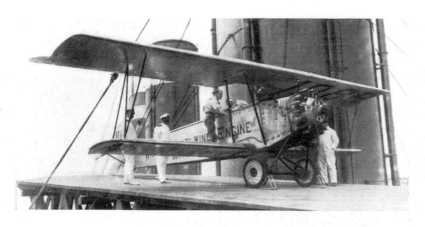

Chamberlin's aircraft on the take-off ramp on board the *Leviathan* before flying back to New York (1 August 1927).

Von Gronau's Dornier-Wal in New York harbour on 26 August 1930. Note the ring-shaped aerial of the radio direction finder.

SPEEDING THE ATLANTIC MAIL

Despite several successful Atlantic crossings, the ocean had, even in 1930, by no means been fully conquered by the aeroplane. Among those confronted with the reality of making transoceanic transport pay, there were many who thought that rather than pursue the Grail of complete domination it would make sense to give aeroplanes without delay those lesser tasks which they could already achieve. One of the solutions proposed was to combine the speed of the aeroplane with the range of the ocean liner.

Aircraft could at that date travel about four times faster than steam ships; an aeroplane could accordingly leave ten hours after a ship and catch up with it eight to ten hours later, 600–700 miles out at sea. Alternatively an aeroplane could take off from a ship 600 miles from its destination and arrive up to ten hours before it. The military possibilities of aircraft at sea had already been exploited; take off-platforms, launching catapults and landing decks had all been developed. Their adaptation to civilian vessels would be all the easier because of the more favourable lay-out of the superstructure.

On 1 August 1927 Chamberlin took off from the *Leviathan* when the ship was already 60 miles out on its journey to Europe and flew back to New York without incident. This striking demonstration had required only a lightweight aeroplane and a makeshift take-off platform installed on board the ship. In 1928 a fixed Penhoët catapult 112 ft. long was installed on the *Ile-de-France*. On 13 August a Liouré-Olivier amphibian with a Jupiter engine was launched from the ship

450 miles from the American coast and reached New York 4 hours and 15 minutes later. The ship's mail had been loaded on to the seaplane and arrived at its destination almost 24 hours ahead of schedule. On the return journey the aircraft was launched 150 miles west of the Scilly Isles and landed at Le Bourget having gained nearly forty hours. These successful trial runs, repeated in 1929 with a CAMS flying boat with a 450 h.p. Lorraine engine, were discontinued, but similar experiments were started by the Germans, who installed Heinkel catapults and seaplanes on board the liners *Europa* and *Bremen*.

However, the problem of lifting a seaplane on board a moving ship had still to be solved, and it was again the Germans who came up with the most ingenious solution. This was a trailing strip of tarpaulin which could be unrolled from the ship's stern, up which the seaplane could be winched on to the deck.

At the same time other long-distance air freight companies were trying to secure the use of and even monopolies on the air routes to and from the Azores and Bermuda, the two obvious staging posts in the Atlantic Ocean. Some experts even believed that an artificial landing strip of some kind would have to be constructed at great cost between these two groups of islands if transatlantic services were even to become a reality.

Others looked farther afield. In 1929 von Gronau, the director of the training centre for German civil and commercial aviators, decided to investigate the possibility of establishing a transatlantic route via Iceland and Greenland.

Between 18 and 26 August 1930 von Gronau and three companions flew from List to New York via the southern tip of Greenland in a

seven-year-old Wal (the N-25 used by Amundsen in the Arctic in 1925) which had been refitted with two 500–600 h.p. B.M.W. engines. They covered 4,240 miles in 45 flying hours: the weather had been favourable, except over Greenland where they had been hampered by freezing fog.

In 1931 the same crew took three weeks – from 8 August to 1 September – to reach Chicago via Hudson Bay, this time in a completely new Wal with 600–700 h.p. B.M.W. engines. Bad weather had forced von Gronau to cross Greenland further north on this occasion. Between Scoresby Sund and Godthaab he had flown for 1,250 miles over an icy plateau 10,000 ft. high. The crew were only able to complete this perilous journey thanks to their excellent wireless communications and radio direction-finding equipment.

Von Gronau was wary of drawing over-optimistic conclusions from this double success: he was of the opinion that the route over southern Greenland was safe only during the few weeks when the various harbours were free of ice. Nevertheless the Greenland route seemed commercially viable to several American companies and in 1931 they financed a pilot called Cramer to fly the route from west to east. Cramer left Detroit on 26 July in a Bellanca, which for the first time on a long-distance flight of this sort was fitted with a Packard heavy-oil engine. He disappeared off the Scandinavian coast together with his co-pilot Paquette on 9 August.

Between 22 and 30 July 1932 von Gronau made a third Atlantic crossing in the same aircraft that he had used in 1931, but both the Northern and the Southern routes were shortly to be rendered obsolete by improvements in the range and reliability of the big flying boats.

Launching the CAMS flying boat from the *Ile-de-France* (August 1929).

Winching a seaplane up the Kiwull trailing tarpaulin on the *Norddeutscher Lloyd*

The ten Italian flying boats that had just crossed the Atlantic moored on the Potingy river near Natal on 6 January 1931.

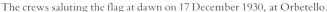

The crews saluting the flag at dawn on 17 December 1930, at Orbetello.

Six of the Savoia-Marchetti flying boats that made the 1931 crossing.

TRANSATLANTIC GROUP FLIGHTS

The great double hulled flying boats which made up the bulk of the Italian naval air force gave in 1931 and 1933 two remarkable displays of their coordination in transatlantic journeys that rivalled Del Prete and Ferrarin's exploit. Long-distance flights across the Mediterranean and to the Black Sea were no longer enough for the Italian airmen. In 1931 the destination of a group of twelve flying boats commanded by the Air Minister, General Balbo, was Rio de Janeiro.

During the night of 5–6 January 1931 fourteen Savoia-Marchetti aircraft with 560 h.p. engines set out from Bolama in Portuguese Guinea, where they had previously assembled after flying out from Orbetello in Italy. Two flying boats manned by maintenance personnel also took part in the expedition; a total of 56 airmen.

Take-off was risky for such heavily laden aircraft – each flying boat carried 4 tons of petrol – and cost two aircraft and five men. General Valle's aircraft also had difficulties in getting airborne and made the crossing separately from the other aircraft, after dumping 45 gallons of fuel. Meanwhile the eleven remaining flying boats flew westwards in group formation; the distance between the aircraft varying according to the weather conditions along the route. The crossing was difficult and the insistence on remaining in a group only compounded the aviators' problems. The aircraft frequently had to change course owing to torrential rain. Nevertheless, eighteen hours after setting out, ten Savoias put down off Natal; General Valle's flying boat had rejoined the main group, but two other aircraft had had to drop out along the way owing to serious destabilisation of their wooden propellers caused by the pouring rain. As soon as these had put down on the sea they were located and towed to the coast; this prompt rescue operation was made possible by wireless communication. One of them subsequently managed to get to Natal, thus bringing to eleven the number of flying boats which, still in group formation, flew on to Rio de Janeiro.

This flight was only eclipsed in 1933 when again under the command of General Balbo twenty five Savoia S55X flying boats set out to fly from Rome to Chicago. The Alps were successfully crossed on 1 July but on arriving at Amsterdam one of the aircraft overturned while putting down on shallow water killing a sergeant and injuring the other three crew members.

The remaining twenty-four aircraft flew on via Londonderry, Reykjavik and Montreal to Chicago. On their return journey they flew down the Hudson River, accompanied by a number of American aeroplanes on 19 July, and moored off Floyd Bennett Field, where they were welcomed by a crowd of 25,000 people and a blackshirted guard of honour. On 25 July they set out on the return journey to Italy.

Left: the accident at Amsterdam on 1 July 1933 that reduced the Rome–Chicago flight to twenty four aircraft; rescue work being carried out on the upturned flying boat, in which one man was killed. Right: the squadron moored off the Floyd Bennett field, New York, on their way back from Chicago.

Lt. Kinkead's supermarine S-5 with 1000 h.p. Napier engine (March 1928)   The Italian Macchi M-39 seaplane which won back the Schneider Cup in 1926.

THE SCHNEIDER CUP AND FASTER AIRCRAFT

The decisive American victory in the Schneider Cup of 1923 had left little hope of its early recovery by the distinctly unimpressive European competition. In fact in 1924 the United States would have been the only nation to field a team had they not sportingly decided not to hold the race that year.

On 26 October 1925 Great Britain and Italy challenged the dominance of the Curtiss at Baltimore. The American planes were now fitted with a 600 h.p. engine and once again confirmed their superiority. Doolittle won the speed trials with an astonishing average of 232 mph. over the seven 50 km. circuits, beating Broad's Gloster-Napier biplane with floats like the Curtiss, by 31 mph., and the Italian Macchi M-33, a monoplane with a hull which had been fitted with a Curtiss 450 h.p. engine, by 97 mph.

A year later the Italians, spurred on by this humiliating defeat, were the only challengers at Hampton Roads on 13 November 1926 bringing three Macchi M-39 monoplanes with floats and brand new 800 h.p. Fiat engines. Aircraft and engines had been entirely designed, developed and tested in Italy in the space of a few months, and they inflicted a convincing defeat on the American planes whose 700 h.p. engines did not perform as well as had been hoped. While Schilt barely managed to reach 231 mph. in a 1925 model Curtiss – slightly less than the winning American speed of the previous year – de Bernardi achieved a speed of 246 mph., thus breaking at the same time the world records over 100, 200 and 300 km. circuits. On 17 November, he increased the basic speed record to 258.7 mph.

The Schneider Cup was back in Europe. At Venice along the famous Lido beach the British team, the only challengers, fielded six seaplanes: four Supermarine S-5 monoplanes and a Gloster

biplane, all powered by 980 h.p. water-cooled Napier engines, and a Short "Crusader" monoplane powered by an 800 h.p. air-cooled Bristol engine. This last was slower than the others and was in any case destroyed in an accident before the trials began. Italy produced three Macchi M-52s, derived from the M-39, each equipped with a 950 h.p. Fiat engine. All the aeroplanes involved in the 1927 trials had floats.

On Sunday 25 September, the date fixed for the

The British victory at Venice in 1927. The Gloster biplane being overtaken by Webster's Supermarine S-5, the eventual winner, with a speed of 281 mph.

trials, special trains brought tens of thousands of spectators from all over Italy. Unfortunately a particularly strong wind forced the organisers to postpone the trials to the next day when the Italians were decisively beaten. One of the Italian team members had to withdraw on the first circuit, another on the second, and the last one on the seventh. Their best average speed had been 258 mph. Meanwhile Kinkead had reached 273 mph. in the Gloster; he dropped out on the sixth circuit, but two of the Supermarine S-5s scored the decisive victory which the British technical preparation richly deserved. Webster was the ultimate victor with a speed of 281.5 mph. over 250 km. (218 miles); Worsley came second with 272.9 mph. The Supermarines had a similar structure to the Macchi, but seemed to owe their victory to a more finely tuned engine, more streamlined metal floats and above all a more efficient cooling system, which allowed the engine to maintain its maximum output. And finally, the airmanship of the British pilots eschewed spectacular effects and aimed for maximum efficiency, especially in the turns.

The winning aircraft had a wing surface of just under 115 sq. ft., a weight of 3,190 lb. fully loaded and a 980 h.p. aero-engine. It therefore weighed 18 lb. per sq. ft. of wing surface and 3¼ lb. per horsepower. Take-off was not surprisingly very difficult and required a long stretch of sheltered water. The Supermarine S-5 had just beaten the basic speed record set by a French Bernard land plane in 1924 by 3 mph. over seven 50 km. circuits. Henceforth the vastly increased speeds made possible by ever more powerful engines could only be achieved by seaplanes; the Schneider Cup therefore became a sort of testing laboratory for high-speed aircraft fitted with immensely powerful engines.

The French decided to take part in the next Schneider Cup trials, which had been fixed for 1929 in order to give time for sufficient preparation. However, despite determined efforts by the

The three Italian seaplanes on their special transport and launching pontoon (7 September 1929).

Speed-trial seaplanes over the Solent on 7 September 1929. Left to right: Lt. d'Arcy Greig in a Supermarine S-5; the Italian pilot Cadringher in a Macchi; Lt. Atcherley making a sharp turn in one of the new Supermarine S-6 aircraft which increased the speed record to 331.5 mph. over a 100 km. circuit.

Bernard, Nieuport and Hispano-Suiza companies, France was still not ready for the 1929 trials that were to be held on 7 September in the Solent. The Italians too only attended in order to honour their promise of two years before and to help defray some of the organisers' costs. The new Macchi M-67s, which were derived from the M-52s, and were fitted with 1,800 h.p. Isotta-Fraschini engines, had not yet been perfected. Neither had the completely new Fiat C-29s and twin-engined Savoias, or the Piaggio P-8 with a watertight fuselage whose test flights before the event remained shrouded in mystery.

Great Britain had been able to make ready two Supermarine type S-6 aircraft, a version of the S-5 equipped with a 1,900 h.p. Rolls-Royce engine. One piloted by Waghorn, completed the course at the incredible average speed of 328 mph., the other, which was flown by Atcherley, was disqualified for a turning error but managed to beat the record over 100 km. with a speed of 331.5 mph. The Italian Dal Molin came second in an improved M-52 with a speed of 284 mph.

The speed trials of 1931 were to be the last. This time both the French and Italian teams withdrew at a late stage. The British government had originally intended not to take part, and only prepared for the competition because it had been challenged to do so and because public opinion and considerable private donations forced the government's hand. The result was the Supermarine S 6-B, the 2,300 h.p. Rolls-Royce "R" engine, and on 13 September a third and definitive British victory, when Lt. Boothman flew over the 350 km. course at 340.3 mph. A few moments later his fellow team member Lt. Stainforth increased the basic speed record to 378.8 mph. On 29 September Stainforth beat his own record in the same S 6-B seaplane fitted with a specially tuned engine yielding 3,000 h.p.; the new record stood at 408 mph.

The speed of the victors in Schneider Cup trials between 1926 and 1931 had increased from 246 to 340 mph. This 38% gain in air speed was achieved

by a 200% increase in engine power – from 800 h.p. to approximately 2,400 h.p. However, the preparations for the Schneider Cup had proved as costly in human life as they had in money spent on research and development. Since 1927 Worsley, Kinkead and Brinton in England, Motta, Dal Molin, Monti and Bellini in Italy, and Bonnet and Bougault in France had all been killed in training on high speed aircraft, as these meteors capable of speeds of nearly 400 mph. were more liable to stall than any other type of aircraft. On take-off, and for a considerable time after it, the

The winning plane of 1931, the Supermarine S 6-B, being fitted with the most powerful aero-engine yet built, a Rolls-Royce of 2,300-2,800 hp.

pilot dared not initiate any manoeuvre, until the aircraft's speed had built up. In the end of course, in spite of the exciting progress that had been made by increasing engine power alone it was decided that the cause of building faster aircraft would be better served by limiting engine capacities and thereby encouraging designers to improve other aspects of their aircraft also.

Although, or perhaps because, the American government had ceased to take part in the Schneider Cup trials after 1926, American aircraft designers and manufacturers continued their re-

search into high-speed aviation but applied the results to everyday air travel and transport. It was a curious fact that in Europe throughout a period in which the speed record increased from 280 to over 400 mph. the speed of ordinary air travel remained somewhere in the region of 90 mph.

It was at this point that reports reached Europe of journeys made by the American airman Hawks, who regularly crossed America at average speeds of around 200 mph. It is probable that many would have continued to view these reports with scepticism, and if they believed them would still have questioned the practical value of the achievement, had not Hawks come over to Europe in 1931 and personally demonstrated that such journeys were possible by flying between Paris, London, Berlin, Rome and various other cities in record time. Indeed, the sheer speed at which he travelled actually made the task of navigating easier, since it lessened the effects of contrary winds and other atmospheric disturbances.

Demonstrations of this kind had led directly to the inauguration of express passenger services in the United States. These services mainly used Lockheed aircraft. From the small monoplane made famous by the polar expeditions of pilots such as Wilkins and Eielson, American designers had evolved a series of transport planes: the Lockheed Vega, which Post and Gatty were to make famous by a lightning-quick flight around the world, and then the Lockheed Orion and Altair, both of which had retractable undercarriages. The Orion indeed was able to carry five people at an operating speed of 185 mph. over distances of 500 to 600 miles. Of course, such "state-of-the-art" performances entailed new risks, and in 1931 it would have been premature to consider extending the use of such aeroplanes over the air network as a whole, but they did serve to emphasize the gulf that was appearing in the European (and particularly French) aircraft industry between the performances of "pot-hunters" and commercial practice.

The *Travel Air* in which Frank M. Hawks made numerous journeys across the United States and Europe at over 200 mph.

The Lockheed Orion high-speed passenger plane fitted with a 550 h.p. air-cooled engine, capable of a cruising speed of 185 mph.

The English airship R-100 over the Saint Laurence after crossing the Atlantic.

THE R100 AND R101

Despite the loss of most of its airship experts in the R-38 disaster, the British government pressed on with the construction of new rigid dirigibles. Two entirely new airships, the *R-100* and the *R-101*, were ordered; the *R-101* in particular represented a quite radical departure from the Zeppelin framework around which most airships were constructed. Both of these dirigibles, which were destined for service on the "imperial air routes", were noticeably shorter than German airships and were supposedly more "aerodynamic".

Between 29 July and 1 August 1930, the *R-100* made the first crossing of the Atlantic by airship from Europe to Canada. She arrived safely and moored at the Saint-Hubert mast in Montreal. The return journey took place in more favourable weather conditions and lasted 57 hours and 5 minutes. The *R-100* was a hydrogen-filled airship with a gas capacity of 5,650,000 cu. ft. She was 708 ft. long and had a diameter of 133 ft. She had been built by the privately owned Airship Guarantee Company, and was designed to carry 100 passengers and 10 tons of mail.

The *R-101*, which was intended to carry 50 passengers, was built at the government workshops at Cardington, and was modified numerous

The R-101 discharging liquid ballast while moored to its mast by a cable.

times before she was finally ready to fly. There is no doubt that this immense airship containing 5,000,000 cu. ft. of hydrogen and measuring 731 ft. in length by 130 ft. across did not fulfil the expectations of its designers. The engines and frame were too heavy and the craft lacked adequate stability owing to the arrangement of the internal gas envelopes; as a result there were grave doubts about its ability to perform effectively over long distances. Nevertheless, after a fairly summary series of tests, the *R-101* set out from Cardington for Egypt on 1 October 1930. After Egypt it was intended that the airship should continue to India, where its destination was the long-established airport at Karachi.

Among those on board were Major Scott, the hero of the *R-34*, the engineers who had built the airship and a number of official passengers, including the Secretary of State for Air, Lord Thomson of Cardington and the Director of Civil Aviation, Air Vice-Marshal Sir Sefton Brancker.

The airship left in bad weather and was soon caught in wind and rain under low-lying clouds. At 2 o'clock in the morning the R-101 was flying very close to the ground over Allonnes as it approached Beauvais. For some unknown reason it briefly hit the ground and caught fire. A terrible explosion occurred almost immediately. Only four men survived the catastrophe; the death toll came to 50, including all the official passengers. The most tragic aspect of the whole episode was the fact that the use of helium would have greatly reduced the loss of life.

The burned out remains of the R-101 at Allones (Oise). The airship collided with the ground at the edge of a wood on a hillside (2nd October 1980).

The Dewoitine D-33 during its record 6,520 mile flight.

The first Dewoitine D-33, *le Trait-d'Union*, which crashed in the Siberian forest.

THE DRAMA OF THE D-33

From 30 May to 2 June 1930, Maddalena and Cecconi, in a Savoia S-64 *bis* modelled on the S-64 of Del Prete and Ferrarin took the closed circuit long distance record to 5,085 miles.

The French now joined the race. In 1929, the French Air Minister had ordered three aeroplanes specially for long distance performances. The first, the 500 h.p. Hispano-Blériot-110, designed by the engineer Zappata and piloted by Bossoutrot and Rossi, flew for 75 hr. 23 min., from 26 February to 1 March 1931, covering 5,468 miles.

Of the two other special aeroplanes, the Bernard-80, a monoplane with a very thick wing with an 80 ft. span piloted by Paillard and Mermoz, covered a circuit of 5,679 miles from 30 March to 3 April 1931. The second, the Dewoitine D-33, carrying Doret and Le Brix, between 7 and 10 June 1931 flew a closed circuit of 6,520 miles.

The Dewoitine D-33 was a very fine-looking monoplane, very long and totally of metal; the wing, with a span of 92 ft. and no shrouds, only had one longeron to which sixteen petrol tanks, containing more than 1,750 gallons, were attached by hinges. For the record flight, the 650 h.p. Hispano-Suiza engine drove – through reduction gear – a metal three bladed propeller. Its all-up weight on 7 June was nearly 10 tons, requiring a take-off run of 1850 yards.

On 11 July, Doret, Le Brix and the mechanic Mesmin left Le Bourget at 0440 on board the *Trait-d'Union* and flew off eastwards. But, in the night of the 12 and 13, the flight was suddenly interrupted when incredibly they ran out of petrol over the Siberian forest, near Sheberta, only 3,850 miles from Paris. Doret, determined at all costs to save the machine, stayed on board and crash-landed the D-33 in a clearing; the thick low wing protected the cockpit and the pilot was unhurt. Le Brix, and Mesmin had parachuted.

On 11 September, in a second D-33 the same crew took off again. This time, there was a tragic reversal of events and Doret was to owe his life to

Mesmin (†F1931), Le Brix (†F1931) and Doret

his parachute. Le Brix and Mesmin were to die in the wreckage. The catastrophe happened in the morning of 12 September, twenty two hours after take off. Doret, struggling to clear the Urals in thick cloud, lost track of the aircraft's position during this long flight with no landmarks and informed Le Brix. They decided to bale out but while Le Brix was helping Mesmin to put on his parachute, the D-33 crashed into the mountains near Ufa.

Wiley V. Post and Harold Gatty at Roosevelt Field.

Clyde Pangborn and Hugh Herndon

AROUND THE WORLD IN EIGHT DAYS

The round the world record was beaten spectacularly in 1931. Leaving New York on 23 June at 0900 on board a Lockheed Vega with a 450 h.p. Wasp engine, Wiley Post and Harold Gatty landed there again on 1 July at 2047; in the meantime at an average flying speed of 155 miles an hour, the land-based aeroplane had crossed the Atlantic, flown over Europe via Berlin and Moscow, and over Siberia via Omsk, Irkutsk and Khabarovsk; it had flown round the North Pacific via Kamtchatka and Alaska, and over Canada and the Great Lakes.

Up until then, there had only been one round the world flight, the one by American crews in 1924 which had taken six months. From a hundred and seventy five days the record went down to less than nine – a striking demonstration of aviation progress.

NON-STOP ACROSS THE PACIFIC

Following in the footsteps of Post and Gatty, Hugh Herndon and Clyde Pangborn crossed the Atlantic in July in a Bellanca with a Wasp engine, but were slowed down by a storm and failed in their attempt to beat the new record. Instead on 4 October 1931, they left the Japanese coast at Samishiro, jettisoned their undercarriage and headed directly east for the American coast which they reached thirty eight hours later at Seattle. Backtracking to Wenatchee, where they knew that they would get immediate assistance in case of an accident, Pangborn and Herndon landed without an undercarriage; with masterly decision and control they sideslipped intentionally, got back into position a few feet from the ground, glided briefly, then nosed up causing the rear of the fuselage to touch first, and the aeroplane slid on its belly, coming to rest after 50 yards.

Post and Gatty's Lockheed Vega at Berlin-Tempelhof airfield

Pangborn and Herndon's Bellanca landing without an undercarriage at Wenatchee

Above: a Schreck-FBA amphibian lands beside the liner *Ile de France* in the port at Le Havre; other aircraft attending the "Transat" rally are moored on the right.

PRIVATE FLYING 1926–1932

Private flying became fully established in Europe between 1928 and 1930. It was aided by promotional gatherings which were all the more effective in that they were aimed to preach to the converted and so tended to become "fun outings" amongst friends.

More and more owners piloted their own aeroplanes to these rallies and were accompanied by their families. This was in large measure because since 1926 a new type of private aeroplane had had become available. Notwithstanding the efforts in France of Potez, Caudron and Morane-Saulnier, in Czechoslovakia of Avia and of Germany by Klemm, it is De Havilland who must be considered the father of private aviation, for his decision in 1925, completely ignoring the sporting regulations of the day, to build the "Moth", a safe, simple, sturdy aeroplane with a good full-powered engine, built for long service in the hands of non-technical amateurs.

Flying clubs also sprang up where the British could combine their taste for social life and sport. In these clubs, which received a modest grant from the government, many amateur pilots, both men and women, received flying instruction which was soon further developed by the practice

of flying from club to club across the country. This led naturally to the amazing profusion of "globe-trotters" who soon found themselves cramped in an often foggy England and went off to find the sun on all the world's great routes.

Record breaking inevitably followed and, although the greatest reservations must be made concerning the "sleepless journeys" which were the final outcome, mention should nevertheless be made here of the successes of Scott, Mollison, Butler and Amy Johnson (later Mrs Mollison) on the Australian route; of Caspareuthus, Lady Bailey, Store and Miss Salaman on the Cape Town route; and of Barnard who specialised in long non-stop flights within Europe.

In 1931 the French government began subsidizing the buying of private aeroplanes and private

aviation became as widespread as in England, encouraged since 1929 by the example of the Baillys and the Goulettes.

Records were established for light aircraft, in which the great professional pilot Lallouette and the young de Permangle triumphed until the day of their fatal crash in the sea, off the Catalan coast. And women's records too, where Léna Bernstein and Maryse Bastié competed for nearly forty hours for the solo flight endurance record.

Above all there were the great journeys. Moench and Burtin flew to Istres and Antananarivo in six days and nine hours; Goulette and Salal improved on this with four days and seven hours, then cut the time to Cape Town to three days and nineteen hours; Dévé, de Verneilh and Munch flew to New Caledonia, between 9 March and 5 April 1932; d'Estailleur-Chanteraine, with Mistrot and Giraud and then Freton as pilots, completed an amazing tour of Africa in 1931, then, in 1932, a rapid Paris-Djibouti-Dakar-Paris circuit, which included the first air crossing of the African continent from east to west; Lefèvre piloted a Mauboussin with a 40 h.p. Salmson engine to Madagascar and back; while the Comte de Sibour, flew from Paris to Peking via Siberia in eleven days and returned in nine, flew off again to rescue Doret after the Ufa drama, and then again to help Maryse Hilsz in the middle of Africa.

Mrs. Elliot Lynn, at the first French competition for private aeroplanes held in August 1926 at Orly, putting her De Havilland Moth, through the official measuring gauge. Right: a meeting of British private aircraft, mostly De Havilland Moths, on the airfield at Bristol.

Left: the Breguet family who have just landed at Bléville in one of their aeroplanes are greeted by M. André Schelcher, organiser of the annual rallies in beret.

R.F. Caspareuthus

Réginensi and Bailly

C.W.A. Scott

Goulette (†*F*1932) and Salel

Lady Bailey

Alan Butler with his Comper Swift Pobjoy

Miss Salaman and Store with their Puss Moth

Damet with the Comte and Mme. de Sibour.

Amy Johnson

C.D. Barnard

J.A. Mollison

Moench (right) and Burtin

René Lefèvre

Marga von Etzdorf

Mistrot, d'Estailleur-Chanteraine and the pilot Giraud (†*F*1932)

Captain Dévé, Munch and Flying Officer Verneilh

271

Gliders at the 1931 Rhön meeting grouped at the summit of the Wasserkuppe.

THE SECOND AGE OF GLIDING

Great endurance performances in gliders had been achieved as early as 1925; at Vauville, Commandant Massaux flew for 10 hr. 19 min. in a Poncelet glider and in the Crimea, the German, Schultz, stayed in the air for 12 hr. 6 min. Seven years later the endurance record – taken to 21 hr. 36 min. on 19 December 1931 by Cocke in Honolulu – went largely unnoticed. The second "age" of gliding was characterised by an entirely new type of performance: "motorless journeys" over distances varying from 50 to more than 150 miles.

On 20 July 1929, Kronfeld covered 88 miles from the Rhön to Hermsdorf. But in 1931, the new technique of "towed take-offs" permitted performances that were all the more striking in that they were not apparently dependent on the terrain flown over. On 13 April, three gliders were released from towing aircraft at 1300 ft. over Darmstadt. The first two landed at Bruchsal after 44 miles; the third, piloted by Groenhoff, reached Fribourg, 134 miles away. On 15 April, Fuchs, launched above Griesheim, turned over Heidelberg 37 miles away, and returned to land at his take off point. On 5 May, Groenhoff was released over Munich for a demonstration flight during an aeronautics display into the front of a thunder storm. After a flight of nine hours he landed in Czechoslovakia, 165 miles from his starting point. During the journey, he had recorded violent changes in altitude of up to 6000 ft. and his glider had been quite severely damaged.

On 30 June 1931 Kronfeld, who had been invited to England by the British Gliding Association, flew from Hanworth to Chatham on his glider *Wien*. Released at an altitude of 1150 ft. on an absolutely calm day, Kronfeld had used the thermal currents, active under cloud, to rise to nearly 4,600 ft. The next day, he was again released by an aeroplane near his landing point, having announced his intention of trying to return to his starting point; after a flight of three and a half hours, he landed at the Hanworth aerodrome. This journey had been one long struggle for lift; Kronfeld, flying very low and almost in despair, had finally gained height by circling over a cornfield lit up by the sun, had been able from there to "leap up" to a cloud making a solitary formation in the sky, climb to 3000 ft. over Biggin Hill and Croydon and thus – circling somewhere between 1300 and 3300 ft., and guided by the movement of the distant clouds – to reach his appointed goal.

But it was the Rhön meeting in 1931 – the twelfth consecutive one – which probably provided the most striking performances; the routes fanned out from the Wasserkuppe from West through North to North East. On 5 August, a day of very light winds, the longest flight had not exceeded ten minutes when Kronfeld left around 1300 in his *Wein*. For half an hour he struggled grimly to stay in the air. Finally, thousands of spectators saw the glider begin to describe very tight circles and spiral slowly upwards; once again, Kronfeld, the ascent 'magician', had found the air current to save him; he went up, then headed towards a vast cloud formation several miles away; that evening it was learned that he had landed near Arnsberg after a flight of 6 hr. 25 min., having covered 108 miles as the crow flies.

Dr Georgii, the meteorologist who contributed so much to German gliding, has explained what such exploits demand in the way of human qualities and experience: intelligent preparation, sensitive and shrewd piloting, sufficient meteorological knowledge to observe, and take advantage of, the sky and to interpret the readings of special precision altimeters. Because for every up current there is a corresponding down current, as harmful as the former can be valuable. Ascents have been recorded of more than 300 ft. a minute and descents of more than 3000; enemies are everywhere, mingled with allies, and the unaided eye of man, without visible signs such as clouds or smoke, is blind to them both.

Thus a new sport was born, but accessible – barring exceptional weather conditions or mountain formations – to very few pilots, in gliders in the same class as the "Wein". Even in Germany, this elite was limited to five or six specialists out of more than 2000 glider pilots – 200 of whom held advanced licences by the end of 1931 – and some 2000 machines, and it was brutally tested during the final Rhön competition. On 19 July 1932, Rudiger, made a fatal dive, and on the 23rd Groenhoff himself was killed in a stall.

Kronfeld in his glider *Wien*

Hirth removing the cockpit canopy from his glider *Musterle*

Lippisch's "tailless" 28 h.p. motor-glider.

The Latécoere-28, in seaplane form. This aircraft held 25 records, 20 of them for seaplanes.

The Bleriot-110 which took the long distance record in closed circuit to 6,583 miles.

The Bellanca Pacemaker, which stayed in the air for 84 hr. and 32 min. from 25 to 28 May 1931.

SPEED Over 3km. (1.86 miles)	ALTITUDE	DISTANCE (In closed circuit)
Bonnet 278.49 mph. Bernard-Hubert V-2 (One 450 h.p. Hispano Suiza) 11/12/24 France	A. Soucek 43,155 ft. Wright Apache (One 450 h.p. Pratt and Whitney) 4/6/30 U.S.A.	Bossoutrot and Rossi 6,587.34m. Blériot 110 (One 500 h.p. Hispano Suiza) 23–26/3/32 France
DISTANCE (In straight line)	**ENDURANCE**	**MAXIMUM LOAD** (Carried to 2,000 m- 6,560 ft.)
Boardman and Polando 5,011.95m. Bellanca (One 300 h.p. Wright Whirlwind J.6.) 28–30/7/31 U.S.A.	W. Lees and A. Brossy 84 hr. 32 min. Bellanca Pacemaker (One 220 h.p. Packard diesel) 25–28/5/31 U.S.A.	D. Antonini 22,000 lb. Caproni 90.PB (Six 1,000 h.p. Isotta-Fraschini-Asso) 22/2/30 Italy

SPEED Over 3km. (1.86 miles)	ALTITUDE	DISTANCE (In closed circuit)
Stainforth 407.10 mph. Supermarine S.6.B. (One 2,800 h.p. Rolls Royce R) 29/9/31 Great Britain	A. Soucek 38,550 ft. Wright Apache (One 425 h.p. supercharged Pratt and Whitney) 4/6/29 U.S.A.	Paris and Gonord 3,113.91 m. Latécoère 28–5 (One 650 h.p. Hispano Suiza) 4–5/6/31 France
DISTANCE (In straight line)	**ENDURANCE**	**MAXIMUM LOAD** (Carried to 2,000 m- 6,560 ft.)
Mermoz, Dabry and Gimié 1,971.79m. Latécoère 28–5 (One 600 h.p. Hispano-Suiza) 12–13/5/30 France	Paris and Gonord 36 hr. 57 min. Latécoère 28–5 (One 650 h.p. Hispano-Suiza) 22/6/30 France	Steindorf 14,190 lb. Rohrbach Romar (Three 500 h.p. BMW) 17/4/89 Germany

MAJOR WORLD RECORDS FOR AEROPLANES AT 1 JULY 1932

MAJOR WORLD RECORDS FOR SEAPLANES AT 1 JULY 1932

Speed	Carrying 500kg. (1,100 lb.)	Carrying 1,000kg. (2,200 lb.)	Carrying 2,000kg. (4,400 lb.)
Over 500 km. (310.69 m.)	J. Kalla 171.74 mph. Letov S-516 (One 800 h.p. Asso) 13/10/30 Czechoslovakia	Lee and Schoenhair 168.2 mph. Lockheed Vega (One 650 h.p. P. and W. Wasp Asso) 20/2/30 U.S.A.	Dubourdieu 140.48 mph. Latécoère-28 (One 650 h.p. Hispano Suiza) 29/3/31 France
Over 1,000 km. (621.39 m.)	J. Kalla 171.05 mph. Letov S-516 (One 800 h.p. Asso) 13/10/3 Czechoslovakia	Voitech and Swozil 156.83 mph. Aero A-42 (One 800 h.p. Asso) 20/9/30 Czechoslovakia	Dubourdieu 139.65 mph. Latécoère-28 (One 650 h.p. Hispano-Suiza 29/3/31 France
Over 2,000 km. (1242.78 m.)	Paris 141.84 mph. Latécoère-28 (One 650 h.p. Hispano Suiza) 11/4/31 France	Paris 141.84 mph. Latécoère 28 (One 650 h.p. Hispano Suiza) 11/4/31 France	Doret and Le Biox 94.05 mph. Dewoitine D-33 (One 650 h.p. Hispano Suiza) 23–24/3/31 France

Speed	Carrying 500kg. (1,100 lb.)	Carrying 1,000kg. (2,200 lb.)	Carrying 2,000kg. (4,400 lb.)
Over 500 km. (310.69 m.)	Rolf Starke 146.6 mph. Heinkel He 9a (One 600 h.p. BMW-VI) 21/5/29 Germany	Rolf Starke 146.21 mph. Heinkel He 9a (One 600 h.p. BMW-VI) 21/5/69 Germany	Prévot 125.58 mph. Latécoère-28 (One 650 h.p. Hispano Suiza) 5/3/30 France
Over 1,000 km. (621.39 m.)	Rolf Starke 138.12 mph. Heinkel He9 (One 600 h.p. BMW-IV) 10/6/2 Germany	Paris 118.07 mph. Latécoère-28 (One 650 h.p. Hispano Suiza) 22/6/30 France	R Wagner 110.16 mph. Dornier Superwal (Four 480 h.p. Gnome-Rhône Jupiter) 5/2/28 Germany
Over 2,000 km. (1242.78 m.)	Paris and Hélbert 115.54 mph. Latécoère-28 (One 650 h.p. Hispano Suiza) 22/6/30 France	Paris and Hélbert 115.54 mph. Latécoère-28 (One 650 h.p. Hispano Suiza) 22/6/30 France	Demougeot, Gonord 101.68 mph. Latécoère-38 (Two 650 h.p. Hispano Suiza) 2/9/31 France

SPEED RECORDS FOR AEROPLANES (VARYING LOADS AND DISTANCES)

SPEED RECORDS FOR SEAPLANES (VARYING LOADS AND DISTANCES)

1932 WORLD RECORDS AND FLYING PROGRESS

Between 1920 and 1932 the officially recognized world records showed the following progression: for speed, from 170 to 407 miles per hour; for altitude, from 33,105 to 43,155 feet, for endurance on a circuit, from 24 hr. 19 min. to 84 hr. 32 min.; for distance on a circuit, from 1,190 to 6,580 miles; for straight distance, from 1,966 (the official record as from 1925) to 5,009 miles.

These figures give some idea of the technical progress made, and the speed records over 500, 1,000 and 2,000 kilometres (310½, 621 and 1,242 miles) with 500, 1,000 and 2,000 kilos (1,100, 2,200, and 4,400 lb.) of cargo, should have been a better guide to the development of everyday working aircraft, but in fact this method of selection did not in any way produce an exhaustive list of the world's best aircraft. Many manufacturers, among them the largest, never showed any interest in world records; moreover many aeroplanes, of remarkable overall design, could not compete with others designed solely to conquer a specific record, and the disservice done to aviation in general by a preoccupation with such records on the part of some European (and in particular French) manufacturers is amply demonstrated by the fact that on 1 July 1932 when the official speed record for aircraft carrying 500 kilogrammes was 172 mph. the Lockheed Orion in the United States was already carrying 5 passengers in commercial service at speeds in excess of 186 mph. Records made with refuelling in flight were however an interesting sideline. Since the thirty seven hours of Smith and Richter (1923), the endurance record had been taken to the disconcerting figure of five hundred and fifty three hours (1930) by the Hunter brothers. Behind the monotony of twenty three days in the air was the serious purpose of demonstrating the reliability of the engines, and the operation of a system that could cut back both all-up weight and the carriage of excessive amounts of fuel.

A Heath V rounding a pylon at Chicago in 1930.

Refuelling in flight. Left: Smith and Richter setting the endurance (37 hr. 15 min.) and distance (3291 miles) records on 27–28 August 1923. Right: the Hunter brothers refuelling on the 21st day. Note the walkways giving in-flight access to the engine.

Essential Existing Air Routes.
Existing Routes equipped for Night Flying
Other Routes equipped for Night Flying
Proposed Routes.

The European air transport network in the spring of 1932

AIRLINES IN 1932

In 1932 the largest commercial air network was still to be found in Europe, although it was precisely there that the greatest difficulty was encountered in providing useful regular services, because trains could average 35 to 40 miles an hour round the clock on the main lines, a speed with which the aeroplane, limited to between eight and twelve hours flying a day according to the time of year, could not compete. Moreover, it was not enough for air transport merely to be as fast as the railways – it needed to offer advantages proportionate to its cost, which was still high. Since, at that time, the public did not seem disposed to pay much more for an air journey than for the same journey by train, a policy of massive subsidies was adopted which led, in Europe more than elsewhere, to a shocking proliferation of unnecessary airlines. Each country wanted to have its own lines which resulted in constant duplication and in an irrational network; on the Vienna-Budapest run for example, six subsidised companies from different countries, were sharing a volume of traffic from which one alone would have had difficulty in breaking even.

There were however, even in Europe, routes where commercial aircraft were useful, and would have been of even more use if they had been left undisturbed by competition. Such were Paris–London, a short link joining two vital world centres and saving passengers the bother of transferring to cross the Channel, and the long Paris-Constantinople line, where by aeroplane, journeys could be accomplished in six to fifteen hours during the summer months, compared to one to three days by train.

Africa, where European activities and interests were so great, had seemed – in 1919 – an ideal place to start up commercial flights. However, with the exception of the "Sabena" services in the Belgian Congo, it was not until 1932 that any of the great transafrican routes – in this case Cairo–Cape Town – was opened for regular public transport, and even then this was merely an extension of the service which, in 1931, opened the northern section of this route from Egypt to Kenya, and which was one of the arteries of the British Empire. This operation was marked by serious difficulties; hazardous landing fields, the difficulty of maintaining them in tropical and equatorial countries, delays in transporting mail and passengers with a standby aeroplane in cases of breakdown, and the need to provide such standbys; all this must have made the local governments, though committed to the rapid air link they were subsidising, have doubts about its actual worth.

In the light of this experience, it is easy to understand why France, however interested she may have been in the link with Madagascar via French Equatorial Africa and the Congo, had not yet decided to open it; the cost was very high and the commercial return doubtful. It was more important to establish the possibility of a fast link in emergencies – by equipping the route – rather than a premature regular air service.

In fact, the only successful African services were regional or local; the Belgian Congo net-

A Dornier Superwal with emergency radio mast.

The "Flèche d'Orient" service (Paris-Bucharest)

An Imperial Airways Handley Page (London-Paris)

A Luftverkehr-Persien Junkers (Teheran-Baku)

The inauguration in 1921 of a French Guianan airline.

Aeroplanes of South West African Airways at Windhoek.

Some of the staff of New Guinea Airways

The Colombian Baranquilla-Bogota service.

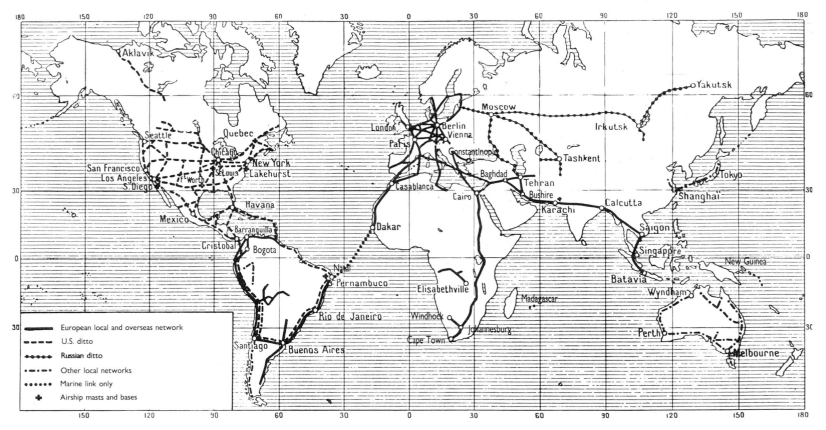

Continental and international air transport networks in the spring of 1932.

work, the development of which was held back by the economic crisis, and the South African network where the postal link between Windhoek and Johannesburg by South West African Airways was especially interesting economically and technically, since it broke new ground by using three small wholly metal aeroplanes with 85 h.p. engines to reduce the running costs to a minimum.

There was even more reason why, on the long transoceanic routes, the aeroplane and the seaplane had not yet succeeded in establishing themselves. Without the security of regular stopping-planes on land or of the natural landmarks of a coast only a fully sea-worthy flying boat could offer sufficient safety and carry a sufficiently specialised crew. In fact, in 1932 there was nowhere in the world where an air service crossed more than 600 miles of sea without a stopover and the Dakar-Natal gap in the France-South America line was still serviced by ship. Long transcontinental links were few, and the services were

generally weekly, such as those between Toulouse and Santiago in Chile and on the Pan American Airways South American circuit. Only on the East Indian line, did the coexistence of Dutch, British and French services, the last inaugurated in January 1931, assure three weekly links to Karachi, two to Burma and then one on to Saigon or Batavia.

Linked up with this long distance line at Bushire and Baghdad, a useful and relatively prosperous local network had been created by Junkers in Persia, a trading country whose precarious communications made it an ideal candidate for an airline, but even this company met with difficulties in 1932, and the service had to be shut down, while other less justified ones continued.

There were, however, exceptional cases which were amazingly successful due to their economic geography, such as the Colombian "Scadta" and New Guinea Airways. The former joined the capital, Bogota, to the coast in eight hours; the only viable alternative being an eight to ten days'

journey by paddlesteamer down the river Magdalena. In New Guinea, the aeroplane revolutionized the exploitation of gold mines and enabled great savings to be made compared with the cost of porterage or of building roads; New Guinea Airways, which had been set up with a modest capital, was thus able by 1929 to distribute dividends of around 40% and to make a free issue of one new share for each old one.

From the United States airmail network set up in 1926 had grown a transport system covering, on U.S. territory alone, some 30,000 miles by 1932, on which around 600 aeroplanes covered more than 130,000 miles each day. A recent law allowed local airlines to be subsidised at generous rates, by granting them postal contracts for the transport of passengers and parcels. In 1931, 522,000 passengers were carried and nearly 4,400 tons of post. The development of the transcontinental services was remarkable; several lines joined the Pacific to the Atlantic in thirty to thirty six hours.

A Lockheed Vega, for passengers and mail, about to leave Los Angeles for New York

A Lockheed Orion, with retracting undercarriage, on Luddington Airlines New York-Washington service in 1931.

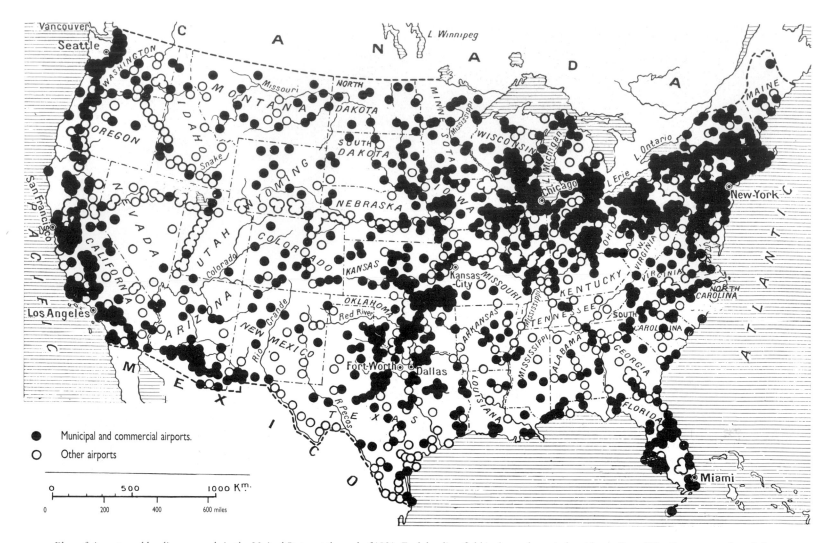

Plan of airports and landing grounds in the United States at the end of 1931. Each landing field is shown by a circle with a radius of 20 miles; an aeroplane flying at a normal height within any one of these circles could glide to the aerodrome situated in the centre in the event of engine failure.

Assistance given to fliers in the United States Centre: routes equipped for night flying by 1 January 1932. Below left: a pilot studying, before take-off, local

weather reports sent by telex to all stops on a route. Below right: Burbank airport in California, with runways aligned to the prevailing winds.

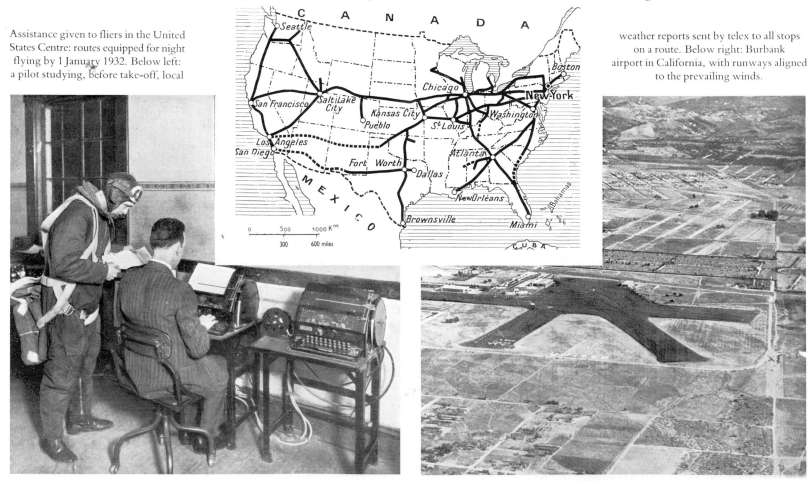

The problems of airports in capital cities. Left: Paris-Le Bourget. Offices and hangars (bottom left), thought excessive in 1919 had by 1932 become insufficient. Buildings had also mushroomed round the perimeter, mainly for military use (top). Right: terminals and apron at Berlin-Tempelhof, where houses come dangerously close to the airport.

Left and right: two views of Marseille-Marignane, France's largest seaplane port. Centre: the mooring pylon for dirigibles at Pernambuco.

AIRPORTS

The rapid American trans continental services which ran day and night for up to 2,500 miles were only possible thanks to very well-equipped air routes. At the beginning of 1932, there were 2,100 airports or landing fields for commercial aviation in the United States and nearly 20,000 miles of marked airways signed by more than 2,000 special lights. Weather reports were transmitted by "telex" over 13,000 miles and nearly 100 radio beacons were in service.

Europe, through lack of political unity, was still far from adopting such a programme of cooperation. Great efforts had been made to make airports worthy of the great capitals they served and there were sufficient landing fields for stop overs or emergencies. What was lacking was unity among the nations to achieve a task that, by its very nature, was "supra-national".

As aeroplanes became more reliable, particularly with the introduction of extremely powerful multiple engines, they became less dependent on ground facilities. Permanent contacts with their stopping points and with radio beacons became much more important than regularly spaced emergency landing fields or guiding lights. The aeroplane navigated freely from one airport to another and, on long distance flights, would turn off its normal flight path many times as a result of weather reports relayed to it by wireless.

The hesitations of those who had thought that "air routes", laboriously installed on land, would be useless, were thus in part vindicated. Building airports is extremely expensive; not only does it involve the buying, levelling and maintenance of

vast areas and the construction of hangars, but also the provision of services and facilities that extend far beyond the airport perimeter.

Supporters of seaplanes have always maintained that the flying boat – and especially the "winged liners" of which the Do-X was the prototype – saved at least on some of these investments. In fact seaplane lines had a modest infrastructure; sea-worthy aircraft, experienced crews, and land-based wireless and radio direction finding stations were the only essential elements for a regular and safe service.

The large dirigible, thanks to its field of action, was even less demanding. The *Graf-Zeppelin* had only one hangar, at Friedrichshafen, and provided services to South America using only quite rudimentary mooring masts.

The Fennings plan for an airport in Central London

The layout of an airport often had a considerable influence on the traffic. When 40 or 50 aeroplanes were taking off or landing each day, the access to the boarding areas, discipline on the runway and the organisation of traffic and customs controls were of vital importance to the customer's well-being.

Naturally, later airports were able to profit from the experience of the earlier ones. This was particularly true in the United States where the development of commercial aviation started in 1928 and airports – built after study trips to Europe – were inspired less by the European constructions than by the criticism of the Europeans of their own airports. In 1925, a French pilot and engineer, M. A.-B. Duval, proposed grouping all the buildings in a triangle extending from one corner to the centre of the landing area to allow runways to be built aligned to all the prevailing winds, and to keep movement on the ground to a minimum for aeroplanes and cargo.

The vast area needed to be able to align runways in more than one direction has itself serious constraints on the siting of airports. Except in exceptional cases where – as at Berlin-Templehof – there is an enormous site in the town itself, the airport has had to be built anything up to 15 miles from the town it serves. In order to remove this formidable handicap, some daringly radical architects have studied airports for town centres either to be built over a river or raised off the ground with runways radiating on stilts over the buildings themselves. Others have suggested that progress may one day lead to catapulted take-offs and braked landings that will eliminate the need for the enormous and distant airport.

Dobkevicius, Lithuania
(†*F*1926)

Del Prete, Italy
(†*F*1928)

Négrin, France
(†*F*1930)

Lefranc, France
(†*F*1928)

Lallouette, France
(†*F*1931)

Casale, France
(†*F*1923)

Loriga, Spain
(†*F*1927)

Rodgers, U.S.A.
(†*F*1926)

Stinson, U.S.A.
(†*F*1932)

Plauth, Germany
(†*F*1927)

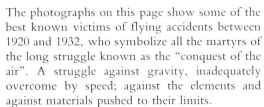

Maneyrol's coffin (†*F*1923) being brought back to Paris

CASUALTIES OF THE 1920s

The photographs on this page show some of the best known victims of flying accidents between 1920 and 1932, who symbolize all the martyrs of the long struggle known as the "conquest of the air". A struggle against gravity, inadequately overcome by speed; against the elements and against materials pushed to their limits.

Dobkevicius, Del Prete, Rodgers and Loriga stand for the service pilots, Lallonette, Casale, Stinson and Plauth for the civilian test-pilots and designers; Maneyrol, for the devotees of gliders and light aircraft; Lord Thomson and Sir Sefton Brancker for the politicians and civil servants; Negrin, airline pilot, and Lefranc, engineer and manager, represent the victims of commercial aviation; Maddalena and Teste, the service test-pilots and technicians; Bougault, Dal Molin and Bettis, the victims of speed; De Précourt and Lhota, the expert "amateurs"; Sperry, both pilot and engineer; Thiéffry and Ross Smith, pioneers of air routes; all serve as a reminder of the diversity of the pilots who risked, and too often gave, their lives.

Sir Sefton Brancker (†*F*1930)

Lord Thomson of Cardington (†*F*1930)

Teste, France
(†*F*1925)

Maddalena, Italy
(†*F*1931)

Bougault, France
(†*F*1931)

Dal Molin, Italy
(†*F*1930)

De Précourt, France
(†*F*1930)

Lhota, Czechoslovakia
(†*F*1926)

Bettis, U.S.A.
(†*F*1926)

Sperry, U.S.A.
(†*F*1923)

Thiéffry, Belgium
(†*F*1929)

Ross Smith, Australian
(†*F*1922)

Orlinski, Poland

Thoret, France

René Panthan, France

Paris, France

Ferrarin, Italy

Koehl, Germany

FLIERS OF 1932

Mittelholzer,
Switzerland

Cobham,
Great Britain

De Havilland,
Great Britain

Orlebar,
Great Britain

Most of the great pilots assembled on this page have already been mentioned for the long distance flights they accomplished, the records they broke or the specialities they mastered. Alongside them are to be found De Havilland, Fokker and Morane, the most well known among the manufacturers who continually strove to perfect and test their aeroplanes themselves, as La Cierva did for the autogiro; Paumier, an engineer and pilot who broke several records; Finat, an indefatigable organiser of meetings who gave superb demonstrations and lost his life this way; and finally René Paulhan, a test-pilot like his father, Louis Paulhan, who was the hero of the 1910 London–Manchester.

Licensed women pilots were rare in France although there were several hundred in the United States and in England. Miss Earhardt came to Europe, flying over the Atlantic alone. Maryse Bastie, also alone, flew for more than thirty-eight hours, longer at that time than any male solo flight; Ruth Nicholls made some fine speed records in the United States, while Lady Heath and Maryse Hilsz made long journeys in Africa.

There were some 5,000 to 6,000 men throughout the world in 1932 who crewed the airlines or flew on charter work. These men, who were of all nationalities are represented here by the Frenchman Mermoz of Aéropostale who, with Dabry, who came from the merchant navy, and represents here the "navigating" specialists, mechanics, radiotelegraphers and navigators, made the first non-stop postal crossing of the South Atlantic.

Brow was the first to exceed 400 kilometres an hour (248 mph.), and Soucek the first to go higher than 13,000 metres (42640 ft.) These two officers are a good example of Service pilots who achieved records while making technical tests. Squadron Leader Orlebar, head of the British speed squadron, was always the first to try out difficult aircraft.

Finally Van Orman and Demuyter, famous for their victories in the Gordon-Bennett Cup, represent the devotees of "lighter than air".

Robert Morane, France

Fokker, Holland

Hawks, U.S.A.

Finat, France

Lady Heath,
Great Britain

Hinkler,
Great Britain

Maryse Bastié,
France

Amelia Earhardt,
U.S.A.

Paumier, France

Maryse Hilsz, France

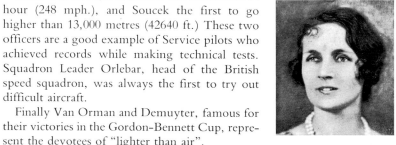

Ruth Nicholls, U.S.A.

Bossoutrot, France

Brow, U.S.A.

Soucek, U.S.A.

Mermoz, France

Dabry, France

Demuyter, Belgium

Van Orman, U.S.A.

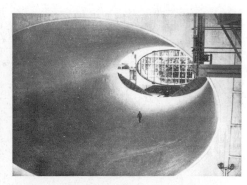

Testing a form of autogiro on the mobile test-bed at Saint-Cyr.

Full scale testing of an aeroplane in the giant wind tunnel of the American N.A.C.A. (1931)

The giant wind tunnel built at Chalais-Meudon between 1932 and 1934.

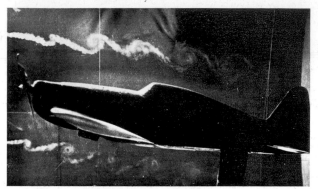

Left and right: studying the disturbance caused by the propeller to the airflow on one-tenth scale models of a Morane Saulnier fighter and a two-engined bomber, using smoke emitters and stroboscopic photography in a wind-tunnel. Centre: Gustave Eiffel (1832–1923)

DESIGN, CONSTRUCTION AND TESTING

From the very beginning scientists, technicians and pilots had collaborated in their research into improving the performance of aeroplanes. Indeed the famous pioneers – Lilienthal and the Wright brothers in particular – had already made many experiments of a truly scientific nature before the secret of flight was discovered. In the course of time, research naturally divided itself into different fields and scientists began to work in more narrowly defined areas.

Two great names dominated the study of aerodynamics in France: those of Gustave Eiffel, who created a laboratory in Paris, and of Joukovsky. To these should be added that of the patron, Henry Deutsch de la Meurthe, who died in 1919 and founded the *Institut Aérotechnique de Saint-Cyr*

before the war and endowed a chair of aeronautics at the *Conservatoire des Arts et Métiers*.

The sole object of this research was to improve the performance and security of aircraft. For the aeroplane, progress was achieved in particular by the reduction of harmful drag, by improving the profile, design and general proportions of lifting surfaces and controls. For this, the aerodynamic laboratory was of prime importance. The wind tunnel, the mobile test-bed and the "merry-go-round" allowed the study of isolated elements, from the standpoints both of their contribution to overall performance and of their individual strength, and enabled the behaviour of different profiles to be studied at varying angles of attack; in sum they provided a remarkably accurate prediction of the future aeroplane's performance.

Test on small-scale aeroplane models in wind tunnels were carried out since the beginning, but it was not until 1927 that the first giant wind

tunnel for testing full-scale aeroplanes was put into service in the United States. Between 1932 and 1934, a second wind tunnel of this type was built in France, at Chalais-Meudon. Parallel with advances in the design of the wind tunnels came improvements in methods of making visible, and of measuring, the aerodynamic phenomena that affect the performance of aircraft: alternating vortices, slipstreams, the separation of air streams near the wing-fuselage junction and interference from the propeller, many of which could be efficiently analysed by the emission and illumination of smoke.

An aeroplane is made up of a number of independent elements, which are joined together at a late stage of assembly, and which in the 1930s could be made of different materials: wooden wings, bodies of welded steel tubes or duralumin sections, canvas coverings for example.

Whether of wood or metal, the wing nearly

One of the first large aeroplanes with a steel frame: the Boulton P-15, built in 1922 by the British company Boulton and Paul Ltd.

Ultra-light wing designed in wood by the engineer Zappata for the Blériot-111, which was specially built to attack the long-distance record.

Wings of a racing seaplane: the Bernard, built in 1929 for the Schneider Cup, with longerons formed from laminated wooden tubes.

The wing of a Gloster monoplane, constructed using the Monospar system with a single steel longeron, placed vertically for the photograph (1931)

Wooden wing structure of a Fokker aeroplane, which will be covered with plywood, and from which the ailerons will be cut out after completion.

Front and central sections of a Junkers Ju-52, made entirely of light aluminium alloys (1931)

Left: an internal view of the framework of the fuselage of a Dewoitine. Centre: the fuselage and attachments for the wings, all in duralumin, for an Amiot SECM-140-M heavy bomber. Right: the point of attachment of the wing longeron to the fuselage of a Loire-II. Note the cut-outs in the metal designed to reduce unnecessary weight.

always included (usually two) main structural elements running in the direction of its span, the longerons; to these were joined, at right angles to them, a series of ribs, shaped so that both sides of the wing were curved in order to provide the necessary lift.

The fuselage was no more than a truss similar to that of a bridge calculated and built in such a way as to allow it support on the fulcrum of the wings, the engine, or engines, in the front, and the stabilizer at the back, and to take the strains of movement in the air or on the ground.

The first aeroplanes were nearly always made of wood, a light material which was easy to work with. However even before the 1914 war, some engineers, such as Voisin, began to build metal aeroplanes. The first all metal-framed aeroplane was Ponche and Primard's Tubavion of 1912.

Twenty years on the change to metal was still not complete, partly because suitable aluminium alloys were not yet available, and steel was heavy, partly because short production runs made the use

of wood more economic, but also in large part apparently through the whim or custom of the manufacturer concerned.

The same diversity was shown in the size and

The steel chassis uniting lower wings and fuselage of a Breguet-27.

number of the wings. Although the monoplane was indisputably in the ascendant, the biplane was by no means abandoned. The sesquiplane, a form

which developed from the biplane but where one pair of wings was at least double the size of the other, was amazingly successful: long distance aeroplanes such as the Breguet-19 often adopted this configuration.

The increasing interest in high tensible steel, in spite of its specific weight, underlined the value of metal in general for aircraft construction. The longerons in a wing for example, work in traction, compression and flexion all at once, and sometimes in torsion as well; wood did not react to all these various demands on it nearly as well as metal, particularly high tensible steel. The use of steel, a much more homogeneous and consistent product than wood, also greatly reduced the risk of aeroplanes breaking up in flight because of a local structural weakness or faulty assembly. Static tests, where the aeroplane was progressively submitted to much greater stress than it could ever be in flight, also contributed to safety and above all allowed practical corroboration of calculated effects.

Left: Static loading to 20g on the inverted wing of a single-seater Dewoitine D-27 fighter. Right: one hundred men standing on the wing of a Rohrbach-Romar flying boat with an unsupported span of 131 ft. (1928)

Left top: Lindbergh examining the 230 h.p. Packard-Diesel, in the summer of 1929

Left centre: the 600 h.p. Junkers S L-I diesel engine (1929)

Left bottom: M. Clerget and his first 100 h.p. diesel engine (1929)

Above left: a typical water-cooled engine: a 12 cylinder 650 h.p. Hispano-Suiza R–Nbr

Above right: a typical air-cooled engine a 9 cylinder 600 h.p. Bristol Mercury

Left: the supercharger of a Jupiter-VII engine

Above right: a variable-pitch all-metal propeller by Ratier

Left: the Farman propeller speed reduction gear

ENGINES IN THE 1930s

Continuous progress in metallurgy, metal-working and construction coupled with greater experience allowed each component of the aeroplane engine to become better adapted to its role, with a consequent saving of materials. This led to a general reduction in weight – over ten years – from over 42 to under 28 ounces per h.p. in the more powerful engines.

The conflict between the two schools of thought – cooling by air or by water – remained unresolved. The first had the advantage of lightness and ease of adaptation to the ambient temperature; the second was more logical, more easily controlled, and gave the best performance. It was thus naturally favoured for military aeroplanes where questions of economy and ease

maintenance were of secondary importance.

The classic internal combustion engine was by 1932 an admirable power source likely to last for thousands of hours, and could often run for more than five hundred hours without servicing. This progress was in part due to improved accessories and, in particular, to components which increased or made maximum use of the power: the supercharger made by Rateau as early as 1916; the reduction gear; the variable pitch propeller.

Diesel engines came into use almost simultaneously, in 1928 and 1929, on both sides of the Atlantic. Packard, in the United States, was the first to fit a 230 h.p. diesel engine, designed by Woolson, to a transport monoplane which first flew on 18 September 1928, and was soon making flights of up to 700 miles, two years later, an improved version of this engine enabled Lees and Brossy to stay in the air for more than twenty

four hours without refuelling. In 1929 in Germany, Junkers produced a 600 h.p. engine, the SL-1, later upgraded to 700 h.p., and Clerget in France, a 100 h.p. engine which led to a 200 h.p. model. Later both developed 500 h.p. versions.

The advantages of using diesel fuel were two-fold. Safety was increased by using a fuel which only produced inflammable vapours at a high temperature and allowed a system of fuel injection which made flashbacks impossible. Diesel engines also consumed less fuel and were therefore capable of carrying greater loads over longer distances: 6 oz. of fuel per h.p. per hour was the norm, compared to around 8 oz. for petrol.

While these improvements to the classical engine continued proponents of propulsion by reaction continued their research; in 1929, Fritz von Opel made a successful flight of two thirds of a mile in an aeroplane propelled by rockets.

A three-engined Rohrbach Roland of the Berlin-Paris service

A three-engined Ford flying over Brooklyn

A three-engined Wibault-210 of the Paris-Bucharest service (1932)

Three-engined German Junkers G-24 of 1930

The Lockheed Sirius with lowered wing

The all-metal Northrop Alpha

TRANSPORT AIRCRAFT

Commercial aviation could have become economically independent much more quickly if it had had equipment better suited to different types of cargo and to the special requirements of the various airlines throughout the world. In addition, many of these airlines were so recently formed that, although they would have liked to have used better equipment when it did become available, were obliged to continue with what they had until they could write off the cost of their original aircraft; an inherently difficult undertaking was thus made even more so, and held back by financial considerations. It was especially unfortunate that the airlines were unable to order on a reasonable scale since, as that very time, the aeronautics industry was benefiting from large credits for research into, and the production of, military aeroplanes and seaplanes. Indeed most of the aircraft in commercial service up till 1930 were "by-products" of research into military and naval aviation. Little by little, however, these rather unsuitable aeroplanes gave way to aircraft specifically designed for public transport. In the United States, in particular, the freer and wider development of commercial avia-tion and the fact that it was in the hands of a few powerful groups, resulted in the creation of a whole range of more suitable aircraft. The Lockheeds have already been mentioned, the Northrops and the Fleetsters were nearly as fast and just as economic. Ford, having proved the worth of its classic three-engined aircraft, started building a long distance de luxe aeroplane for day and night flights. Boeing built a two-engined aircraft, derived from its "Monomail", while Bellanca, whose wings with wide fairings on the struts had proved their effectiveness, transformed these fairings into additional lifting surfaces on their new Airbus.

The rapid transport aeroplane, the Boeing "Monomail", for passengers and mail, with undercarriage raised

The most powerful French flying boat: a Latécoère-300, with four 650 h.p. Hispano-Suiza engine, being launched at Biscarosse for a transatlantic service.

The Bellanca Airbus, with the auto-stabilising W-shaped lower wing developed from the Bellanca faired struts.

A three-engined low-powered mail plane: the Couzinet-30, with three 40 h.p. Salmson engines

What an aerial attack would look like; twin engined American bombers flying over the Hudson during the American Army Air Corps manoeuvres in 1931

AIR FORCES IN 1932

The costs of research and the development of aircraft in the world's leading countries were still almost totally dependent on government credits for military aircraft. More than 75, and in some countries more than 90%, of the turnover of all the manufacturing companies put together, not only of aeroplanes but of engines and equipment, resulted from military orders.

This new "arms race" provoked strong competition since all countries believed themselves to be threatened from the air as, in Europe particularly, there were few regions far enough away from a border to be out of the range of bombers. There were, however, in fact, only a very small number of squadrons in each country equipped with heavy bombers which were the only type that could actually mount a military significant attack. The Italians and particularly General Douhet, were the leading advocates of offensive aviation but either because of resistance from the other services, or because the policies actually followed differed greatly from those announced in her propaganda, most of the resources available for aircraft production in Italy as everywhere else continued to go to the fighter, reconnaissance and observation squadrons, in other words to defensive and inter-service liaison aircraft, and not to the "independent air force" that Douhet believed capable of decisive action right from the outbreak of a war.

Dummy bombs ranging from 20 to 500 lb. for a simulated attack on London by RAF aircraft.

The French manoeuvres of 1931. Left: shock troops boarding a D B-70 transport aeroplane, presumably requisitioned. Right: the detachment in the enormous cabin during the flight towards the supposed place of intervention.

The Aérienne Bordelaise AB-20 night bomber with four 600 h.p. Lorraine engines, twin fuselages and ventral gun-turret.

More than 600 Italian aircraft preparing for the fly past at Bologna which ended the great aerial manoeuvres of August 1931

Nieuport-Delage-N-62s (Hispano 500 h.p. engine)

The Polish PZ L-11 (Mercury 500 h.p. engine)

A row of Fokker D-XVIs (Panther 500 h.p. engine)

The Dewoitine D-27 (Hispano 500 h.p. engine)

The Morane-Saulnier-224 (Jupiter 500 h.p. engine)

SINGLE-SEAT FIGHTER AIRCRAFT

The Blériot Spad-91 (Hispano 500 h.p. engine)

The Breguet-27 (Hispano-Suiza 500 h.p. engine)

The Potez-50 (Lorraine 500 h.p. engine)

TWO-SEATER OBSERVATION AND LIAISON AIRCRAFT

The Douglas O-25 (Curtiss 600 h.p. engine)

Other reasons for this general reluctance to develop offensive airforces were the undoubted enormous cost of heavy bombers, their probable vulnerability and possibly a realisation of the ultimate futility of developing such a force in peace time since no country could allow another one to have a monopoly.

All these ideas were exposed to world opinion during the Arms Limitation Conference. Agreement was difficult between nations which had very different interests and among which the overseas territories and possessions of some always posed particular problems of defense and policing. It seemed, however, after the conference, that a significant advance had been made

Numbers of military aircraft (front-line and first reserve) of the Great Powers at the beginning of 1932. Note that Germany does not figure on the list.

towards ruling out the threat of "total air war", at least in Europe where the danger was greatest. In the field of defense, and also in the army and navy, aviation kept its place; but progress in artillery and anti-aircraft machines guns, and the practical impossibility at that stage of providing bombers with effective defenses meant that they were regarded in official circles as virtually suicidal, a quite different impression from that held by the general public as a result of regular highly publicised air manoeuvres.

As a result in 1932, about a quarter of military aviation units consisted of single seater fighters and about half of two-seater liaison and observation aircraft, leaving very few bombing units equipped with heavy aircraft in the various armies and navies of Europe.

Lioré and Olivier-203 bomber (4 Titan 300 h.p. engines)

The SPCA-III multi-seat (2 Lorraine 650 h.p. engines)

The Farman-211 bomber (4 Farman 250 h.p. engines)

The C A M S-55 flying boat (2 Hispano 600 h.p. engines)

The Levasseur P L-14-T (Hispano 600 h.p. engine)

MULTI-SEAT BOMBERS AND OTHERS

The ANF-Mureaux-120 (2 K-7 300 h.p. engines)

The American all metal airship *ZMC-2* or *Metalclad*, during construction and after completion.

THE METALCLAD AND THE AKRON

As early as 1925, work was underway in Detroit on a totally metallic dirigible whose envelope, made of bands of light alloys in a spiral, was designed to hold the helium directly.

This bold technical departure was incorporated in an aircraft of 204,000 cu. ft., 149 ft. long, which made its first highly successful flights in 1929. Built by the Aircraft Development Corporation, this dirigible, called *ZMC-2* or *Metalclad*, was flown from Detroit to Lakehurst, a flight of 560 omiles, where it joined the *Los Angeles*.

Before the ZMC-2 could be built, a sort of sewing machine had had to be devised to assemble, by three rows of rivets, the sheets of "alclad", a sheet of duralumin sandwiched between two very thin sheets of pure aluminium which protected the stronger metal against corrosion. This machine, which fixed 135 rivets a minute, had fitted three and a half million, with a wastage of 3 per 10,000 before the two halves of the envelope which were each assembled vertically were ready

to be repositioned horizontally to be joined together.

The internal framework consisted of five principal transverse circles, seven secondary ones and twenty four longitudinal ribs; the interior, totally free and airtight, held, besides the helium, two small air balloons for regulating the pressure which took up a quarter of the total volume.

Towards the rear of the envelope, but far enough from the stem still to be in the slipstream during movement, the eight stabilizers and rudders were placed radially and equally distributed round the periphery. The aspect ratio of the balloon, which was less than 3, (it had a diameter of 52 ft. 6 in. for a length of 149 ft. had been chosen after meticulous aerodynamic tests.

The ascensional force of this first model reached 12,210 lb. of which 3125 lb., or over 25 percent, was pay-load, a remarkable proportion for a small experimental balloon.

The performances achieved, with two Wright 220 h.p. engines, were sufficiently encouraging for the Aircraft Development Corporation to plan a 100 ton airship, but the economic crisis that

from 1930 affected the United States put an end to this project.

On 23 September 1931, the first flight of the *ZRS-4*, the largest dirigible in the world, took place in the United States in an atmosphere of national rejoicing. Christened Akron, after the city where it had been built and from which it took off, the majestic airship carried 113 people on this maiden flight, a sign of the confidence shown in the classic technique of the large rigid balloon. It was destined for the American navy and had a length of 787 ft., a height of 157 ft., and a gas volume of 6,529,000 cu. ft. for a displacement of 7,340,000. With 123,000 lb. of fuel, it could cover more than 12,000 miles at 45 miles per hour or 5,500 miles at a maximum speed of 75 mph.

Powerfully armed with machine guns, the *Akron* was also designed to carry, in a special hangar, from four to seven aeroplanes which could leave and return in mid-flight. The engines, placed inside the envelope since there was no risk of fire from the helium, drove through remote linkages orientable propellers.

The largest dirigible in the world at 1 August 1932; the *ZRS-4*, the Akron, under construction in a special hangar.

The De Havilland "Puss Moth" (inverted Gipsy engine)

The Caudron C-232 with foldable wings (100 h.p. Renault engine)

The Klemm 1-25-1a (40 h.p. Salmson engine)

The Curtiss-Wright Junior (60 h.p. Szekely engine)

The Portez-36 with covered cabin and "anti-stall flap" (100 h.p. Renault engine)

The Mauboussin M-11 with covered cabin (40 h.p. Salmson engine)

AIRCRAFT FOR PRIVATE FLYING

Aircraft destined for private flying were generally smaller than other types in order to make it a less expensive undertaking; nevertheless a wide variety of models were created. British flying clubs, which had an impressive number of members, inspired a following in Europe which was encouraged by government subsidies. The amateur pilot was therefore able to acquire, for the price of a 10 h.p. car, a good two-seater, several hundred of which were sold. Naturally, these aircraft gave very different performances according to their engine power and whether they were designed for sport, for touring or for simple "fine weather flying". Some of the most popular or famous touring aeroplanes are shown on this page. Note the closed cabin, with two seats side by side, of the Potez-36 and the "anti-stall flap" – a fixed flap added to the leading edge of the wing – which decreased considerably the speed at which the aircraft would stall. The Curtiss-Wright Junior, which had a pusher propeller, owed much of its success to the open views which it allowed its passengers.

The first tests on a jet propelled manned aeroplane: Fritz von Opel in his rocket-propelled aeroplane, flying at Frankfurt on 30 September 1929.

GIANT AIRCRAFT

The giant Caproni triple tri-plane flying boat, the "Capronissime", designed to carry 100 passengers, which crashed during flight tests on Lake Maggiore in 1921.

The first passenger plane with an engine room: the Breguet-Leviathan, tested in 1921. Left: the fuselage and the power unit. Right: the "engine room", with two superimposed Bugatti engines

The great "Flying Wing", Left: the Junkers G-38 in flight. Top right: the engines, mounted inside the wing cavity, were accessible in flight. Bottom right: maintenance men give an idea of the size of the wing area.

The Dornier Do-X-II during trials on Lake Constance; the stabilising fins gave additional lift in flight.

The efforts made after 1915 to increase the range and, above all, the carrying capacity of bombers first led the Germans to consider the question of giant aircraft. Their elephantine 10 to 20 ton aircraft needed a total of 1,200 to 2,500 h.p. to fly at a time when engines had a maximum power of 200 to 250 h.p. In order to avoid putting engines all over the airframe, they were led to daring solutions such as transmitting power from a distance by means of shafts and pulleys and even the "engine room" approach of grouping all the motors together; this at least made it easy to keep an eye on the power, to stop, restart and even repair the engines during the flight, and was used to drive several propellers or sometimes – as in the case of the Linke-Hofmann – a single propeller of gigantic proportions.

Once the war was over, this research was ready to be applied to long distance aircraft especially since surplus power and its distribution were the main elements of regularity and security, *provided* that the engines were accessible in flight. The first step made in this direction after the war was by the engineer Rohrbach, whose four-engined transport aircraft the *Zeppelin-Staaken*, destroyed after test flights by Allied orders, included in the thickness of its single wing an access passage to the engines. The Italian manufacturer Caproni adopted a diametrically opposite approach with his "Capronissime" in 1921, a large triple triplane flying boat with the engines spread out over the wings. This bold but reasonable solution – for tandem wings had a lot to offer – was abandoned after an accident when the prototype was destroyed.

At the same time in France, Breguet was flying his "Leviathan" which was admittedly much smaller but which had arrived independently at the "engine room" solution.

The technical restrictions imposed on German aviation after the war constrained them to limit their new designs to the permitted scale; for this reason the Junkers F-13, the Dornier-Wal and the Rohrbach Rocco were much smaller than their predecessors. However there then followed, by a methodic transition, the Superwal, the G-24 and the Romar, and finally the "giants" of almost incredible size, the Dornier Do-X and the Junkers G-38.

Research was started on the first of these, a straightforward but bold development of the Wal, in 1926, and it was to achieve almost the same worldwide fame as the *Graf-Zeppelin*. On 24 June 1932, the Do-X-1 landed on the Muggelsee, near Berlin, after a journey of 28,000 miles which had taken it from Europe to South America and to the United States, crossing the Atlantic – for which it had not been designed – twice.

Its 12 Fiat engines of 600 to 700 h.p. consumed approximately 350 gallons of fuel an hour, sufficient to absorb its entire lifting capacity in a flight of 1500 miles: the Do-X was infact designed for sea crossings of 750 to 500 miles; it could in these conditions carry 40 to 80 passengers in extreme comfort owing to the size of its hull which had a volume of over 14,000 cu. ft.

The Junkers G-38 had only four engines, giving a power of 2,000 to 2,800 h.p. for a lifting surface of 3225 sq. ft. The four engines were mounted within the structure of the 148 ft. span wings, which were very deep, allowing access to the engines in flight. They drove the propellers through flexibly-mounted shafts. A considerable amount of the cargo was also carried in the wings, as was the fuel, which reduced the flexional moments at the wing roots and allowed the structure to be considerably lightened. Weighing 12 tons when empty and 18 to 22 tons when loaded, it was designed to carry modest loads over long distances, for example 3 tons over 2000 miles. Researched with the help of the Japanese who were interested in it for military reasons, the G-38 was better suited for carrying freight or bombs than passengers. Junker's dream of a "flying wing" in which passengers could have cabins with forward views, aligned along the leading edge of the single wing would have to be deferred until he could build a machine of double the size and five times the weight.

Overleaf are grouped scale drawings of the largest aeroplanes and hydroplanes built between 1918 and 1932, with the exception of the 1921 "Capronissime", which crashed prematurely. The aircraft run from top to bottom in more or

The Dornier Do-X-I on the Muggelsee, near Berlin, at the end of its Atlantic journey (June 1932)

An American Sikorsky S-40 amphibian, with wheels raised. Furnished with four 575 h.p. Hornet engines it was designed to carry 40 passengers over 400 to 500 miles.

The control room for the twelve 650 h.p. Fiat engines on the Dornier Do-X flying boat.

less chronological order. It is immediately obvious that the Siemens-Schuckert and the Dornier-Zeppelinwerke of 1918, which went into service during the war, were hardly exceeded in size by the much later giant aeroplanes and flying boats.

Five years after having built a flying boat with a span of 118 ft., Dornier produced the Wal – much smaller but much more efficient – and it was only three years later that the started research on the Do-X; nothing gives a better idea of the transitions necessary to successfully tackle the domain of "giant aircraft". Junkers, also, made three or four intermediate aircraft over eight years before starting work on the G-38, a decisive advance towards his aim of the flying wing.

Finally, it is important to remember that, apart from the 1918 aircraft, only one, two or three models of each of the largest aeroplanes and flying boats shown here were built, although they were undeniable technical successes. Giant aviation had not yet become a practical reality; the three largest aircraft to have been mass produced, the Junkers G-24, the Farman-Goliath and the Dornier Wal, seem tiny by comparison.

The Dyle and Bacalan DB-70 transport, fitted with three 500 h.p. Hispano-Suiza engines, tested in 1929, which inspired the four-engined AB-20 bomber of the Société d'Aviation Bordelaise.

The Italian Caproni 90-PB bomber, fitted with six 1,000 h.p. Isotta-Fraschini engines. Note the unusual inverted sesquiplane configuration.

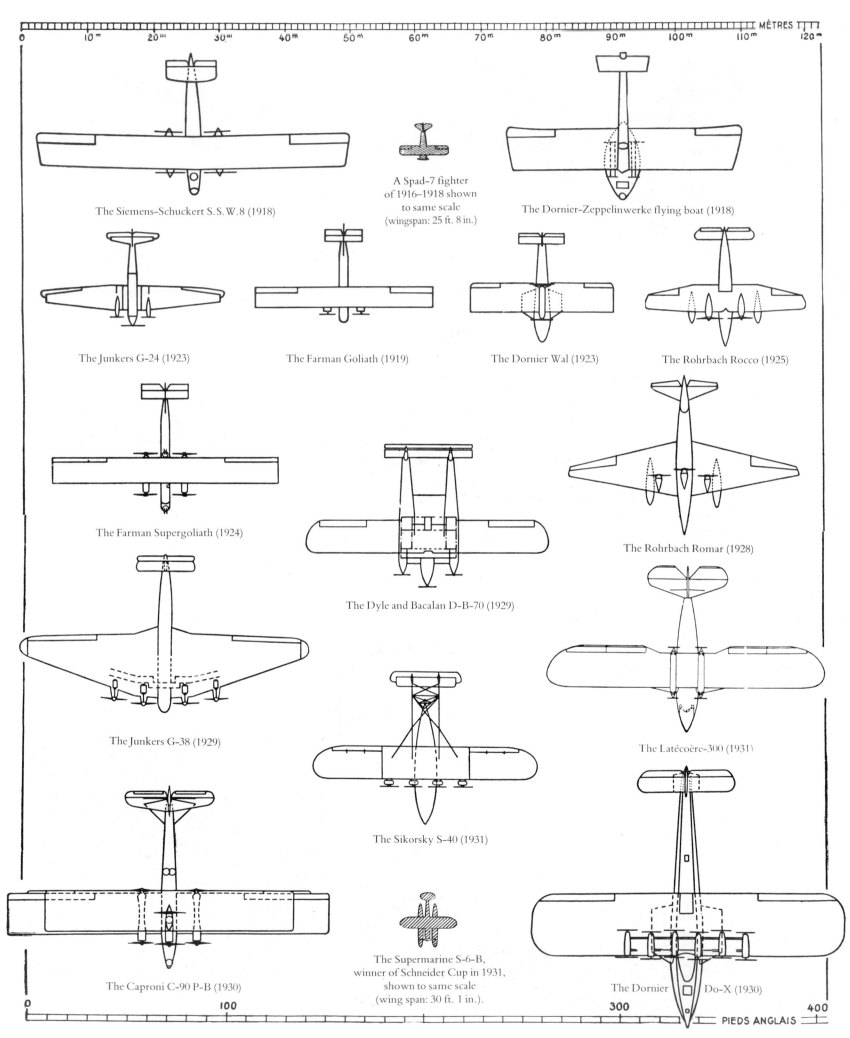

The Siemens-Schuckert S.S.W.8 (1918)

A Spad-7 fighter of 1916–1918 shown to same scale (wingspan: 25 ft. 8 in.)

The Dornier-Zeppelinwerke flying boat (1918)

The Junkers G-24 (1923)

The Farman Goliath (1919)

The Dornier Wal (1923)

The Rohrbach Rocco (1925)

The Farman Supergoliath (1924)

The Dyle and Bacalan D-B-70 (1929)

The Rohrbach Romar (1928)

The Junkers G-38 (1929)

The Sikorsky S-40 (1931)

The Latécoère-300 (1931)

The Caproni C-90 P-B (1930)

The Supermarine S-6-B, winner of Schneider Cup in 1931, shown to same scale (wing span: 30 ft. 1 in.).

The Dornier Do-X (1930)

GIANT AIRCRAFT 1918–1932

Two helicopters tested in Europe in 1930. Left: the last Pescara with a 40 h.p. Salmson engine. Right: the Ascanio on which each rotor blade had its own stabiliser and which reached a height of 60 ft.

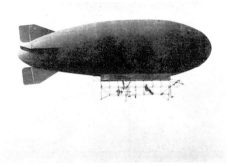

Left: the Oehmichen helicostat, a helicopter stabilised and partly lifted by a balloon of 14,000 cu. ft. capacity (1931) Centre: an autogiro built and tested in 1931, which had a closed cabin and a three bladed rotor without stays. Right: the first autogiro with a pusher propeller: the American two-seater Buhl (1931)

HELICOPTERS

The helicopter took a long time to achieve its theoretical ability to take off and land vertically, and to glide at any angle. The freely turning rotors of the autogiro, which was the first machine to disassociate lift from forward speed, was, until well into the Thirties, the only example of the principle which had proved its worth, and even that was a compromise. Moreover, the death of M. de La Cierva killed in an aeroplane accident in December 1936, had left the few researchers working on auto-rotating wings without a leader.

At the same time, sometimes using some of the mechanisms of the autogiro – in particular, doubly articulated blades – two or three helicopter specialists obtained remarkable results. In France, Louis Breguet and Dorand continued improving their "gyroplane"; the tests, supervised by the engineer and pilot Claysse, enabled new world records to be established in 1937. But these were put in the shade a few months later by the astonishing performances of the German helicopter Focke-Wulf Fw 61, invented by Professor Focke. This machine had a 160 h.p. engine, cooled by a small propeller, which drove two lifting propellers placed symetrically on either side of the longitudinal axis. Built in great secret, the Fw 61 revealed itself to the world only by its records: ascent to 7,700 ft., speed exceeding 75 mph., journeys of 50 miles on a circuit, then of 140 miles in a straight line, flying backwards at 20 mph., gliding descent – with the motor cut – using only the propellers, released into self-rotation, to brake its fall.

These performances were greeted with some scepticism until the aircraft's public unveiling inside the Deutschlandhalle in Berlin in 1938.

Left: the Breguet-Dorand gyroplane with two coaxial propellers, piloted by M. Claysee, taking off from Villacoublay.
Right: Professor Focke's Fw 61 helicopter, piloted by Hanna Reitsch, demonstrating its evolution, in all senses, inside the Deutschlandhalle in Berlin, in 1938.

The ascent of Piccard and Kipfer, 27 May 1931, at Augsburg. Left: Professor Piccard, in the light metal sphere which served as a basket, talking to Kipfer. Right: the balloon ready for departure. Centre: the balloon just after departure showing the characteristic elongated shape.

EXPLORING THE STRATOSPHERE

It was purely for reasons of scientific research that the Swiss Professor, Piccard, who taught physics at Brussels University, made his great ascent into the stratosphere, the name given to the atmosphere above 40,000 ft. The object of the expedition was to observe cosmic radiation and to measure its effects. To achieve this it was necessary to go above 49,000 ft., which effectively meant to exceed the previous records which were: 43,155 ft. in an aeroplane by the American, Lt. Apollo Soucek; 28,500 ft. in a balloon by another American, Lt. Gray, who lost his life on this attempt.

Piccard devised a special, very large balloon of 500,000 cu. ft. capacity, extremely lightly built and needing only 70 to 100,000 cu. ft. of hydrogen to lift it and the basket; the remaining space was necessary for the expansion of the gas as the atmosphere thinned. The basket, entirely in duralumin, was a sphere 6 ft. 10½ in. diameter, absolutely airtight so as to maintain an atmosphere of oxygen at normal pressure around the pilots. In spite of its very small dimensions, the basket contained numerous scientific instruments connected to sensors outside. The balloon was made by Riedinger in Augsburg and the basket by Lhoir in Liège.

Two attempts to take off were made in 1930: each time the enormous sail formed by the balloon during filling caused difficulties which meant that it had to be deflated. The envelope

which would have a diameter of 100 ft. and a total height of 150 ft. when full, stretched, when barely inflated at ground level, to a height of 180 ft.

At last on 27 May, at 0357 the balloon, named F.N.R.S. (Fonds National de Recherches Scientifiques, a Belgian institution), left Augsburg and rose vertically at an enormous speed, carrying Professor Piccard and his assistant Kipfer. Twenty eight minutes after departure, the balloon stabilized at 49,200 ft. in the sun and above the clouds.

Almost immediately Piccard and Kipfer had to work to seal a fissure due to the rupture of an electric insulator that passed through the wall of the cabin. At the same time, they discovered that they could not operate the gas release valve: their only hope of descending lay in waiting for night and a drop in the temperature. In the basket the heat was extreme, more than 40°C, while the outside temperature was −30°C. Jettisoning 110 kilos of ballast, the pilots recorded an outside pressure of 76 millimetres; they had nine tenths of the atmospheric mass under them and the altitude was at that point 51,761 ft., as accepted by the official records.

For the whole day the balloon, which was supposed to have come down before 11 o'clock, floated gently over the Alps, causing indescribable consternation. The sight became even more worrying when night fell and it remained lit up like a star and visible from 60 miles away. The descent, however, began in the evening and speeded up after 8 o'clock.

At 2050, at 15,000 ft., Piccard and Kipfer were able to open the basket's port-holes and, several minutes later, in calm weather, they landed easily

on a glacier, seventeen hours after their departure. They were in the Austrian Tyrol, near Obergurgl, a few miles from Italy and only 120 miles from Augsburg. After a night on the glacier, the two scientists were joined by guides sent up to rescue them.

Professor Piccard, assisted this time by Max Cosyns, made a second completely successful ascent on 18 August 1932. Leaving Dubendorf, in Switzerland, at 0507, he landed at 1710 near Cavallaro di Monzambano, in the province of Mantua, having reached an altitude of around 54,120 ft.

Strangely enough, Piccard's technique of using a very small amount of gas for a very large capacity balloon was not followed in France, Germany, Great Britain or Italy. In Spain, Colonel Herrera adopted it while testing a very interesting space suit which would have done away with an airtight basket. But it was Soviet Russia and the United States who continued exploring the stratosphere with manned aircraft.

On 3 October 1933, the balloon U.S.S.R., manned by Prokofiev, Godunov and Birbnaum, took off near Moscow. The dimensions of the aircraft and the length of the shrouds once the envelope was upright, led them to use the novel technique for last minute check-ups of sending inspectors up in little captive balloons to whatever part of the envelope needed to be examined. Under the round airtight basket, a wicker base served as a shock absorber to facilitate landing. A height of 58,700 ft. was attained.

A few months later, on 30 January 1934, a second Russian stratospheric balloon, christened Ossoaviakhim I, after the famous association

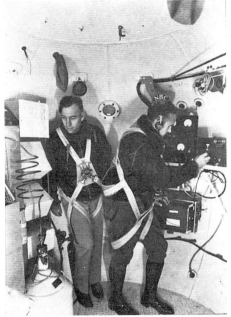

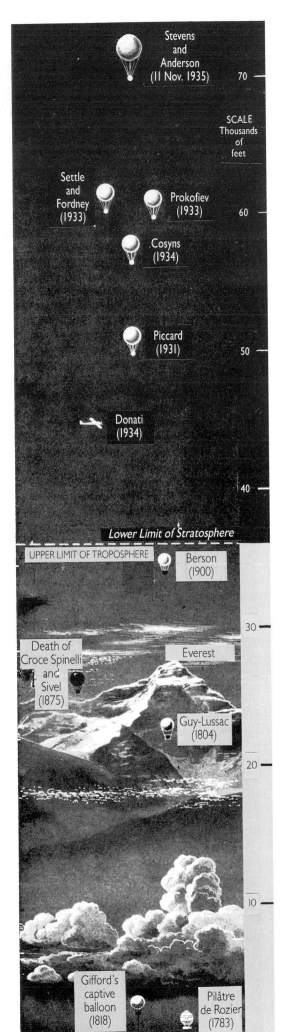

Above: the ascent of Stevens and Anderson, 11 November 1935, from Rapid City, S. Dakota. Clockwise from top left. The night departure of Explorer II; three stages of the landing at White Lake; Stevens and Anderson in the cabin of Explorer II. Extreme right: altitude records for aeroplanes and balloons.

which had sponsored the venture, took off. The three man crew observed for several hours, noted that an altitude of around 72,000 ft. had been reached, started the descent and at 1613 were still writing in the log book. Ten minutes later, the basket crashed to the ground and the three men were killed. Later, it was possible to reconstruct this drama: too much ballast had been jettisoned and they had stayed too long in the stratosphere; giving way to the temptation to go even higher they had started the descent with half the ballast that they needed to land normally. From 39,000 ft. the descent became uncontrollable.

Three months later, in the United States, Settle and Fordney reached 61,300 ft. sponsored by the National Geographic Society, who also sponsored the other 1934 and 1935 ascents.

Success was not obtained without difficulty or risk. On 28 July 1934, Stevens, Anderson and Kepner took off on board the Explorer I, a stratospheric balloon which had a volume of 3,000,000 cu. ft. and which could theoretically go higher than 72,000 ft. At 59,000 ft. the envelope became torn by an abnormal strain and they

decided to descend. At 20,000 ft. they opened the port-holes in the basket while the balloon continued to destroy itself by the wind from its descent. At 6000 ft., after having sent down the main recording instruments by special parachutes, the three men jumped in turn. The crew arrived on the ground safe and sound; the basket crashed; the instruments were recovered and yielded some of the scientific data required. It was decided to make a second balloon.

On 11 November 1935, the Explorer II . . . took off from a magic circle of searchlights from Rapid City in South Dakota. Piloted by Stevens and Anderson, the balloon landed under perfect conditions near White Lake, 250 miles to the west, after a flight of 8 hr. 13 min. On departure, the giant envelope only held 250,000 cu. ft. of helium; at the highest point, that is to say at 72,375 ft. the helium had expanded to fill 3,670,000 cu. ft. of the balloon.

Between 1936 and 1938, only one further attempt was made in the stratosphere, by a Russian balloon in the summer of 1937; it came nowhere near the 1935 record.

TOWARDS GREATER SAFETY

By 1932 considerable progress had been made in flying safety. The public was not always aware of this, however, because whereas flying accidents inevitably made headline news, little was heard of the rapidly increasing number of people taking to the air, both as passengers and pilots. However, so-called propagandists who went round saying that the aeroplane was "as safe as the train, and safer than a Sunday drive in the car" did flying a great disservice. The risk of flying could be not denied and was indeed at that time greater than

A typical accident: a stall on final approach, and four dead under the torn-off canvas of the wing (Avignon, June 1932)

A Farman F-190 equipped with Constantin stabilising gear

The Gastambide-Levavasseur aeroplane with variable surface area.

that of any other means of transport.

In the first place, flying, by the very act of leaving the ground, amplified some of the risks common to all transport. A fire in a car rarely claims lives because the driver can nearly always brake and jump out in time with his passengers and does not need a parachute; a collision between two cars usually only causes damage to the car itself; the accident is limited and does not automatically lead to a spiralling fall which ends up with the crew crashing unless they have had the time to use their parachutes.

Fires, collisions, crashes and breakdowns were accidental risks inherent in any form of transport liners also caught fire or got split open on reefs, trains "telescoped" and car steering wheels broke, but, just as there were good ships, there were good aeroplanes which were solid and stable. The public, however, did not have the same confidence in the aeroplane as in a ship because it suspected that the aeroplane was subject to an *intrinsic additional risk*. And it knew the name of

that risk: it was called "the stall". The wings of an aeroplane could only carry it through the air by converting speed into lift; however, since the wings were invariably and rigidly joined to the aeroplane, the speed and angle of attack (that is the angle between the plane of the wings and the direction of motion any instant) of the carrying surfaces was also that of the aeroplane itself; if by too sudden a reduction in the engine power or by the nose of the aircraft being lifted too high for the power available the speed dropped below a critical minimum or the angle of attack rose above a critical maximum the wings would suddenly cease to provide lift and the aeroplane had only the potential energy locked up in its height left to rely on. Certainly a well designed aeroplane ought always to have been able to get back into a safe attitude (a position corresponding to the engine power – reduced or non-existent – at its disposal); it did so by diving. But this dive resulted, by definition, in a sudden and predetermined loss of height; if the aeroplane was too near

to the ground for the dive to be completed and airspeed recovered, catastrophe was inevitable. It was for this reason that a stall on take-off or landing was so often fatal. An accident was even less avoidable and the outcome even more serious because the lateral control ailerons had a much reduced effect at such a low speed, and the aeroplane could "lose a wing" or "go into a spin" which meant losing all the lift on one wing marginally before the other; as a result instead of coming down in a horizontal attitude and crash landing with its undercarriage first, it would turn on its side and dive into the ground.

Much research had gone into trying to find ways of protecting aeroplanes against this danger. Warning or correcting systems had been around for a long time; the Etéve paddle and the Constanin stabiliser for instance. But the most efficient remedy was the "slotted wing", invented and perfected by Constantin, Thurston, Lachmann and Handley Page.

This was a wing formed of several shallow slats

The "safer aeroplanes" of the Daniel Guggenheim contest (United States, 1929): Left and top centre: the Handley Page Gugnunc: flaps front and rear on both wings.
Right: the Russel aeroplane parachute, carried in the fuselage. Bottom centre: the Curtiss Tanager: slotted wings and adjustable sections prolonging the lower wing

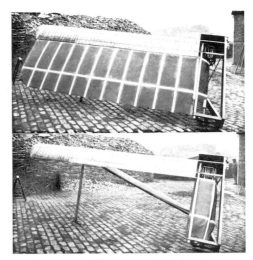

Left: the Makhonine aeroplane with telescopic wings, tested in 1931, shown here with its maximum (69 ft.) and minimum (43 ft.) spans. Right: the variable depth Gerin wing, tested experimentally in 1931, which gave the greatest reduction in surface area for normal flight.

whose contours were separated by "slots" parallel to the span which let through controlled amounts of air from the underside of the wing to the top and by doing so kept the airstream flowing smoothly over the top surface. Laboratory and flight tests showed that a single slit made in the leading edge of the wing by adding to it a fixed or mobile flap could increase the lift by 30 to 40%. And if opening the leading edge flap was combined with lowering a flap articulated at the back of the wing so as also to produce a "slot effect",

A Polish light aircraft, competing for minimum take-off "hangs" in the air in front of the obstacle, thanks to its "slotted wing".

this could also produce a variation in the curve of the wing which again increased the lift without noticeably disturbing the aerodynamic balance of the system since the lift was being improved both at the front and at the back of the wing. Finally, if such a system was applied to the outermost sections of each wing, activating the pair of flaps on one wing or the other could allow the lateral stability of the aeroplane to be controlled at speeds where this control would no longer have

been effective in the case of an ordinary wing fitted with ailerons alone.

In fact, the slotted wing – which had the drawback of needing a more complex structure and produced some additional drag – reduced the stalling speed by about 30% and thereby pushed back the danger zone by as much. It was real progress, but not decisive – for its use was limited. Special aeroplanes, lavishly provided with wings with slots and curved flaps which – in 1929 – led the field in the Guggenheim competition, were not built for the open market until much later.

Research was also carried out into reducing take off and landing speeds by varying the size of the lifting surface in flight: the systems tested usually entailed such complicated and heavy structures that the reduction obtained of between 10 and 15% was not justified. It seemed more profitable to reduce the surface of an ordinary wing in flight and thereby considerably increase the maximum flying speed. M. Makhonine did just this in 1931 with his "telescopic" wing. The wing area on Makhonine's prototype could be reduced from 355 to 204 sq. ft.; an even larger variation could be obtained with the Gerin system, though this had other inherent disadvantages.

By the end of the 1930s the problem had become acute. In 1937 and 1938 new civil and military aeroplanes came out which could cruise, using two thirds of their total power, at between 200 and 250 miles an hour. In order to land at speeds which would allow their brakes to bring them to rest within the confines of existing airfields they had to be able still to fly and be controllable at no more than 60 to 90 mph., as they made their final approach to the runway.

The slender wing profiles that allowed these aeroplanes to achieve such high cruising speeds were simply not suitable for the much lower landing speeds. As a result, pilots often got dangerously close to the limits of the stall. This caused many accidents and efforts were redoubled to give these very slender and very fast aircraft the benefit of increased lift at low speeds.

Flaps and slit wings became widely used and their underlying principle of applying additional energy to the air passing over the top surface of the wing to keep it flowing in a smooth laminar

The Focke-Wulf "flying duck" with a self stabilising wing layout, flying away from the camera.

manner extended. "Suction wings" or "blown wings" were tested in the laboratory which used fans operating at speeds up to 30,000 rpm. to apply additional air to the upper wing surfaces of models, though their practical use for aeroplanes – subject to turbulence, brutal acceleration and icing – still appeared to be some way off. However they had opened new horizons and it was hoped that their development would allow the next generation of even higher-performance aircraft to continue to use existing or even reduced airfields for take-off and landing.

Left: the Fairey Battle light bomber with flaps and wheels lowered for landing. Right: the same aeroplane in flight, with wheels lifted and flaps merged into the wing. In later models the main wheels and tail wheel retracted completely.

Waterman's "flying arrow"

The first experimental Weick aircraft inspired by the official American "safe flying" programme

Cambell's "economical aeroplane" using an automobile engine

The Gwinn Aircar.

PRIVATE FLYING 1932–1938

Private aviation entered a period of almost total stagnation in Europe between 1932 and 1938, partly because research and industry had been almost completely taken over by the creation and construction of military aeroplanes and equipment, and partly because the demand for new equipment had disappeared because one of the principal reasons for joining a flying club in the twenties, the sense of exhilaration, could be much better satisfied in the thirties by part time training with the airforce reserves which had sprung up in almost all countries.

In the United States, some of the smaller but sound companies, like Aeronca and Taylor, continued to produce on a modest scale low powered aircraft which complied with normal regulations. They succeeded in satisfying the needs of a very restricted market but not in expanding it. Further expansion on anything like the earlier scale obviously depended on making real progress towards an entirely new level of security which

would make flying a light aeroplane as safe, cheap and convenient as driving a car or a motorboat; the American civil aviation authority's intervention, in May 1934, with a second competition for the design of "the safe aeroplane" was therefore timely. With government backing, Hammond, Weick and Waterman demonstrated some interesting aircraft where, once again, the various possibilities of wings with slots were explored, and they also tried to make undercarriages with three wheels become standard equipment. Other small manufacturers were encouraged to build their various light aeroplanes with modified car engines which could be produced cheaply. The Autogiro Company of America was contracted to make a little autogiro able to travel on the road under its own power. But in spite of all these efforts, the days of universal private flying – even in the United States – had not yet arrived.

One of the few new aircraft launched in Europe was Mignet's "Pou-du Ciel" or "Flying Flea". With this tiny original machine it was hoped to achieve automatic, or rather instinctive, stability by the unusual configuration of its lifting surfaces and the controlled mobility of its front wing. This was a daring and ingenious concept which should have been thoroughly and scientifically resear-

ched but which was prematurely launched in "kit form" for home construction and then flown by young people many of whom had never flown a conventional aircraft. This resulted in too many accidents for which lack of control by the French government was partly responsible: from September 1935 to September 1936, the "Pou-du-Ciel" claimed eleven lives, among them the excellent pilot Robineau, one of the movement's pioneers, before being officially banned.

From 1936 as free pilot training, designed to produce a reserve of airforce pilots became widespread, private flying virtually disappeared. It survived, however, and even explored new fields in the new sport of gliding, which now entered a new stage of cross-country circuits without an engine. The records of distance, of endurance and of altitude (which eventually reached a startling 21,933 ft. above the starting point) were continually being improved on, particularly by the German specialists, who had invented techniques of observation and the use of air currents which made it possible to make long distance glides to predetermined spots, and closed circuit glides with fixed control points on pre-selected days, of which the Rhône meetings in 1937 and 1938 provided striking demonstrations.

Left: two views of a "Flying Flea", a popular little machine, around 200 of which were built by less well-off amateurs between 1934 and 1936. Its was abandoned after a series of fatal accidents. Right: German high-performance gliders – a Rhonsperber in the foreground – at the summit of the Wasserkuppe.

The Duetsch Cup: the retractable undercarriage of the Potez 53, with Potez engine, winner in 1933.

Hélène Boucher (†*F*1934) with Delmotte, her instructor.

On the starting line at the Etampes aerodrome, 19 May 1935: the Caudron-Renaults grouped as a team, following the tradition of the great automobile races.

THE DEUTSCH CUP AND THE WORLD SPEED RECORDS

There were two categories of event for air speed records between 1932 and 1938. The former was for seaplanes and very powerful record-breaking aeroplanes. The latter, a fortunate reaction against the monstrous engines used in the Schneider Cup, led to a new set of rules and the Deutsch Cup.

The regulations which limited the engine, or engines, to a total capacity of 8 litres, obliged the engineers to incorporate in the aircraft high performance mechanisms which were then starting to prove their worth: retractable undercarriages, supercharged engines, variable-pitch propellers and flaps which modified the angle of descent and slowed down the landing speed.

From the beginning, the results were amazing: in the first year, a little Potez 53 monoplane, piloted by Detre, which had an air-cooled Potez radial engine of less than 300 h.p. covered the 2,000 kilometres (1,242 miles) of the competition at 206 miles an hour.

In 1934, the event was won by a first class amateur pilot, Arnoux, in a Caudron C 450 with a Renault 310 h.p. engine. The average speed was increased to 241.6 mph. even though the Caud-rons – designed and tested by Riffard – had had to fly with the landing gear extended and hastily streamlined. For the first time variable-pitch propellers – Ratiers with just two positions – were used in flight and had contributed to the success.

In 1935, Caudron-Renault again won the competition; this time the chief pilot Delmotte, on a C 460 with an engine producing 370 h.p. from the 8 litres allowed, covered the twenty laps of the 100 kilometre (62 mile) circuit at an average speed of 275.7 mph. This time the undercarriage had been retracted in flight; the pilot was totally enclosed in his little aeroplane, flying inside a streamlined cockpit with his head touching the top and a foam rubber cushion in between.

From 1933 to 1935, numerous speed records were established by aircraft that had originally been designed during the Deutsch Cup. The most famous was by Delmotte who, on 25 December 1934, won the landplane speed record for France with a speed of 313.6 mph. beating by 9.3 mph. with a 370 h.p. engine (with a capacity increased to 9.5 litres) the record of the American Wedell established on 4 September 1933 using a 1,000 h.p. engine.

On 24 August 1935, it was again Delmotte who won the speed record, over a 1,000 kilometre (621 mile) circuit, increasing it to 279.5 mph. This time, he beat the record established a year earlier by his pupil, Hélène Boucher, an excellent woman pilot, who had had a fatal crash on 30 November 1934.

Earlier, on 23 May 1933, a top class pilot, Ludovic Arrachart had died while trying out one of the new aeroplanes entered in the competition. Obviously, the "Deutsch Cup technique", which attracted high performance aeroplanes, implied high risks. However, it was not from these risks that the competition was to die out, but from official indifference to a sporting event whose conditions did not directly favour the creation of powerful military aeroplanes. In 1936, the results were inferior to those of the previous year, and there was no Deutsch Cup in 1937 and 1938; it had been killed by the aerial arms race.

In the autumn of 1938, the air speed record of 440 mph. had been held for four years by the Italian pilot Agello on a Macchi-Castoldi seaplane with two Fiat 3,100 h.p. engines. The record for landplanes, which Howard Hughes had held for two years with 351 mph., was taken to 379 mph. on 11 November 1937 by the German pilot Würster, in a single-seater Messerschmitt-Bf 109 with a Daimler-Benz 1,000 h.p. engine; on 5 June 1938 this record was easily beaten by Udet who, in a new Heinkel aeroplane with a 1,800 h.p. Daimler-Benz engine, flew at an average 393.7 mph. over a 100 kilometre (62 mile) circuit.

A single-seater Messerschmitt Bf 109 fighter, a version of which took the aeroplane speed record to 379 mph.

The aeroplane in which Howard Hughes flew from Los Angeles to New York in 7 hr. 28 min.

The Macchi-Castoldi seaplane in which Agello took the world speed record to 440 mph.

Left: Lunch being served on a TWA flight. Right: the T.W.A. fleet of Douglas DC 3s which made transcontinental flights of 2,800 miles in 15 to 16 hours

The Boeing 307 Stratoliner put into production in 1938 for the U.S. market.

Douglas aircraft of Trans-World Air Lines operating all night from Kansas City.

Wing sections stored vertically in the Douglas factory at Santa Monica.

PLANNING FOR THE FUTURE

By 1936, after two bad years due to political in-fighting, the American national air-transport system was just about breaking even. At the beginning of the year, three of the main companies serving the enormous internal network and the company contracted to handle overseas flights decided to pool their technical and financial resources to enable them to build the larger aeroplanes that would soon be needed. They decided on a 27 ton four-engined Douglas with a tricycle undercarriage, but it was not until the summer of 1938 that testing began on the first Douglas DC 4.

However the financial situation of the smaller companies operating the internal network remained precarious. Moreover, a much debated anti-trust law prevented companies not only from amalgamating but often even from having ordinary commercial agreements. Finally in 1937, a series of serious accidents – which particularly affected public opinion since the aeroplanes were carrying 12 to 20 passengers – resulted in a marked drop in the number of passengers: 82,000 in November compared with 130,000 in the same month of the previous year. The financial situation was therefore critical and even more urgent because companies wishing to operate transcontinental and panamerican services would soon have to replace their current aeroplanes with others like the DC 4 which would cost between

five and three times as much per aircraft, even if thirty to fifty were built.

It therefore seemed that the 20 odd American airline companies would have to divide more rigidly than in the past into distinct categories. On the one hand would-be operators of the new long distance aircraft which would fly at 220 to 250 mph. over distances of 1000 to 1250 miles, reducing the number of time-consuming stops to a minimum. On the other, feeder airlines filling in the meshes of the national net with subsidiary networks of purely local importance.

This second group, which would concentrate on increasing the number and frequency of its services, would almost certainly use medium size aeroplanes, like the twin-engined Lockheed 14s which could carry 10 to 12 passengers at 205 mph. and which, for the same reasons, already had a large market in Europe. For long internal passenger flights and those to South America, the United States was expected soon to have imposing machines like the Douglas DC 4 or the Boeing 307, "Stratoliner", a development of the B-17 bomber that would have a pressurised cabin allowing it to cruise at 20,000 ft. at 235 mph. with thirty passengers and 5 tons of freight.

For crossing the ocean, the Americans would soon have large flying boats like the Boeing 314, of which Pan American Airways had ordered six, and which would carry, with four 1,500 h.p. engines, up to 74 passengers over the stages of the transpacific line; the same aircraft, like some of the Shorts then being built in England, would

also be able to fly non stop over the North Atlantic, from New York to Southampton for example, with 1 or 2 tons of post.

Looking even further ahead, in 1937, the technical committee of Pan American Airways, presided over by Lindbergh, had asked the largest aircraft manufacturing companies to design an even larger flying boat, of which they would order between 10 and 25, capable of carrying a crew of 16 men, 100 passengers and 5 tons of freight over 5,000 miles in still air, at 220 to 250 mph. Several designs were submitted and these "dream aircraft", as they were called, were due to be built in 1941 and 1942.

Flight safety too would have to keep pace with the increase in air traffic; both airports and air traffic control essential elements of the infrastructure, had to be made safer.

By the summer of 1938, the American government had instituted a new, independent and powerful organisation responsible for all aspects of civil aviation and had been careful to give it, at the same time as its responsibility the means of enforcing its requirements. It was to be hoped that Europe would soon have such an organisation which could establish, in spite of national divisions, a standard infrastructure, subject to the same rules and regulations. It was all very well to build large airports, and even grandiose terminals as at Paris, Berlin, Rome and London, but many passengers felt that it would be preferable to institute a system that allowed them to fly safely from one to another in all weathers.

Stockholm airport on the American model (1937)

The new terminal at Le Bourget (1937)

Part of the grandiose planes for Berlin Tempelhof.

At Le Bourget airport, at 0100 on 12 July 1938. Hughes about to leave for Moscow on his Lockheed 14, on his round-world flight.

THE LAST PIONEERS

Soon only the memory of the old long distance trips would remain when such flying times as were being contemplated were achieved. There were, however, still a number of old-style achievements made between 1932 and 1938. From 21 to 23 January 1932, Codos and Robida made the Hanoi-Marseilles trip in 2 days and 23 hours, in a Breguet 33 with a 650 h.p. engine; in 1936, 1937 and 1938 there were rapid journeys by Broadbent, Clouston and Joan Batten on the British Empire routes and by the Japanese, Ihinuma and Tsukakoshi from Tokyo to London.

There was a price to pay for these ventures. In France, Doret and Japy escaped but Moench died, while America lost her great and charming pilot Amelia Earhardt, who disappeared in the Pacific during a trip round the world.

There was also the tragic death of the excellent one-eyed pilot, Wiley Post, on 16 August 1935, in Greenland, almost at the beginning of one of those fast flights which had made him famous. In 1933, from 15 to 23 July, in 7 days and 19 hours, he had flown round the northern hemisphere via the Atlantic, Europe, Siberia and Alaska; alone on board his faithful Lockheed he beat his own 1931 time by 21 hours.

Five years later, this time was halved by another American crew. Between 11 and 14 July 1938, Howard Hughes with Thurlow, Connor, Stoddard and Lund, covered a circuit of 14,300 miles around the northern hemisphere in 91 hours 16 minutes, including stops totalling about 18

Amelia Earhardt (†*F*1937)

hours. This meant an overall average of 156 mph , and an average flying speed of 194 mph., a performance very near the aircraft's theoretical limits. For this journey Hughes chose a standard transport aeroplane, the Lockheed 14, fitted with two Pratt and Whitney 1,100 h.p. engines. The only modifications were those necessary to give it a still-air range of some 5,000 miles; its radio equipment played an important part in the success

of the journey.

Post's had been a sporting performance. The one-eyed pilot, with the aid of an automatic pilot, had accomplished a prodigious personal feat in 1933. He also had used a standard Lockheed transport aeroplane, but his was a single-engined one. American industry had therefore achieved two exploits five years apart, both striking in the eyes of the rest of the world, but which *were in fact no more than a demonstration of the performance of regular air transport in the United States.*

Far greater speeds over long distances had in fact already been achieved by specialised aircraft. As early as 1934, in the London-Melbourne race the winning crew of Scott and Campbell Black had covered the 11,200 miles of the competition in less than three days, to be precise, in 70 hours and 54 minutes; with two 225 h.p. engines, Ratier variable propellers and retractable undercarriage, their De Havilland Comet (one of three specially designed for the race) had flown at more than 230 miles an hour.

But behind Scott and Campbell Black's racing aeroplane, a standard American transport plane came second, covering the 11,200 miles in 90 hours 10 minutes with seven people on board; it was a Douglas DC 2, piloted by Parmentier and Moll, which had been entered by the Dutch company KLM.

Scott and Campbell-Black's winning Comet at Melbourne (23 October 1934).

Clouston

Joan Batten after flying from Australia to England

Ilinuma and Tsukakoshi arrive in London from Tokyo

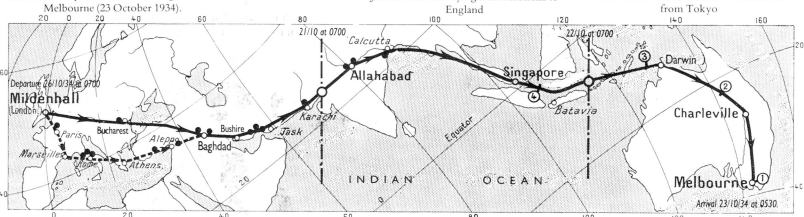

The 1934 London-Melbourne race showing daily stages of Scott and Campbell Black's Comet, and positions of other competitors when they finished.

The Short *Mayo* composite, *Maia* and *Mercury*, separating during a display, 23 February 1938.

The Dornier Do 18, with two Junkers 205 diesels, which flew from Plymouth to Brazil

THE NORTH ATLANTIC

The most difficult ocean crossing to tackle and potentially the most lucrative still remained without a regular service. Between 1918 and 1932, there had been 98 attempts to fly over the North Atlantic, 52 of which had failed. 12 crews had been lost and 15 others, forced to come down in the sea, had been saved. The most remarkable rescue was that of Rody, Johanssen and Veiga, who had taken off from Lisbon for New York on board a single-engined Junkers aeroplane, and were picked up near America after their aircraft – which was all metal – had floated for 158 hours.

From 1931 on, there was a tendency to reduce the risk of these air crossings by using the fastest aircraft available. On 15 and 16 July 1931, the Hungarian crew Endresz-Magyar, on board an American single-engined Lockheed Sirius, flew from Newfoundland to Budapest at 125 mph. On 20 and 21 May 1932, Amelia Earhardt in a Lockheed Vega flew solo from Newfoundland to Londonderry (Ireland) at 136 mph.; several days later the pilot Reichers, alone on board a Lockheed Vega, crossed the Atlantic at 186 mph., but had to put down before reaching the coast; on 5 and 6 July, Mattern and Griffin, again in a Lockheed Vega, flew from New York to Berlin – with a stop – at 156 mph.

During all this time, Lufthansa was accelerating the mail across the North Atlantic each summer by using seaplanes launched by catapult from the

A Lufthansa Blohm and Voss Ha 139 about to be hoisted on board the base-ship *Friesenland* in 1937.

Europa and the *Bremen* as they neared land. From 1930 to the end of 1935, these aircraft made 200 flights of 600 miles on average, and their crews gained valuable experience.

Germany was also the first to put a complete air service into operation. From 10 September to 19 October 1936, the small twin-engined diesel Dornier Do-18s, the *Aeolus* and the *Zephyr*, launched by catapult from Horta in the Azores and from New York, made four return crossings – sometimes with a stop in Bermuda – at 125 mph. The same autumn, the large dirigible, the *Hindenburg* of the Deutsche Luftreederei made twenty commercial flights between Frankfurt and Lakehurst. It seemed that Germany, with mail planes flying the Berlin-Lisbon-Azores-New York route and with an airship crossing the Atlantic non-stop with passengers, was the best placed of the great powers to operate in the rich domain of the North Atlantic.

However, Great Britain and the United States were ready to come on the scene. One of the large Short flying boats of Imperial Airways was sent to Bermuda to run a regular service from there to New York with the cooperation of Pan American Airways; two others, the Caledonia and the Cambria, were fitted with additional tanks to enable them to cover 2,200 miles against a 35 mph. wind. This was the distance that had to be reckoned on for a direct crossing on the "North-

The Sikorsky *Bermuda Clipper* (foreground) and the Short *Cavalier* which recall the American and British test flights over the North Atlantic in 1937 made with similar aircraft

The Pan American *Bermuda Clipper* which carried out the test on 5 July 1937 seen on its arrival at Foynes.

The short "G" class flying boat, *Golden Hind* launched on the Medway on 17 June 1939

The Boeing *Yankee Clipper* arriving at Southampton via the Azores on 4 April 1939

ern Route" which had been chosen by the two companies, the longest stage being Foynes-Botwood, from Ireland to Newfoundland.

By the summer of 1937, the two Imperial Airways Shorts and two Pan American Airways Sikorsky S 42-Bs had made a series of journeys: in a period of a few weeks there were 16 successful crossings between Foynes and Botwood with an average time of 16 hours towards the United States and 13 hours towards Europe.

Lufthansa in turn was continuing and developing its efforts of the preceding year. This time, still on the Southern line, two new seaplanes – Blohm and Voss Ha. 139s with floats and four 600 h.p. Junkers diesel engines – made fourteen journeys between Horta and New York at an average speed of 150 mph. over the 2,400 miles; the aircraft were launched from two ship-bases, the *Friesenland* and the *Schwabenland* on this section of the route and then flew between Horta and Germany without assistance.

In 1938, the Germans were still the most active. To the two Ha. 139 seaplanes of 1937, a third was added – an Ha. 139 B – which had a cruising speed of 170 mph.; there were to be 28 crossings, again on the Southern route.

France finally launched the large Latécoère on the North Atlantic; it made two crossings by the Southern route, but experienced considerable trouble with rough seas in the Azores.

The Americans were too involved in the trans-pacific route and postponed developing their services and the British had delays with their four-engined De Havilland Albatross aeroplanes; Imperial Airways' only activity on the route was the experimental return crossing with the "composite aeroplane" *Maia/Mercury*.

By 1938 transport aeroplanes or flying boats were taking-off with wing-loadings of 25 to 30 lb. per sq. ft. which was double what could have been risked in 1932; the repercussions on the size

of aeroplanes, their capacities and the performances had been considerable.

A catapult, as used by the Germans on the Southern North Atlantic route, was the accepted way of increasing still further the possible load at take-off but a new solution was tried in 1938, the Short *Mayo* composite aeroplane, where a large aeroplane – a flying catapult – launched a smaller aeroplane that it had taken up with it. The first public demonstration of the system was made on 6 February 1938; the little four-engined seaplane *Mercury*, with a total power of 1,280 h.p. separated in flight, at a height of 750 feet, from the large flying boat *Maia* which had a power of 3,200 h.p. and was carrying very little fuel. Under the total power of nearly 4,500 h.p., the little aircraft could easily reach, before having to rely on its power alone, the speed needed to sustain its very heavy wing loading. In this way mail which was a relatively small and light cargo in proportion to the charge that could be made for carrying it, could be transported over distances of 3000 to 6000 miles employing – during the actual journey – only a modest engine power.

Putting this simple idea into practice led to many original solutions of detail. The principle was established when the first composite aeroplane made a remarkable crossing of the North Atlantic, between Foynes and Botwood, on 20 and 21 July 1938 at 150 mph. with half a ton of freight.

Then, between 6 and 8 October, the *Mercury* achieved fame with a world distance record for seaplanes of 5,960 miles from Dundee to the mouth of the Orange River in South Africa; it covered this long journey in 42 hours 6 minutes, at the remarkable average speed of 142 mph., constant adverse winds having prevented it by 325 miles from reaching its hoped-for goal of Cape Town and the distance record for all types.

The "composite aircraft" might have had furth-

er applications for both civilian and military aviation; the system provided both high performance and extended range, and could have been further improved by using diesel engines like those which had allowed a catapulted Dornier Do. 18 to set between 27 and 29 March 1938, the distance record for seaplanes which the *Mercury* had just broken.

Events however overtook it. On 4 April 1939 the first of Pan-American's six new Boeing flying boats, the *Yankee Clipper* arrived at Southampton by the Southern route with a crew of 12 and 9 passengers, all official observers and experts. This aircraft could carry 70 passengers and 5000 lb. of cargo or 40 passengers in berths, and was powered by four 1500 h.p. Wright Cyclone radial engines each with 14 cylinders arranged in two rows. The engines were accessible in flight from a catwalk inside the giant wing.

On June 17 Shorts launched the *Golden Hind*, the first of the new "G" class flying boats, with four Hercules engines designed to carry up to 150 passengers over 6000 miles. Construction had been delayed by a shift of priorities at the factory to the production of Sunderlands for the Royal Air Force, but Imperial Airways hoped to have at least three of these in service by the following year. Meanwhile a mail service only began on 5 August when the *Caribou*, a converted "C" class, with the aid of flight refuelling and the expenditure of some ten tons of fuel delivered just half a ton of mail to New York. The inauguration of the Northern route therefore fell to Pan-American alone; the *Yankee Clipper* arrived once more at Southampton on June 28, 18 hr. 42 min. after leaving Botwood, Newfoundland, carrying 19 passengers, besides her crew of 12 and 16,000 lb. of mail. At the same time her sister craft, the *Dixie Clipper*, began a regular passenger service on the Southern route.

Just nine weeks later Europe was at war.

The recreation lounge, sleeping accommodation, flight deck and 15-seat dining room on board the 37 ton *Yankee Clipper*

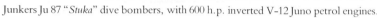

Junkers Ju 87 "*Stuka*" dive bombers, with 600 h.p. inverted V-12 Juno petrol engines.

Junkers Ju 86 bombers, with two diesel engines, flying to Nuremburg for a rally.

PREPARING FOR AN AIR WAR

The international problems that had been apparent since 1932 and the failure of the Disarmament Conference in October 1933 unleashed the "air arms race" in Europe. This immense effort was characterised, on the one hand, by the reconstitution of German military aviation and, on the other, the partial application – in Ethiopia, Spain and China – of modern methods of air war, an essential instrument of "total war".

In 1935, Germany made public the fact of the creation of its military air force, and claimed that it had already reached parity with that of Great Britain. That autumn, some hundred aeroplanes – single-seater fighters and two-engined bombers – took part in the great Nuremberg parade. In spite of this it was still argued by many that it was going to be an extremely long and difficult task for the Germans to build from scratch, after an interruption of fifteen years, a military airforce commensurate with her strength as a nation.

An enormous effort was however undertaken, favoured by the "totalitarianism" of the national-socialist state and by the understandable interest of a young "flying mad" generation, still threatened by unemployment in civilian life, in the alternative of prestigious positions and commissions which were offered by the thousand. But, there were great difficulties even in training this flying personnel; in spite of strict secrecy, news leaked out of numerous fatal accidents.

Equipment posed as many difficulties. an aeronautics industry had to be entirely recreated which, apart from two or three companies, had not had the occasion to produce in quantity since 1918. Particular difficulties were experienced in the manufacture of engines which, in their latest supercharged from, were the monopoly of the half dozen or so French, American and British companies which had been able to maintain a

Chancellor Hitler and General Goering watch Heinkel III bombers fly past at Nuremburg in 1937.

reasonable volume of production since 1918. The determined efforts of Junkers, however, to develop the diesel engine had already led in Germany to their incorporation in mass-produced military aircraft. The reduced consumption of these engines enabled the range of the aircraft to be increased by 20 to 30% for an equal payload.

The reconstruction of the fighter arm of the German Luftwaffe on an independent and solid basis was however still dependent on the large

scale production of very high performance petrol engines. Technically, this result was achieved by the end of 1936; industrially, results began to show in the summer of 1937, when the German aeroplanes – equipped with new Junkers or Daimler-Benz engines – carried off the main events at the international Zurich air show. From the military point of view, the massive production of these engines – in amazingly well equipped factories – resulted, between mid 1937 and the autumn of 1938, in the creation of more, and on the whole better equipped, combat units than those of any other European country. Technical advance continued, helped by rapid production not only of prototypes but of whole series; the single-seater Heinkel fighter, in which General Udet took the speed record over 100 kilometres to 393.7 mph. on 5 June 1938, was designed and built in record time.

The Third Reich made good use of its air force; in the Austrian Anschluss affair its mere vigilant presence sufficed; from the early hours of the operation several squadrons of fast bombers immediately occupied all airports and particularly Vienna-Aspern, where transport planes landed the Nazi "security detachments".

Further afield Germany took advantage of events in Spain to put her equipment and tactics to the test. Here she joined the Italian airforce, whose "legionnaires" had begun forming units in Spain after July 1936 where they played a continually increasing role in Nationalist operations.

There is no doubt that from 1932 to 1938, the "Regia Aeronautica" of Fascist Italy had become

A Nationalist Fiat C.R.52 shooting down a Russian copy of the American Boeing single seat fighter

The pilot of a Republican Dewoitine D.371 jumps to safety

Italian Savoia-Marchetti S 79 bombers flying horizontally in Spain, but made to look as if they are diving for greater effect

A French all purpose monoplane capable of about 300 mph: the Potez 63.

The Morane-Saulnier 405, single-seat fighter with a cannon firing through the propeller boss.

very effective. Italy, totally dependent on others for oil and petrol, nevertheless played the aviation card with energy. Of course, she was still far from following fully the doctrine of the Italian general Douhet ("hold fast on land, and strike from the air"), but those responsible, the Balbos, then the Valles, directly inspired by Mussolini, increased as best they could the role of aviation in the Italian military machine. They also never hesitated to use foreign techniques in the interests of their country; a lively industry of aircraft engines, its expertise first acquired from licences granted abroad, notably in England and in France, was progressively added to the well established and independent aeroplane manufacturing industry.

Hawker Huricanes (Max speed 335 mph.)

Spurred on by events, wanting to be strong and also to make an impression abroad at difficult moments, Italian military aviation built the first modern ultra-powerful bombers: twin-engined Breda 88s which, at the end of 1937, took the speed records, unloaded over 100 kilometres, and with 500 and 1,000 kilo loads over 1,000 kilometres, to 344 and 325 mph. respectively, and three-engined Savoia S.79s which filled the first three places in the international Istres-Damascus-Paris race, the winner covering the 3850 miles of the competition at an average speed of 219 mph.

Large numbers of both these aircraft were built, and the training of crews was speeded up and extended by the creation of new flying schools. A liaison between the Italian and German military air forces was also established, which France and Great Britain had to take into serious consideration, particularly as for these two countries, the problem of acquiring and maintaining an adequate air strength was proving very difficult.

France, forced into a defensive position, had to extend this defense to a vast colonial empire; her technical and industrial resources, which were limited, had been prematurely engaged in 1934 in an unfortunate effort, a so called "aeronautical renovation" which resulted in the mass production of all purpose aeroplanes, known as "multi-seat fighting planes", which were soon outdated. Their manufacture was slow and uncertain but nevertheless exhausted an industry that was totally unprepared for the effort and which later the State had to take under its control and responsibility by "nationalising". The quality of the French prototypes was still good; all that was needed was for them to be built quickly enough to ensure that the aircraft that would reach the front line in 1939 and 1940 were not already outdated when they came into service, as the 1935 and 1936 ones had been. In any case, France, which had a considerable land army to support, could not produce air arms on the scale of Germany, which was industrially much stronger, or of Great Britain.

Great Britain, which had entered the race in 1936 after the Ethiopian alert, embarked on it with method and decision. In the 1938–1939 budget, the funds amounted to nearly 130 million pounds and were allocated to a four-fold effort: doubling the size of the aircraft industry, increasing the number of flying schools and recruiting personnel, the mass creation of military units, and the construction of new airfields. The Royal Air Force went from 52 metropolitan squadrons in 1934 to nearly 140 in 1938 with 1,600 front line aeroplanes. By March 1940 it was estimated that the number of home-based aircraft would be increased to 2,370 (not including immediate reserves of about 50%); the Navy would have 500 aircraft and the overseas squadrons another 490.

This was an enormous effort. It was however insufficent to appease a by now worried public, whose nerves had been continuously played on by the Press and certain politicians.

Where then should additional aid against Germany be sought? It was mainly for this reason that after many years attention was again being paid to the Russian air force.

There was an uncertainty about Soviet military air strength which, until 1936, owed much to the propaganda efforts of the Russian leaders towards their official visitors. As early as 1933, on the occasion of the May Day parade, foreign representatives in Moscow could see flying past over

Vickers Supermarine Spitfires (Max speed 360 mph.)

Red Square more than fifty four-engined modern bombers capable of delivering 1,500 to 2,000 bombs over a range of 600 to 700 miles; at that time, no European power could show an equivalent group of such effective offensive squadrons. The impression this show made was reinforced by the strictly industrial shows which in the summers of 1933 and 1936 were given to the members of official missions who visited the Russian aircraft factories. From then on it was admitted that the U.S.S.R. had a great, and some said the greatest, air force.

Estimates of this kind were extremely subjective; in any case, they needed to be completed by precise information on the wartime "replacement

British aircraft production. Left to right: Armstrong Whitworth Whitleys, Fairey Battles and Vickers Supermarine Spitfires.

Russian parachutists during manoeuvres in 1935

American 4,000 h.p. Boeing B-17 "*Flying Fortresses*" over Langley Field.

capacity" of the aircraft industry of the country in question. Considering the recent rapid changes in air-frame design and the mechanical complexity of the latest supercharged engines, it was impossible to believe that Russian industry could in the near future be on a par with those of Great Britain, Germany or France.

Nevertheless, in October 1936 the U.S.S.R. was able to engage several hundred crews and aeroplanes in the Spanish Civil War. The strict discipline and the real worth of these formations then had to be acknowledged; at the same time, the quality of two or three types of aeroplanes – in particular the rapid twin-engined "Katyuska" bombers – surprised military experts.

The ability of Russia to sustain her aeronautical effort in a major war where she would be totally engaged was therefore still debatable; but there could be no doubt that results argued a strong industry. This was also unusual in several respects, in particular the unprecedented development of "military parachuting", armed interven-

tions of a new kind where troops could be flown near to the chosen point of intervention and then reach the ground by parachute. On the occasion of the Red Army manoeuvres in 1935 the Russian High Command had shown the assembled military attachés, and through photographs and films, the world, the spectacle an entire battalion launched by parachute behind the enemy lines by successive waves of aeroplanes.

Specialists of national defense were thence forward obliged to consider the possibility of this type of surprise intervention behind the enemy lines, or, at the beginning of sudden hostilities, near key points such as bridges, warehouses, factories, etc., that could easily be destroyed or made unusable. This represented a new form of danger from the air, as well as a new contribution from aviation to the technique of "total" war.

Another possible source of aid was that of a powerful industry, not directly engaged in the air arms race, which could provide – political circumstances permitting, for no State allows its nationals to enter into arms contracts without its own at least tacit approval – preferential delivery of mass-produced aeroplanes and engines.

The United States was the only country to have such an industry. From 1937 France and Great Britain entered into negotiations with her which led to a considerable but still insufficient trade. American military and naval aviation were expanding rapidly and there was a surplus of no more than 600 military aeroplanes a year for export. There was no lack of buyers; China and Japan, for example, were serious customers from 1936. But the American authorities could obviously not authorise the export of the latest equipment intended for their own forces; obolescent machines only were offered, although this was off-set by the indisputable lead that American aviation had been able to acquire, thanks to its research laboratories, raw materials and high performance motor industry.

Moreover, European military leaders were certainly conscious of the fact that the Americans, separated from the principal scenes of action by thousands of miles of ocean, were certain to be able to continue manufacturing and even developing their industry on demand in the case of a major war in Europe, in a way impossible in Europe itself, and especially was this true for those industries which would naturally be the object of surprise attacks from the beginning. For the first objectives of enemy bombers would

certainly be aircraft factories, along with air bases.

This high-lighted a new advantage for the great modern empires who possessed overseas territories or, better still, could cooperate with dominions all over the world. It was therefore not surprising that a subsidiary aircraft industry was organised in Canada at the end of 1938 which – in liaison with American and British industry – could make a large contribution to resupplying Great Britain and France in case of need.

If precautions against air attack were considered of prime importance for these two countries, which had well organised overseas connections and supplies, they must have appeared absolutely vital for a country like Germany which was even more exposed since it was organising itself to be self-suffcent and concentrating on its small territory, so recently unprovided with any air force at all, all the means of independent military action.

Lingering doubts about the reality of the relative air strengths of the major European powers still preoccupied their leaders. After the crisis of September 1938, the balance in Europe seemed too precarious for the question of limiting air arms to be raised. Everyone was aware, however, that the problem existed, and the courtesy visits made by General Milch to France and Britain and General Vuillemin and British Air Staff to Germany, were an indication of these preoccupations. It was by then, however, far too late to recover the position. German production had overtaken France and Britain by 1934; she achieved air parity with Britain in 1935 and with France shortly after. Britain woke up in 1936, and by 1939 had at least recovered the lead in production if not in aircraft in service, France's out-put in 1939 was still only a third of that of Germany.

Once landed the parachutists immediately regroup ready for action beind the enemy lines.

Curtiss B.D. 2-C 1 Navy dive bombers with 1,000 h.p. engines and retractable wheels.

CHRONOLOGY OF AVIATION

The list that follows attempts to draw together in chronological order the truly great moments in the history of manned flight, events that have had an important influence on new developments, technical improvements and established practice. Also included are events which can be seen as remarkable human achievements.

1782 *(around 15 November):*
Joseph Montgolfier sends up the first miniature hot air balloon at Avignon.

1783 *(4 June):*
Joseph and Etienne Montgolfier give the first public demonstration of a hot air balloon ascent at Annonay.

1783 *(27 August):*
Charles and the Robert brothers send up the first un-manned hydrogen-filled gas balloon in Paris.

1783 *(19 September):*
A sheep, a cockerel and a duck become the first living creatures to make an ascent in a hot-air balloon at Versailles.

1783 *(15 October):*
Pilâtre de Rozier becomes the first man ever to ascend in a captive hot-air balloon.

1783 *(21 November):*
Pilâtre de Rozier and the Marquis d'Arlandes make the first flight in free hot-air balloon from La Muette to the Gobelins.

1783 *(1 December):*
Charles and the younger Robert make the first flight in a hydrogen-filled gas balloon, from Paris to Nesles.

1784 *(25 April):*
Guyton de Morveau and Bertrand carry out the first experiments in steering a balloon at Dijon.

1784 *(4 June):*
Madame Thible becomes the first woman to ascend in a balloon at Lyons.

1784 *(19 September):*
The Robert brothers and Colin-Hulin make the first flight of more than 100 km. (62 miles) from Paris to Beuvry (115 miles in 6 hours and 40 minutes).

1784 *(16 October):*
First use in ballooning of a rotating apparatus for propulsion, by Blanchard in London.

1785 *(7 January):*
Blanchard and Jeffries make the first flight across water and from one country to another, from Dover to Guines by balloon.

1785 *(15 June):*
Ballooning claims its first victims, Pilâtre de Rozier and P.-A. Romain. Both die in an accident at Wimereux.

1786 *(10 & 11 June):*
Tétu-Brissy makes the first night flight in a balloon, from Paris to Breteuil.

1794 *(2 June):*
The first military use of a balloon, a captive hot air balloon sent up by Coutelle at the siege of Maubeuge.

1797 *(22 October):*
First descent by parachute from a balloon by Jacques Garnerin in Paris.

1798 *(10 November):*
First balloon flight made entirely by women, Mademoiselle Labrosse (Madame Jacques Garnerin) and Mademoiselle Henry in Paris.

1803 *(3 & 4 October)* – **1807** *(22 & 23 September):*
Jacques Garnerin makes the first long-distance flights (Moscow to Polova, 200 miles and Paris to Clausen, 250 miles).

1809 George Cayley makes the first designs for an aeroplane and carries out experiments on models and a full-scale glider.

1821 *(19 July):*
Charles Green makes the first ascent in a balloon filled with coal gas in London.

1836 *(7 & 8 November):*
Charles Green, Hollond and Monck Mason make the first flight of more than 500 km. (310 miles) in a balloon, from London to Weilburg (372 miles in 18 hours).

1842 *(29 September):*
W.S. Henson designs a steam-powered aeroplane.

1844 *(9 June):*
First use of steam in a model balloon by Dr Le Berrier in Paris.

1848 First sustained flight by a model aeroplane with a steam-powered mechanical engine, designed by John Stringfellow.

1849 *(7 October):*
F. Arban becomes the first man to cross the Alps by balloon from Marseilles to Stubini near Turin.

1852 *(24 September):*
First manned flight made in a mechanically driven aircraft: Henri Giffard, the inventor, ascends in a steam-powered dirigible.

1858 First photograph taken from a captive balloon by Nadar at Petit-Bicêtre.

1859 *(1 & 2 July):*
J. Wise, La Mountain and two passengers make the first flight of more than 1,000 km. (621 miles) from Saint Louis to Henderson (802 miles in 20 hours and 40 minutes) as well as carrying the first air mail by balloon.

1870 *(23 September to 28 January 1871):*
First air mail service linking besieged Paris and the outside world. A total of sixty six postal balloons were used.

1872 *(13 December):*
First use of an internal combustion engine on Haenlein's dirigible at Brno.

1884 *(9 August):*
Charles Renard and A. Krebs make the first round-trip from Chalais-Meudon, near Paris, in an electrically powered dirigible.

1886 *(12 & 13 September):*
Henri Hervé and Alluard make the first flight lasting more than 24 hours from Boulogne to Yarmouth (24 hours and 10 minutes).

1890 *(9 October):*
First manned flight in an aeroplane fitted with an engine, Ader's *Eole*, which flew for 50 yards at a height of 8 inches at Armainvilliers.

1896 *(6 May):*
First unmanned flight of over 1 km. (1093 yds.) made by a powered aeroplane. Trial flight carried out by Langley above the Potomac (1750 yards in 1 minute and 30 seconds).

1896 *(9 August):*
Otto Lilienthal, who pioneered the use of gliders to obtain experience in the art of flying, dies when his bi-plane glider breaks up in the air. Lilienthal had made over 2,000 test flights.

1896 *(28 August):*
A petrol engine is used for the first time on an aircraft, Wolfert's dirigible *Deutschland* in Berlin.

1897 *(14 June):*
Wolfert and Knabe are the first victims of an aircraft powered by an engine when their dirigible explodes in Berlin.

1897 *(11 to 14 July):*
Andrée, Strindberg and Fränkel fail to return from the first journey of exploration in a balloon, taking off from Spitzbergen in the direction of the North Pole.

1897 *(3 November):*
First flight of an entirely metal dirigible, the *Schwartz* in Berlin.

1899 *(12 June):*
The Count de La Vaulx and Monsieur Mallet are the winners of the first ballooning distance trials held in Paris.

1900 *(3 July)*:
First flight of a rigid Zeppelin-type airship over Lake Constance.

1901 *(31 July)*:
Dr Bersen and Dr Suring are the first men to fly to a height of over 10,000 metres (32,800 ft.) in a balloon (34,400 ft. over Berlin).

1901 *(19 October)*:
Santos-Dumont in his airship *No.6* wins the Deutsch prize by flying from Saint-Cloud to the Eiffel Tower and back in less than 30 minutes.

1901 *(October)*:
First use of an internal combustion engine on an aeroplane by W. Kress, in Austria.

1903 *(8 May)*:
Juchmès and Rey make the first cross-country circuit from Moisson to Mantes (23 miles) and back again in a dirigible powered by an internal combustion engine, the *Lebaudy*.

1903 *(12 November)*:
Juchmès and Rey make the first cross-country flight using an internal combustion engine, again in the *Lebaudy*, this time from Moisson to Paris (39 miles).

1903 *(17 December)*:
Orville and Wilbur Wright make the first sustained flights in an aeroplane powered by an internal combustion engine at Kitty Hawk (12, 13, 15 and 59 seconds, 852 ft.).

1904 *(15 September)*:
Wilbur Wright makes the first turn in an aeroplane at Dayton.

1904 *(20 September)*:
Wilbur Wright makes the first closed circuit and flies over one kilometre (1,093 yards) in an aeroplane at Dayton (1,355 yards in 2 minutes and 15 seconds).

1905 *(4 October)*:
Orville Wright makes the first flight in an aeroplane lasting more than half an hour (33 minutes and 17 seconds).

1906 *(13 September)*:
Santos-Dumont gives the first public demonstration of powered flight in an aeroplane in Europe, at Bagatelle.

1906 *(23 October)*:
first sustained flight in an aeroplane in Europe, again by Santos-Dumont at Bagatelle (240 yards).

1907 *(13 November)*:
first take-off by a helicopter and its pilot, Paul Cornu, near Lisieux.

1908 *(13 January)*:
Henry Farman wins the Deutsch-Archdeacon prize for the first officially recorded flight over one kilometre (1093 yards), at Issy.

1908 *(28 March)*:
Henry Farman becomes the first passenger to be carried in an aeroplane, by Delagrange at Issy.

1908 *(9 September)*:
Orville Wright makes the first flight lasting more than one hour at Fort Myers (1 hour, 3 minutes and 15 seconds).

1908 *(18 September)*:
Lieutenant Selfridge, a passenger in Orville Wright's aeroplane, becomes the first victim of an accident involving an aeroplane fitted with an internal combustion engine.

1908 *(30 October)*:
Henry Farman makes the first cross-country journey by aeroplane, from Bouy to Rheims (17 miles in 20 minutes).

1908 *(18 December)*:
Wilbur Wright is the first man to fly more than 100 km. (62 miles) in an aeroplane, at Auvours (75 miles in 1 hour, 53 minutes and 59 seconds).

1908 *(18 December)*:
Wilbur Wright becomes the first man to fly above an altitude of 100 metres (328 ft.), at Auvours (375 ft.).

1909 *(25 July)*:
Louis Blériot becomes the first man to cross the English Channel by aeroplane, from Calais to Dover.

1909 *(7 September)*:
Eugène Lefebvre is the first pilot to be killed in an aeroplane accident, at Juvisy.

1909 *(18 October)*:
Count de Lambert becomes the first man to fly over a major city by aeroplane (Paris).

1910 *(7 January)*:
Latham flies above an altitude of 1,000 metres (3,280 ft.) at Mourmelon.

1910 *(8 March)*:
The Baroness de Laroche receives the first pilot's licence issued to a woman.

1910 *(28 March)*:
Henri Fabre makes the first flight in a seaplane at Martigues (550 yards).

1910 *(27 April)*:
Louis Paulhan is the first man to fly over 100 kilometres (62 miles) in a straight line, from Hendon to Trent Valley near Lichfield (110 miles in 2 hours and 39 minutes) on the first stage of the London to Manchester flight for the Daily Mail Prize.

1910 *(Spring)*:
Henry Farman and Roger Sommer make the first night-flights by aeroplane at Mourmelon.

1910 *(9 July)*:
Léon Morane flies at a speed of over 100 kph. (62 mph.) at Rheims (66 mph.).

1910 *(23 September)*:
Chavez becomes the first man to cross the Alps by aeroplane from Brig to Domodossola.

1910 *(16 October)*:
First crossing of the Straits of Dover by airship: Baudry's *Clément-Bayard-II* flies from La Motte-Breuil to Wormwood Scrubs.

1910 *(21 December)*:
Legagneux makes the first round-trip of over 500 km. (310 miles) by aeroplane, at Pau (317 miles in 5 hours and 59 minutes).

1911 *(18 January)*:
Ely successfully lands and takes off from a ship at San Francisco.

1911 *(12 April)*:
Pierre Prier makes the first non-stop flight from London to Paris.

1911 *(3 August)*:
Colliex makes the first flights in an amphibious aircraft, Voisin's *Canard*, at Issy and on the Seine.

1911 *(22 October)*:
First military use of an aeroplane: the Italian Captain Piazza reconnoitres the Turkish lines near Tripoli.

1912 *(1 March)*:
Berry makes the first parachute descent from an aeroplane at Saint Louis.

1912 *(5 March)*:
First military use of airships: the Italian airships *P-1* and *P-3* reconnoitre the Turkish lines west of Tripoli.

1912 *(6 September)*:
Garros flies above an altitude of 5,000 metres (16,400 ft.) at Houlgate.

1912 *(11 September)*:
Fourny makes the first round-trip of 1,000 km. (621 miles) and the first flight lasting more than 12 hours at Etampes (631 miles in 13 hours, 17 minutes and 57 seconds).

1912 *(27–19 October)*:
Bienaimé and Leblanc travel more than 2,000 km. (1242 miles) by balloon from Stuttgart to Ribnoye in Russia, thus winning the Gordon-Bennett cup (total distance 1360 miles).

1912
Ponche and Primard make the first flight in an entirely metal aeroplane, the *Tubavion*, at Issy.

1913 *(24 April)*:
Gilbert is the first man to fly over 500 kilometres (310 miles) in a straight line, from Villacoublay to Vitoria in Spain (5122 miles in 8 hours and 23 minutes).

1913 *(23 September)*:
Garros makes first non-stop crossing of the Mediterranean by aeroplane, from Saint-Raphaël to Bizerta.

1913 *(29 September)*:
Prévost flies at a speed of over 200 km. per hour (124 mph.) at Rheims (124 miles in 59 minutes and 45 seconds).

1914 *(8–10 February):*
Berliner, Haase and Nikolai travel more than 3,000 km. (1863 miles) by balloon from Bitterfeld to Perm in Russia (total distance 1895 miles).

1914 *(10–11 July):*
Boehm makes the first 24-hour flight at Johannisthal (24 hours and 12 minutes).

1914 *(9–10 August):*
The airship *Fleurus*, piloted by Lieutenant Tixier, is the first Allied aircraft to enter German air-space during the hostilities.

1916 *(20 June):*
Anselme Marchal flies over 1,000 km. (621 miles) in a straight line from Nancy to Cholm (total distance 807 miles).

1917 *(26–31 July):*
The Zeppelin *LZ-170* makes a journey lasting more than 100 hours (3791 miles in 101 hours)

1917
First flying ambulance service begins operations in the Moulin-de-Laffaux zone at the instigation of the medical-officer Chassaing.

1917
First flights of aeroplanes equipped with 1,000 h.p. engines and weighing more than 10 tons, the Zeppelin-Staaken R-III (6 × 180 h.p. engines, 25,520 lb.) and the Linke Hofmann R-II (4 × 260 h.p. engines, 26,400 lb.).

1918 *(27 & 28 June):*
First parachute descents from disabled aircraft by the German pilots Steinbrecher and Udet.

1919 *(19 January):*
Védrines lands an aeroplane on the roof of a department store in Paris.

1919 *(5 February):*
The first passenger service is established by the Lufttreederei between Berlin, Leipzig and Weimar.

1919 *(8 February):*
The first international passenger service is established by the Farman Company between Paris and London.

1919 *(4 April):*
The first airship passenger service using an M-type semi-rigid dirigible containing 635,000 cu. ft. of gas is established between Rome and Naples.

1919 *(16 & 17 May):*
First crossing of the Atlantic by seaplane, by Commander Read and crew of 5, from Newfoundland to Horta in the Azores and then to Lisbon in the Curtiss flying-boat *NC4*.

1919 *(14 & 15 June):*
First crossing of the Atlantic by aeroplane, by Alcock and Brown, from Newfoundland to Clifden in a Vickers Vimy.

1919 *(2–6 July and 10–13 July):*
First return journey across the Atlantic, from East Fortune to New York and from New York to Pulham, by the airship *R-34* captained by Major Scott.

1919 *(24 August):*
First regular airship passenger service established between Freidrichshafen and Berlin by the small Zeppelin *Bodensee*.

1919 *(12 November to 10 December):*
First flight from Europe to Australia by Ross Smith and crew of 3.

1920 *(11 February to 31 May):*
First flight from Europe to Japan by Ferrarin and Masiero.

1920 *(18 February):*
First crossing of the Sahara by air from Tamanraset to Menaka by Vuillemin and Chalus.

1920 *(27 February):*
Major Schroeder flies above an altitude of 10,000 metres (32,800 ft.) at Dayton (33,105 ft.).

1920 *(20 October):*
Sadi Lecointe flies at over 300 kph (186.3 mph.) at Villacoublay (188 mph.).

1921 *(23 October):*
Tampier demonstrates his "automobile-aeroplane" both on the ground and in the air in Paris and at Etampes.

1922 *(30 March to 5 June):*
Sacadura Cabral and Gago Coutinho make the first crossing of the South Atlantic by seaplane.

1922 *(18 August):*
Martens makes an hour-long flight in a glider at Rhön (1 hour and 4 minutes).

1923 *(31 January):*
Gomez Spencer makes the first successful flight in an autogiro at Cuatro Vientos.

1923 *(2 & 3 May):*
MaCready and Kelly make the first non-stop crossing of the North American continent by aeroplane.

1923 *(26 June):*
first successful refuelling of one aeroplane from another while in flight, carried out by Lieutenants Smith and Richter at San Diego.

1923 *(2 November):*
Brow flies at over 400 kph. (248.4 mph.) in New York (259 mph.).

1924 *(29 January):*
Pescara stays airborne for over 10 minutes in a helicopter (10 minutes and 10 seconds).

1924 *(19 March to 28 September):*
Smith, Wade and Nelson travel around the world by air in three convertible aeroplane-seaplanes.

1924 *(4 May):*
Œhmichen flies one kilometre (1093 yards) in a helicopter at Valentigney.

1925 *(3 & 4 February):*
Lemaître and Arrachart fly more than 3,000 km. (1,863 miles) in a straight line from Etampes to Villa Cisneros (1,966 miles).

1925 *(26 July):*
Commander Massaux stays airborne for over 10 hours in a glider at Vauville (10 hours and 19 minutes).

1926 *(9 May):*
Byrd and Floyd Bennett fly over the North Pole in an aeroplane.

1926 *(11–14 May):*
The Amundsen-Ellsworth expedition crosses the polar ice cap for the first time in the airship *Norge* from Spitzbergen to Alaska via the pole.

1926 *(31 August to 1 September):*
Challe and Weiser fly more than 5,000 km. (3,105 miles) in a straight line from Le Bourget to Bandar Abbas (3,213 miles).

1927 *(20–21 May):*
Charles Lindbergh first flies non-stop from New York to Paris.

1927 *(3–5 August):*
Edzard and Ristics stay airborne for more than 50 hours in an aeroplane.

1928 *(30 March):*
Bernardi flies at more than 500 kph (310.5 mph.) in Venice (318 mph.).

1928 *(12 & 13 April):*
First east-west Atlantic crossing by aeroplane, by Koehl, Hünefeld and Fitzmaurice.

1928 *(15 & 16 April):*
First crossing of the polar ice cap by aeroplane, by Wilkins and Eielson.

1928 *(31 May to 9 June):*
First flight from the United States to Australia across the Pacific by Kingsford Smith and crew of 3.

1928 *(13 August):*
First express air-mail service across the Atlantic established using a seaplane catapulted from the deck of the liner *Ile de France*; Demougeot was the pilot.

1928 *(18 September):*
First flight of an aeroplane fitted with a heavy oil engine, at Utica, U.S.A.

1929 *(25 April):*
Nehring climbs to more than 1,000 metres (3,280 ft.) above his take-off point in a glider at Bergstrasse (3966 ft.).

1929 *(20 July):*
Kronfeld glides non-stop for 100 km. (62 miles) in a straight line from Rhön to Hermsdorf (88 miles).

1929 *(20 July):*
Kronfeld climbs to a height of more than 2,000 metres (6,560 ft.) above his take-off point in a glider at Rhön (7,481 ft.).

AVIATION INDEX

B